Tony Devon

Cata

The Open University

Faculty of Technology

'Systems Performance: Human Factors and Systems Failures' Course Team:

G. Peters (Chairman and General Editor)
R. J. Beishon
V. F. Bignell
S. Brown
K. Cavanagh
P. Duchastel
H. Dunkelman
J. Groom (BBC)
C. Holloway
J. N. T. Martin
A. Millington (BBC)
J. Naughton
C. Pym
I. Roth
R. Spear
A. J. C. Wright

Catastrophic Failures

by Victor Bignell, Geoff Peters
and Christopher Pym

with bibliographies by
Caryl Hunter-Brown

THE OPEN UNIVERSITY PRESS

The Open University Press, Walton Hall, Milton Keynes MK7 6AA

First published 1977

Printed in Great Britain by
Staples Printing Group
at the Priory Press, St Albans, Herts.

ISBN 0 335 00038 X

1.1

Preface

The Open University course 'Systems Performance: Human Factors and Systems Failures' uses systems concepts, techniques and methodologies to illuminate three different areas of systems failure or potential failure.

These are catastrophes, where the failure element is obvious; 'hard' systems, such as nuclear power station protection; and 'soft' systems, such as the provision for treating the mentally ill, which may or may not have failed. One common feature of such failures is the involvement of human beings at various stages in the design, development, operation or maintenance of each system.

Catastrophic Failures is the first of two Course Readers designed to provide essential background material for students of the course. It presents seven case studies of disasters that have occurred as a result of systems failure. The course uses each case study to demonstrate how systems methodology might be developed to investigate failure.

In the course, the performance of these and other systems is studied in relation to the objectives and expectations of the people most concerned. The human aspects are closely examined, and an attempt is made to identify the knowledge which is available about the 'human component'. The course aims to give students the ability to conceptualize unstructured problems at an advanced level.

The second Course Reader *Human aspects of man-made systems* is a collection of papers on ergonomics and human factors, which is also to be published by the Open University Press.

As the authors of this Reader, we should like to thank the members of the 'Systems Performance' course team as well as tutors and students for reading and commenting on these case studies when in draft form; the Department of Mechanical Engineering at the City University which facilitated the involvement of Victor Bignell in the work of the course team; Caryl Hunter-Brown of the Open University for researching photographs and background material, and for preparing the bibliographies; Andrew Reilly of the Open University Press for editorial advice; and Sue Parrott who typed the manuscripts.

V.F.B.
G.P.
C.P.

CONTENTS Page

INTRODUCTION

A book telling the stories behind various catastrophes may seem a strange production for a group of learned academics in partnership with a university press. The subject has much more commonly been the province of Sunday journalists and the writers of those sensational paperbacks most often to be found in airport bookshops.

Before I explain our reasons for exploring this subject area I should make quite clear what the book contains, and what it leaves out. The articles in this Reader present many of the known details about various catastrophes. In each case the primary source has been the official Inquiry, but in most cases there has been little attempt to acquire new information or even to examine all the information that was presented. The articles do not contain anything but the simplest of analyses, and certainly do not go beyond the findings of the official Inquiries.

So who needs a book that is a digest of the official reports of Inquiries? We know that the Open University course for which it is set does, because that was the chicken that laid this particular egg. However, we are convinced that a good many other groups of people need source material like this as well, for a variety of reasons.

First of all there are those people involved in the control and management of organizations, large or small. It is important that if society is to learn from its mistakes, the correct lessons about them should be retained. This certainly does not happen when we rely solely on newspaper reports and our memory of them. I wonder how many people can actually say what the causes of the Summerland fire disaster or the Trident air crash really were? I suspect that many people think that the Summerland building burnt down because of the use of a material called Oroglas, and that the rescue work after the Trident air crash was impeded by the hordes of sightseers who clogged up the road and generally got in the way. When you come to read these reports you will realize that both of these conclusions are far from true. So not only are we failing to learn the right lessons from particular disasters, we are actually learning wrong ones. The second and more important lesson for those involved in the management and control aspects of organizations is that it is only when one collects together digests of a whole series of catastrophes that one can begin to see any general lessons emerging.

The second major group for whom this book is intended consists of teachers and students. Many people in teaching are committed to some sort of case-study approach, particularly in the applied and social sciences. However, most of the material available in this area is of a highly structured nature, and is designed purely for one particular discipline. In the Open University, we have found an overwhelming need for material that simply details an actual situation, and we have had to resort to researching and compiling this material ourselves. Previously, the results of our labour have appeared in correspondence texts together with the particular teaching points that we wished students to extract. Our discussions with other teachers of many different subjects have convinced us that we are not alone in this predicament. We trust that we will have helped at least some of them by producing this book.

This brings me to our own use of the case studies presented in this Reader. The course for which it is a set book is entitled 'Systems Performance: Human Factors and Systems Failures'. It collects together the case-study material for the first block of the course, on catastrophes. Students are expected to read the details of a particular incident, and are then either presented with some more detailed and higher level analysis by a member of the course team, or are required to conduct their own similar analysis for evaluation by their course tutors. The course itself is the fourth and last in a series of four systems courses prepared by the Systems Group at the Open University. The previous three were: 'Systems Behaviour' and 'Systems Management' which are second-level courses, and 'Systems Modelling' which, like this course, is a third-level course. The prime objective of all these courses is to encourage students to approach the world in an holistic manner, to see the similarities that exist between situations which are said to be different, and to realize the disadvantages of a reductionist approach. In this particular course we are looking at situations in which something has gone wrong or has been said to have gone wrong. From this investigation we expect that students will learn more about the human aspects of systems, and how people behave in unusual circumstances.

We hope that the articles in this Reader will lead you on into a variety of different areas. If you have an interest in systems or the comparative study of catastrophes, then we hope that you will look at the correspondence texts produced for the 'Systems Performance' course. If you are interested in working at a particular case study in more detail, the bibliographies we have prepared, with the help of Caryl Hunter-Brown of the Open University Library, will give you the necessary pointers. The entries in the bibliographies are arranged chronologically to give an impression of how far people appreciated or ignored various aspects of a problem at different times before and after a particular accident. Perhaps a weakness or danger was recognized by one profession, but remained unnoticed by another. How did people respond to the disaster?

You may wish to follow up a detailed technical point or to gain a wider perspective on the social, professional or academic context of the disaster, to relate it to previous accidents and warning incidents, or to trace through varying responses to the accident and Inquiry report.

Of course, none of the bibliographies is exhaustively comprehensive, but just one paper may have further references to lead you on. Conversely, many of the articles will cover more or less the same ground, so obviously there is no need to read everything. You will, of course, be using a library to locate books or articles, or to obtain them as loans or photocopies. The more familiar you are with its resources, methods of arrangement and so on, the easier you will find it to pursue a line of inquiry of your own. In particular, most people have access to a library which will have some of the indexing and abstracting periodicals which make it possible to follow a theme through the published material without too much difficulty.

Although this book stands on its own as a collection of interesting case studies, we hope that many people will be fired by one or more of the articles to carry out further research. This could take the form of a study of a particular failure or an attempt to gather together their own thoughts about the patterns that emerge, or a continuation of the work that others have done on these patterns. The area of systems failures is, for us at least, a fascinating one, the source of endless anecdotes and amazing tales. We had tremendous pleasure in preparing the material and our only major problem has been limiting the number of case studies to be examined. The whole area of systems failures is an important one, and sooner or later much more serious consideration will have to be given to it. We hope that in some small way we can contribute to speeding up that process with this book.

The Open University **Geoff Peters**
May 1976

You [illegible] a question [illegible] or to gain a wider [illegible] professional [illegible] the [illegible] and [illegible] incidents [illegible] responses [illegible] and the [illegible] approach.

Of course [illegible] the [illegible] references [illegible] the article [illegible] the survey [illegible] everything [illegible] about [illegible] Beyond [illegible] most people have access to a library which will [illegible] some of the [illegible] and [illegible] the books [illegible]

[illegible] of this [illegible] will [illegible] further research [illegible] patterns that [illegible] contribution [illegible] We find [illegible] The whole area of [illegible] future [illegible]

[illegible] G. [illegible]
[illegible]

Case Study 1

The Hixon Level Crossing Accident

by Victor Bignell

CONTENTS

THE RAILWAY REGULATION ACT 1842

(5 & 6 Vict. c. 55)

An Act for the better Regulation of Railways and for the Conveyance of Troops

(30th July 1842)

9. Gates, where railways cross turnpike or other roads, shall be kept closed across each end of the turnpike or other roads

And whereas by an Act passed in the second and third years of her present Majesty, and intituled "An Act to amend an Act of the fifth and sixth years of his late Majesty King William the Fourth relating to highways," it was enacted, that whenever a railway crosses or shall hereafter cross any turnpike road, or any other highway or statute labour road for carts or carriages, in Great Britain, the proprietors or directors of the said railway shall make and maintain good and sufficient gates across each end of such turnpike or other road at each end of the said crossings, and shall employ good and proper persons to open and shut such gates, so that the persons, carts, or carriages passing along such turnpike or other road shall not be exposed to any danger or damage by the passing of any carriages or engines along the said railway: And whereas by the Acts relating to certain railways it is provided that such gates shall be kept constantly closed across the railway, except during the time when carriages or engines passing along the railway shall have to cross such turnpike or other road: And whereas experience has shown that it is more conducive to safety that such gates should be kept closed across the turnpike or other road instead of across the railway: Be it therefore enacted, that, notwithstanding anything to the contrary contained in any Act of Parliament heretofore passed, such gates shall be kept constantly closed across each end of such turnpike or other roads, in lieu of across the railway, except during the time when horses, cattle, carts, or carriages passing along such turnpike or other road shall have to cross such railway; such gates shall be of such dimensions and so constructed as, when closed across the ends of such turnpike or other roads, to fence in the railway, and prevent cattle or horses passing along the road from entering upon the railway while the gates are closed: . . .

HIXON LEVEL CROSSING ACCIDENT

At midday on Saturday 6 January 1968 an express train travelling at 75 miles per hour, carrying some 300 passengers and weighing nearly 500 tons, collided at an automatic level crossing with a road transporter bearing a 120 ton transformer. Eleven people on the train died in the collision; many more suffered injuries. A formal inquiry was constituted under Section 7 of the Regulation of Railways Act 1871. The present account narrates the events leading up to the collision, using details taken from the official report:

> 'Report of the Public Inquiry into the Accident at Hixon Level Crossing on January 6th, 1968.' Presented to Parliament by the Minister of Transport by Command of Her Majesty, July 1968. Published as Command Paper 3706 by Her Majesty's Stationery Office.

BACKGROUND

Of the many obstacles met by early railways, the rivers and estuaries demanded expensive tunnels or bridges; roads on the other hand offered the possibility of a level intersection – hence level crossings.

Road vehicles can stop more quickly than trains, and can rapidly accelerate away again after a delay. So at level crossings road traffic was stopped in favour of rail rather than the reverse. The procedure was that four heavy gates resting across the railway track would be swung around to close off the complete width of road on each side while the train passed. This barrier not only had an air of solidity, it also possessed considerable weight and physical strength, and left in the mind of the user a feeling of confidence in the system. If a human attendant could be employed to halt the traffic before closing the gates, and if the gates were interlocked with railway signals in such a way that unless the gates were across the roadway the signals could not be set in favour of the train, it could then be arranged that an oncoming train was assured a clear route through the crossing. To achieve complete safety, if for any reason road vehicles obstructed the crossing, the signals had to be sited far enough ahead to stop the train in time. In this way the speed of the fastest trains fixed the sites for signals.

The system halted road traffic for at least three minutes, and if a slow goods train came along, or a train in the opposite direction, the delay to road traffic could be doubled.

THE NEW CROSSING

Such lengthy delays to road traffic came to be regarded as unacceptable as road traffic increased in the 1950s. Also the initial cost and upkeep of traditional crossings with heavy gates and an attendant became prohibitive. To solve the problem the Ministry of Transport and British Railways looked at a system much used abroad for dealing with road–rail intersections. In this *Automatic Half-Barrier* system the road and rail routes are both open until a train heralds its approach by actuating a treadle: this was normally placed so that the fastest train using the line would reach the crossing in 24 seconds. Actuation of the treadle and (lest the treadle mechanism should fail) completion of an electric circuit through the rails set red stop lights flashing and bells ringing at the crossing. These signals continued for eight seconds, after which pole-type pivoted barriers descended in the next eight seconds to close the approach lanes of the road.

Far from being physically bulky, half barriers are as light as possible, narrow to reduce the effect of wind forces, and incorporate a weak 'fracture segment' near the pivot. The whole appearance has an air of flimsiness compared with old fashioned gates. By covering only the approach lanes, half barriers allow vehicles already on the crossing to move off. The barriers remain down until the train arrives (a minimum of eight seconds in the case of the fastest train). To complete the sequence, the last vehicle of the train actuates another treadle just beyond the crossing, returning the barriers to a raised position and extinguishing the flashing lights.

The economy provided by the system was dramatic. Road traffic hold-ups could be as small as half a minute, and at Beckingham crossing for instance, whereas 43 vehicle hours had been lost per day with manned gates, only $3\frac{1}{4}$ vehicle hours were lost when automatic half barriers were used. To achieve these benefits and discourage misuse of the crossing the time intervals were deliberately short. Of course, a slow goods train would extend the hold up, and if another train was expected soon, the barriers stayed down. Additionally, if the crossing was skew, or more than two tracks were crossed, the 24 second minimum was increased. At Hixon crossing, however, the standard 24 second timing was used, comprising 8 seconds warning, 8 seconds for the barriers to be lowered and 8 seconds wait with the barriers down before the train arrived.

The automatic half-barrier crossing was not manned; the train driver and signalman had no knowledge of events at the crossing during the 24 seconds, and even if they did the train would be too near to stop. The motorist was thus responsible now not only for the safety of his own vehicle and its occupants, but also for the safety of any train bearing down on the crossing as he came up to it. Further, the train could well be beyond the motorist's field of view until too late.

THE ACCIDENT

The new system worked well enough for normal vehicles, but the transporter approaching the automatic half-barrier level crossing at Hixon in Staffordshire on 6 January 1968 was not a normal vehicle (Figure 1). It consisted of a 32 wheeled trailer having its own steering cabin, drawn by one six wheeled tractor at the front and assisted at the rear by another. Inclusive of the load the vehicles together weighed 162 tons, and occupied a continuous length of 148 feet. It was not surprising that five crew members were needed, together with a police escort in a car.

If the transporter had crossed at a speed of six miles per hour all would have been well, but on the approach to Hixon crossing speed was reduced to two miles per hour. At this reduced speed the transporter would obstruct the barriers and rail tracks for one minute. Unluckily, when the unit was only part way across, the barrier sequence started, activated by an oncoming express.

Not one among the crew or police knew that without prior intervention only 24 seconds would elapse before the arrival of a train. None realized that an oncoming train would bear down irresistibly on the crossing. None knew that the train crew could not be warned at the last moment and would be unable to stop when the crossing came into visual range. So although the engine crew in the last few moments of their lives applied full braking on seeing the obstruction, and although the transporter crew tried to accelerate away on seeing the train only a few hundred yards away, a collision was now unavoidable. The locomotive split the trailer and tossed the 120 ton transformer aside like a toy (Figure 2). The electric locomotive and five leading railway coaches were destroyed; three other coaches were derailed. All the 11 dead and 45 injured were from the engine and train.

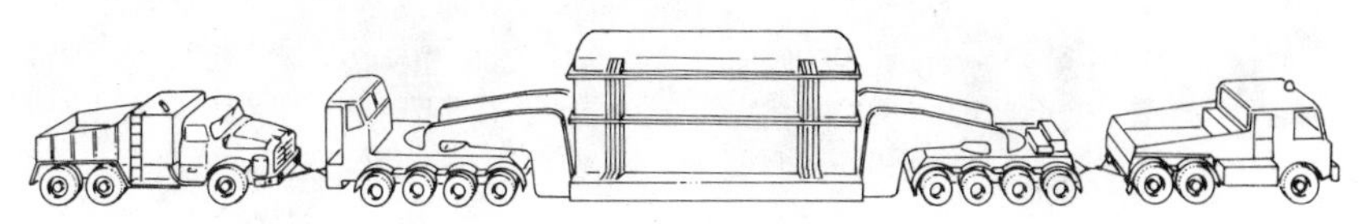

Figure 1 Model of the transporter involved in the Hixon accident.

Figure 2 Aerial view of wrecked train.

THE TELEPHONE

A special telephone had been incorporated in the crossing system to help drivers cross safely with awkward loads, but it was not used on this occasion. It occupied a niche in the pedestal of each barrier, and was connected to the nearest signalbox, where the signalman had precise instructions displayed next to a similar telephone. These instructions met every eventuality. According to the needs and capabilities of vehicles reported by telephone as desiring to cross, the signalman could give or withhold permission, could stop an oncoming train, caution it, or allow it to proceed at normal speed.

The road vehicle, train, signalman, barriers, etc., were all ostensibly equipped for safety; however, for system effectiveness the components had to be suitably linked together. Only via the telephone could information be fed back either way to enable safe control of road and rail traffic. Unless the telephone was used only normal road traffic could cross in safety. As the transporter carrying the transformer was not normal traffic, ignorance of the telephone link invited disaster. It came.

SAFETY AT CROSSINGS

Consideration of safety at automatic half-barrier crossings in Britain had begun in 1956, when a joint Working Party of the Ministry of Transport and British Railways visited the Continent to see automatic crossings in use prior to introduction here. They found the background situation different however. Railway tracks had not been fenced as they are in this country, and railways had not been required to provide manned barriers or massive gates. Thus the Continental public had not come to expect physical protection when near railways, and the limited protection of half barriers was seen as an improvement in safety. On their return the Working Party submitted a report advocating cautious experimental introduction of automatic half-barrier crossings, and after consideration of the matter by a committee of the House of Commons, the British Transport Commission introduced a clause in a Parliamentary Bill permitting the crossings. The first was installed in 1961 not far from Hixon, and by cautious stages the installed total reached 207 in January 1968. British Railways intended converting to automatic half-barrier some 1500 more crossings.

The new automatic crossings were not the only type lacking protection by interlocked signals, for (in 1968) 811 crossings of various types were without that provision. However, 1407 did have specific signal protection to prevent collisions.

Replacing traditional crossings by automatic half barriers shifted the onus away from railway employees on to the road user, for it was now possible for a train to bear down unknowingly on to a crossing obstructed by a vehicle wilfully disobeying the remotely actuated lights, bells, and barriers, or indeed unable to obey. Manning of crossings and interlocking of gate position with signal aspect had formerly protected users of rail and road alike. In transferring responsibility, the Ministry of Transport had to give attention to new dangers, assess new hazards and educate the public.

THE MINISTRY OF TRANSPORT

Several parts of the Ministry played a role in the history of the Hixon accident, but notwithstanding the help of the Inquiry Report the internal workings of the Ministry are still not clear, in that some of the connections in the Hixon affair disappear from view inside the Ministry as do connections in an electrical circuit when they encounter a 'black box'. Further, as a sub-system of the main story the Ministry itself consisted of many sub-groups of people, and in this situation lack of liaison links is not infrequent.

Special Orders

For a vehicle so large and so heavily laden to use the highways at all needed a *special order* obtained from the Ministry before each journey. An order stipulated among other things the route to be followed and the giving of notice to highway and bridge authorities (which might include British Railways). The police were to be informed, and their instructions obeyed. The origin of detailing routes lay in protection of bridges from overloading, so routes were dealt with by the Route Section of the Bridges Engineering Design Standards Division of the Highways 2 Group of the Ministry. Although the route was prepared by the Ministry, who from their central position could have an unrivalled knowledge of roads, the responsibility for the route (no less than actual safety on the journey) lay with the haulier. All relevant road engineers, highway and bridge authorities, together with the police, received a copy of each proposed new route. Any need for caution expressed in reply appeared in the route instruction for the haulier, who then passed copies of the order complete with route and cautions to the authorities and the police. Although some hazards such as roundabouts, sharp corners and overhead wires came to be pin-pointed in routes, these special orders continued to be issued by Bridges Engineering.

Being a visible and self-evident hazard, no level crossing was inserted as a caution unless the difficulty was peculiar to that crossing. Hixon crossing apparently possessed no such snags, so the route devised for movement of the transformer from the English Electric works at Stafford to the depot just beyond the Hixon crossing contained no reference to that crossing whatsoever (Extract 1).

Extract 1

Route for Stafford–Hixon Journey

Leave English Electric Works via A.34 Lichfield Rd, turn left A.449 Wolverhampton Rd to junc M.6 Motorway turn right join northbound carriageway of M.6 turn right join northbound carriageway of A.34 to junc A.51 turn right A.51 Stone By Pass, (CAUTION: vehicles must proceed at crawl speed, keeping to the centre of carriageway, with no other vehicles to be on the structure at the same time when crossing the bridge carrying the A.51 over the River Trent and the Trent and Mersey Canal) (CAUTION: headroom restriction 16′6″) Sandon, A.51 (CAUTION: when crossing the bridges carrying the A.51 over Gayton Brook and the L.M.R. at Weston, vehicles to proceed at crawl speed, keeping to the centre of the carriageway, with no other vehicles to be on the structure at the same time) Weston to junc class III road approx 2 miles past Hixon turn left class III road turn left access road to English Electric Works and destination.

Notices

Each of the average of 870 vehicles per day using the Hixon crossing (Figure 3) would pass various notices. The first (just over 170 yards in advance of the crossing) told the motorist a crossing was ahead (Figure 4). The form of this sign has been criticized as not depicting an automatic half-barrier crossing properly: it was however a standard approved sign used internationally. The notice below the sign added that traffic must stop when the lights ahead flashed. Sixty-six yards nearer the crossing, another standard sign (Figure 5) warned there was only 16′6″ headroom below the overhead electric conductor wires of the railway. At the crossing itself (Figure 6) were red lights (flashing during barrier operation) and a sign on the offside verge: ‘Another train is coming if lights continue to flash.’

Figure 3 Approach to Hixon level crossing

Figure 4
First notice

Figure 5
Second notice

Lastly, there stood the notice referring to the telephone procedure. The wording had been modified from an earlier version used at a different type of crossing, so it now read:

In emergency
or before crossing with
exceptional or heavy
loads or cattle
phone signalman

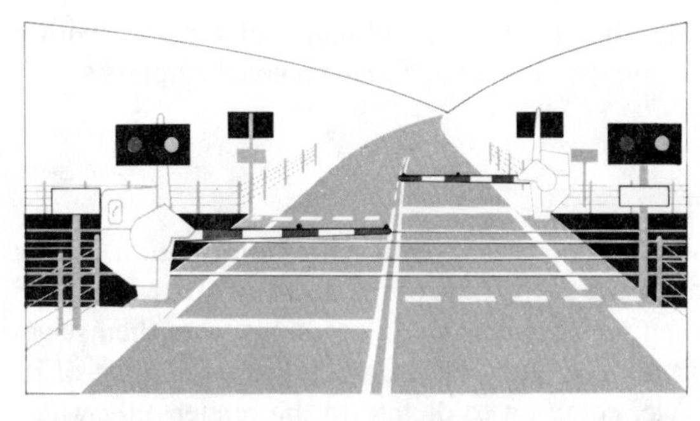

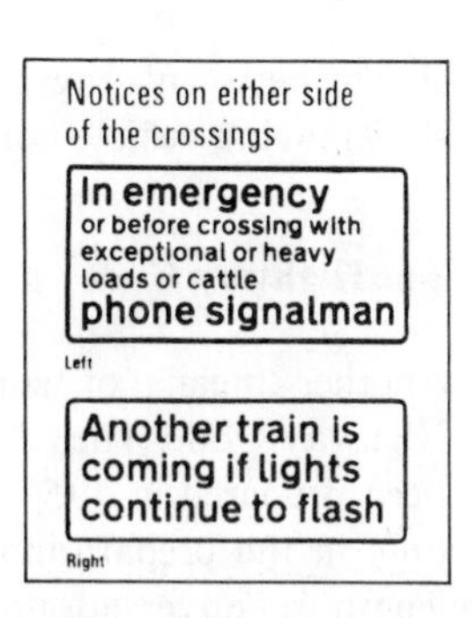

Figure 6 The appearance of a crossing

At the Inquiry there was some doubt about the direction the notice had faced before the accident. According to evidence it stood at an angle to the road, readable by drivers of vehicles approaching the crossing and also by drivers actually on the crossing. But no matter how the notice was placed, whatever the form of words on its face, its message would have been reinforced if the transporter driver had been told in his written instructions to contact the signalman by telephone, or had learned of the dangers and the appropriate remedies from effective publicity.

National Publicity

The Ministry had taken responsibility for national publicity of the automatic half-barrier system, but as no one among the driver and crew of the Hixon transporter and the police patrol were aware of how to use the crossing safely, the publicity had been ineffective. It had failed to impress in the minds of the right people the brisk operation of the barriers, the rapid arrival of the train and the vital need for drivers of certain vehicles to use the telephone.

However, this is not to accuse the Ministry of disregarding all aspects of safety in respect of these crossings. Indeed, they gave great attention to the danger to ordinary motorists, who were expected to be so foolish as to try to beat the descending barriers, or to zig-zag round the half barriers using the wrong side of the road. To counter these misuses of the system the time period for each stage of barrier operation had been minimized. Brisk operation, it was believed, would make zig-zagging or squeezing under both barriers unnecessary and foolhardy.

National publicity went out through the Press and the motoring organizations, by wall-charts in schools, and in short television films to be shown between programmes. But neither the difficulty of crossing with a slow moving vehicle nor the provision of a telephone received emphasis.

The Highway Code

Another means of supplying road users with vital information is the Highway Code. The edition in use at the time of the accident (Extract 2) had been prepared in 1959, when the first automatic crossings were themselves only in the preparation stage. The entry on crossings runs for most of its length in conversational style, going on to dictate to the reader only where zig-zagging is concerned. In this early publication, telephones receive no mention.

Extract 2

Crossings in the Highway Code (italics added)

'58. Some level-crossings are being equipped with the Continental type of short barrier, which covers only half the width of the road and is worked automatically by approaching trains. The barriers are timed to fall *just before a train reaches the crossing.* Red flashing signals and gongs will be provided, and they will operate before the barriers begin to fall, in order to warn traffic. Do not pass the signals when they are flashing, and do not zig-zag round the barriers.

Never cross before the barriers are lifted; there may be a second train coming.

BE PATIENT–NEVER ZIG-ZAG.'

As in other published statements describing the new crossings the reader is allowed to misconstrue the word 'automatic', and imagine the train is automatically aware of the presence of road traffic on the crossing, and will stop in time automatically. In other areas of activity the prefix 'automatic' applied to a system is used to denote a system modification which removes the need for continual human attention, decision and intervention. Examples of this are automatic washing machines and automatic gearboxes in cars.

Automatic Half-barrier Level Crossings
The Requirements and Explanatory Note

The document referred to as the 'Requirements' (Extract 3) was issued to official bodies such as the Magistrates' Association, the Royal Society for the Prevention of Accidents, the Road Haulage Association and, via the Home Office, to police forces. The document laid down the conditions to be fulfilled before a crossing could be converted to automatic operation. It went on to specify in detail such requirements as equipment employed in crossings, light output of the flashing signals, provision of stand-by batteries, etc. An 'Explanatory Note' (Extract 4) issued with the 'Requirements' diminished them by pointing out that they were not statutory, but served as an essential guide for the Railways when selecting sites and making preparations, and for the highway and local authorities, who would be consulted later about each individual crossing. The Note did not make clear the entire absence of signal protection at the crossings and did not mention the telephone; indeed the Requirements followed official policy of the time (July 1966), saying only that a telephone 'may be necessary' despite the decision by British Railways at about the same date to equip all these crossings with telephones.

Extract 3

REQUIREMENTS OF THE MINISTER OF TRANSPORT IN REGARD TO AUTOMATICALLY OPERATED HALF-BARRIERS AT PUBLIC LEVEL CROSSINGS (JULY 1966)

THE GUIDING PRINCIPLE FOR THIS SYSTEM, WITH THE BARRIERS COVERING THE NEARSIDE HALF OF THE ROAD ONLY, IS THAT ROAD TRAFFIC MUST BE STOPPED FOR THE SHORTEST POSSIBLE TIME. THE HALF-BARRIERS SHOULD BE FULLY LOWERED ONLY JUST BEFORE THE ARRIVAL OF A TRAIN AT THE CROSSING, AND BE RAISED IMMEDIATELY AFTER IT HAS PASSED UNLESS ANOTHER TRAIN ON ANOTHER TRACK IS ABOUT TO ARRIVE.

. . .

(b) Specification

The specification for the optical performance of red flashing lights is as B.S.505, paras. 25 and 26, in regard to colorimetric properties and transmittance, and as B.S.505, para. 21, modified as shown below, in regard to distribution:—

Horizontal distribution:	not less than 1,000 candelas at $1\frac{1}{2}°$ from centre; not less than 200 candelas at 10° from centre; and not less than 70 candelas at 25° from centre.

Vertical distribution: not less than 1,000 candelas at $1\frac{1}{2}°$ from centre;
and not less than 200 candelas at 10° below centre.

. . .

(e) Arrangements of Lights

The lights to be arranged horizontally so that there is a distance of between 1 ft. 9 in. and 2 ft. 3 in. between the centres of the lenses of the lamps, and a single rectangular black backboard with white border if required to be provided for each signal of a size that the sides of the board are not less than 1 ft. from the centre of each lamp lens. The red flashing light signals to be placed so that the height of the centre of each lens is between 7 ft. and 11 ft. 6 in. from the carriageway and the centre of the light nearest the carriageway is not less than 2 ft. 6 in. and not more than 5 ft. from the edge of the carriageway. Where the signals overhang a footpath a minimum headroom of 7 ft. to be maintained.

. . .

18. Telephones

(a) If abnormal loads or cattle pass over the crossing frequently a telephone available to the public may be necessary. A notice displaying the words "In emergency or before crossing with exceptional or heavy loads or cattle, telephone signalman" will also be required. The notice boards to be reflectorised. The door of the cabinet containing the telephone to be marked in reflectorised material with either the word "Telephone" or the appropriate symbol.

(b) If a telephone is not required, "Plug-in" connections to be provided for an emergency telephone to be connected at site by railway staff when required for emergency working or maintenance.

(c) A suitable notice to tell road users how to contact the Railway in an emergency should be provided at all crossings where a special telephone is not required.

Extract 4

EXPLANATORY NOTE ON THE REQUIREMENTS (JULY 1966) FOR AUTOMATIC HALF-BARRIER PROTECTION AT LEVEL CROSSINGS

The most revolutionary of the new types of level crossing protection, and the most valuable to road users, is the half-barrier worked automatically by the approaching train.

The saving of delays at busy level crossings by installing automatic half-barriers can be very great. At a crossing worked by an attendant, the level crossing is protected by railway signals and the attendant must close the gates in time to lower the distant signal which may be $\frac{3}{4}$ mile or more away, so that the approaching train can pass it without checking. The majority of attended crossings must therefore be closed about 3–4 minutes before even a fast train passes and, if a train in the opposite direction should approach just as the first one passes, the gates may remain closed for 6–7 minutes or more at a time. With the automatic half-barrier, which is not associated with railway signals, the timing is such that the red flashing light stop signal is given to road traffic, and the barriers come down just before the fastest train reaches the crossing. The delay to road traffic for each train to pass may thus be of the order of only half a minute for a fast train increasing to about $1\frac{1}{2}$ minutes for a slow-speed freight train. The chance of a prolonged closure of the crossing when another train in the opposite direction is also approaching is thus diminished and the delay when it arises very much less. The reduction in delays at level crossings where both rail and road traffic is heavy may well be sufficient to obviate or postpone the need for bridge construction in certain cases.

The principle of using automatic half-barriers in Great Britain has already been accepted and legalised. The original conditions under which they might be installed proved too restrictive and a fresh examination, which included a further study of this equipment on the Continent, was made to decide what could be done to enable automatic half-barriers to be used more widely.

The recommendations arising from this examination have been approved by the Ministry of Transport, the Scottish Development Department and also the Welsh Office, and are incorporated in the attached Requirements. These Requirements now make it possible to use automatic half-barriers at far busier crossings than previously permitted. In no way do they infringe the principles for safety on which this type of protection is based.

These Requirements are not statutory but serve as an essential guide to the Railways when selecting sites and in preparing each automatic half-barrier proposal for submission to the Ministry for approval. They also serve as a guide to highway and/or local authorities, who must be consulted by the Railways about each individual case.

For further automatic half-barrier installations, particularly those at busy crossings, precautions will be taken to make road users acquainted with their working as has been done for the few existing installations. These include:–

(a) national publicity at the appropriate time;

(b) local publicity, with special attention being given to children from schools in the vicinity of the crossing;

(c) attendance of a railway worker at the crossing for some weeks after the installation has been introduced;

(d) an invitation to the police to assist in inculcating road discipline at the crossings.

Ministry of Transport.

July 1966

Meetings held at the Crossing

Hixon crossing was felt to be ideal for conversion to automatic half barriers, but before and after each conversion, meetings were always held at each site to explain the system and discuss problems.

For Hixon crossing a Ministry Railway Inspector took the first meeting in January 1966. He was joined by representatives from the road traffic signal engineers, the Parish Council, the County Council as Highway Authority, the police and British Railways. The police representative reported back to his superiors in a report containing an intelligent appreciation of the situation, including the traffic which might be expected between the English Electric works at Stafford and the depot at Hixon, although no exceptional load had yet used the rather narrow road. At that time Hixon was to be without a telephone.

By the time similar representatives met in June 1967 for the site inspection of the completed crossing, not only was a telephone installed, but application had been made for two special order movements, and the road had been widened to take bulky vehicles. Yet the possibility of exceptional vehicles using the crossing was not discussed at the inspection, nor was the relevance of the new telephone and its notice pointed out.

Application for the Special Order

In devising the route the Ministry used part of one previously cleared with the police, County Council and British Railways for a journey on 7 December 1967 from Hixon depot to Manchester. When devising the route for this earlier journey the Bridges Engineering Group of the Ministry asked the Chief of Heavy Transport at English Electric to confirm that adequate clearance existed under the wires at Hixon crossing. This official used the crossing almost once a week, and confirmed the clearance as adequate. If the actual figure had been sent it would have appeared in the route instruction as a caution. Neither the crossing nor the overhead wires were mentioned as cautions for that December journey, but the driver on that occasion confirmed the wire clearance with his office by telephone the day before. It must also be noted that unlike his counterpart one month later, this driver asked one of the police constables escorting the vehicle to telephone from the crossing when they arrived.

BRITISH RAILWAYS

Local Publicity

British Railways had been conscious since 1964 of the need to make provision for special categories of crossing users, including not only stalled vehicles but also long, slow vehicles. To deal with the problem the telephone and notice system was introduced, and as the Road Safety Group of the Ministry of Transport had approved it, British Railways thought it sufficient. Having thus established a control system loop in which the driver of a problem vehicle had only to telephone the signalman in order to be fed back information on whether the vehicle could cross safely, it only needed publicity to ensure safety.

British Railways took charge of local publicity themselves for each crossing. For Hixon 1000 leaflets and 45 posters were sent to the Education Officer, County Librarian, the County Council and the police.

Unlike some previous systems the half-barriers allowed pedestrians to reach the tracks, even when a train was passing. To deal with the group of pedestrians most likely to stray on to the line, special efforts were made to instruct schoolchildren, but the adult population received little information, and local haulage companies were not directly informed of the new responsibility laid upon their drivers.

Even if they had seen the British Railways' leaflet (Extract 5), drivers could well have missed the point, for like other key documents the leaflet lacked vital emphasis. As in the Highway Code (Extract 2) the possibility could still rest in the mind that automation of the system would stop the train if it was in danger. Perhaps what should have been said was something on the lines of:

> **ONLY a prior telephone call** can stop an oncoming train actuating the crossing. When the lights begin to flash you will have only eight

seconds to pass under the barrier, and then sixteen seconds more to leave the crossing. Unless you can cross in twenty-four seconds do not attempt to do so. **TELEPHONE FIRST.**

The leaflet reproduced here (Extract 5) was prepared for Hixon. In those prepared before the end of 1966 the reference to the prior telephone call was written to apply to drivers of heavy vehicles or exceptional loads which might stall. Reference to stalling later disappears from leaflets, leaving the wording shown.

Leaflets were not the only means of directing attention to the telephone. At the crossing stood the notice, surely plain for all to read and understand!

Extract 5

Part of British Railways' leaflet on crossings

Automatic lifting half barriers

are not yet familiar in Britain although commonplace in the United States and on the Continent where they have proved to be safe and very satisfactory in saving the time of road users.

HOW THEY WORK

A train approaching the crossing automatically sets warnings in motion to stop road traffic and pedestrians. These are unmistakable. A bell gives audible warning and twin red lights flash at both sides of the road. Two red and white striped barriers, carrying fixed red lights, finally descend to seal off the half of the road to oncoming traffic. Within a few seconds the train will pass and, if no other train is approaching, the half-barriers lift automatically to clear the road.

REMEMBER If the barriers do not lift immediately it means another train is approaching. **Obey the red stop lights, your wait will be brief.**

The red stop lights apply to all road users. Pedestrians will have time to cross even if the warnings start as soon as they have stepped on to the crossing. Because each barrier closes only half the road it is impossible to be shut in on the crossing.

PHONES are provided at each barrier post in case of emergency.

BUT– if you intend to herd animals over the crossing you should first use the phone to find out if you have time to cross before the next train.
– drivers with exceptional or heavy loads should also phone the signalman before crossing.

The Telephone Notice

The telephone notice has been referred to before, but its exact wording calls for comment:

> **In emergency**
> or before crossing with
> exceptional or heavy
> loads or cattle
> **phone signalman**

If a driver had confidence that he was not involved in an emergency, he might read the first two words, which were in large, heavy type, then return his attention to the road ahead. But the notice does not deal merely with a stalled vehicle or a road accident, it goes on to instruct in the every-day task of taking a slow load across the railway.

British Railways made no attempt to find out whether the notice drew attention to the telephone effectively. Not until after the Hixon accident was a rough survey carried out nationally to gauge the extent to which the telephone procedure was used. The survey revealed blatant and widespread neglect of the telephone procedure in the months preceding the Hixon accident, thus putting the notice under strong suspicion of ineffectiveness. Moreover a sample survey for the crossing involved in the incident described next (Leominster) showed a similar disregard of this vital part of the control system, even after the Hixon disaster on January 6, 1968, and the subsequent publicity.

Lesson at Leominster

Leominster automatic crossing was notable both for its heavy use by industrial traffic and the massive hump in the road where it crossed the rails.

More than a year before the Hixon collision, a low-loader articulated vehicle carrying a crane became grounded on the hump at Leominster crossing. Only after violent efforts on the part of the lorry driver was the loader driven off before an express arrived. The driver of the vehicle, surprised at the brisk operation of the system and the rapid arrival of the train, reported the incident to his employers, who wrote to British Railways expressing concern that there had nearly been an accident.

In answer to the letter, British Railways replied that Leominster crossing was of standard Ministry-approved design. They went on to say blandly that vehicles must not become immobile on crossings. The reply did not even enclose a standard leaflet. Again railway operators had lost a chance for further thought, together with an opportunity to tell at least one haulier about the telephone. By a strange twist of fate the same haulage company was used by English Electric for the fatal journey to Hixon.

ENGLISH ELECTRIC

This firm, owning both the transformer and the depot to which it was dispatched just beyond the crossing, had contacted British Railways in 1964 about road widening at Hixon, and the haulier a year later about problems imposed by overhead electrification. The Chief of Heavy Transport used the crossing almost once each week, and one month before the accident had taken responsibility for checking the overhead clearance under the electrified wires. English Electric had initiated previous requests for special order journeys over that crossing and now applied for the special order for the fatal movement of their transformer. None of the written instructions received back from the Ministry mentioned the danger on the doorstep of the Hixon depot.

One last opportunity occurred for correcting previous omissions. Because the route was new to the transporter driver he asked English Electric's haulage chief for directions. Hixon crossing was thus mentioned in conversation as an identifying feature on the last lap to the depot, but not described as a hazard. The only party which could intervene now was the police patrol.

THE POLICE

The Patrol Constables

The police have only a general duty to prevent anyone proceeding in a dangerous fashion, so, although the transporter driver assumed the police would look after the passage of his vehicle, the main responsibility of the police patrol on these non-statutory escort duties is to secure a safe and trouble-free journey for other vehicles encountering the escorted load. Of course this might involve halting oncoming traffic briefly but their duty can best be described as overall traffic control rather than clearing a way for the transporter and piloting it past charted hazards.

The police patrol accompanying the transporter comprised two constables in a car. On arrival at the crossing, one constable went ahead to the other side, then returned to tell the transporter driver he was on the right road but faced a 16′6″ headroom restriction and a hump in the road at the rails. Both constables then proceeded over the crossing in advance of the transporter. The policemen did not see the telephone notice. They did not know the crossing worked with guillotine briskness. They took no specific steps to forestall a collision.

The Police Authorities

We have encountered several opportunities for this large system (the police force) to comprehend the workings of automatic crossings. To the list of opportunities must be added inclusion of a copy of the Requirements and the Explanatory Note among the material each officer is expected to read at his Station. We have already noted the excess of detail in the Requirements and the absence of due emphasis in the Note. It is said that one government department (here the Home Office for the police) does not rework material issued by other departments (the Ministry and the Railways). Although the police could complain that they received vital information in an unacceptable form, they have also been criticized for failing to pick out those points necessary for proper execution of their duties.

THE HAULAGE COMPANY

This is a large firm, owning 170 vehicles and specializing in abnormal loads, but somehow they missed, or were missed by, the publicity on the new crossings, for they denied knowledge of the operation of half-barrier systems. However, the Leominster incident involved this very company, and details in their letter to British Railways revealed they knew of the timing and that a lorry driver could not stop an oncoming train. It must be admitted that the vehicle involved at Leominster was not large enough to need a special order, and that the incident was not a direct indication of the danger to a slow moving vehicle as distinct from a stationary vehicle; but even the drivers of normal vehicles in the firm received no warning of any kind from their management. Whether the Leominster driver circulated details of his experience by word of mouth is not known.

THE DRIVER AND CREW

Immediate responsibility for safe passage of the load lay with the crew and driver. As leader of the crew, the driver tackled what was to him a new hazard without reading the roadside notice intended for his assistance. Not only did he ignore the telephone notice, he also acted rashly in another way. His load towered to a height of 16′9″, reducible by six inches after adjustment of the running gear. But faced with the news from the police patrol that clearance under the electrified wires was only 16′6″ he nevertheless drove on. Admittedly, drivers commonly found overhead wires to be higher than stated; agreed he did slow down and arrange for crew members to watch the clearance; but on the other hand he did not stop to reduce his vehicle's height beforehand. Moreover he checked the clearance by advancing the transformer up to the wires. If the clearance had been insufficient, allowing the cable to arc on to the transformer, the load would have been immobile across the tracks for some time.

The mate on the leading tractor had duties as a 'statutory attendant' on a vehicle of this specification. One of these duties was to warn of any danger; his only idea of his duties however was that he should do what the leading driver told him. Also, in common with the whole crew he would expect the police patrol to keep a look out.

CONCLUSION

This is not the place to apportion blame; judgement of the share attributed to each participant is explained and presented in the Report of the Inquiry. Without repeating the names of the components of the system whose objective was safety but whose consequence was the Hixon accident, it is possible to see grave deficiencies in many components of the system and the links between them.

The story of Hixon began with a willingness to satisfy a desire to quicken the pace of one system of transport without slowing down another. The protagonists satisfied themselves that no greater danger would ensue. By cautious experiments experience was gained, some new aspects were considered. But one aspect – the slow moving load – never received the degree of attention that hindsight would show to be necessary. Provision of a telephone at the crossing catered for the needs of this special user of the crossing, but the groups involved in the system failed, some in not publicizing the safety device, some in not being aware of it.

Surprisingly, introducing a system labelled automatic had added to the level of responsibility carried by road users, rather than diminishing it. This was not explained forcefully by the originators of the new scheme; it was not grasped by recipients of information or by users of the new crossings. Then on 6 January 1968, as in many other incidents, men who were confident of their skill and experience found that they had something new to learn. Hixon was the first accident of its type; hopefully there will be no other.

Select chronology of the Hixon Crossing Accident

	1956	Joint Working Party visits the Continent
1 May	1958	Provisional Requirements issued
February	1961	First automatic half-barrier level crossing
	1963	Telephone notice designed
August	1963	English Electric write to British Railways about road widening
22 June	1964	Barriers demonstrated at Marylebone to Press
	1964	British Railways aware of slow vehicle problem
October	1965	English Electric meets haulier about problems raised by electrification at Hixon crossing
12 January	1966	Hixon crossing site meeting
	1966	British Railways widen roadway at Hixon crossing
July	1966	Requirements issued, 'telephone may be necessary'
July	1966	Explanatory note issued
Mid	1966	Telephones to be almost universal at crossings
August	1966	Requirements and Explanatory Note to Chief Constable
8 November	1966	Leominster incident
End	1966	Stalling deleted from leaflet text
1966–January	1967	TV fillers shown
19 January	1967	Hixon Crossing Order signed
January and February	1967	Two 'special order' journeys over Hixon crossing
2 April	1967	Hixon crossing open, converted to automatic half-barrier
2 June	1967	Hixon site inspection
July	1967	Hixon crossing keeper withdrawn
7 December	1967	Manchester journey across Hixon crossing requires special order
18 December	1967	English Electric request route from Ministry
22 December	1967	English Electric told by Ministry that special order is signed
29 December	1967	Haulier sends route to County Council, Police and Railways
6 January	1968	The Hixon accident

photographic [illegible] by the [illegible] of the [illegible] it was [illegible] or by [illegible] of the [illegible] the [illegible] on a [illegible] were [illegible] of [illegible] experience found that they had something new to learn. [illegible] Hixon, was the first accident of its [illegible] hopefully there will [illegible] that.

Select chronology of the [illegible] Crossing Accident

	1956	[illegible] Working Party visit the Continent
1 May	[illegible]	Provisional Requirements [illegible]
February	[illegible]	[illegible] Automatic [illegible]
	[illegible]	Telephone notice designed
[illegible]	[illegible]	English Electric [illegible]
		[illegible]
[illegible]	1964	[illegible]
		[illegible]
[illegible]		[illegible]
		[illegible]
		[illegible]
		[illegible]
[illegible]	1965	[illegible] requirements [illegible] may be necessary
[illegible]	1966	[illegible]
[illegible]	1966	Telephones to be [illegible]
[illegible]	1966	Requirements and Explanatory Note [illegible] Council
[illegible]		[illegible]
[illegible]		[illegible]
[illegible]		[illegible]
[illegible]	[illegible]	Hixon [illegible]
[illegible]		[illegible]
[illegible]	1967	[illegible]
[illegible]	[illegible]	Hixon [illegible]
		[illegible]
[illegible]	[illegible]	[illegible]
[illegible]	[illegible]	[illegible]
[illegible]	[illegible]	[illegible]
[illegible]	1967	[illegible]
[illegible]	[illegible]	[illegible]
[illegible]	1967	[illegible]

Case Study 2

The Aberfan Disaster

by Victor Bignell

CONTENTS Page

At 9.15 a.m. on Friday, 21 October 1966 many thousands of tons of mine rubbish from Tip number 7 of Merthyr Vale Colliery in South Wales swept down the Merthyr Mountain and into the village of Aberfan. Saturated by water, the black slimy mass overwhelmed two cottages, engulfed a school and destroyed some eighteen houses. Other houses and a second school suffered damage. One hundred and sixteen children, five teachers and twenty-three other adults died.

The following account is based on the official report:

> 'Report of the Tribunal appointed to inquire into the Disaster at Aberfan on October 21st 1966', House of Lords paper 316, House of Commons paper 553, published by Her Majesty's Stationery Office, August 1967.

THE VILLAGE BELOW THE MOUNTAIN

Aberfan and nearby Merthyr Vale are villages on the River Taff in South Wales. Aberfan lies mainly on the west bank; Merthyr Vale Colliery is on the east bank. The river shares the valley with a disused canal, railway tracks, and a road (Figure 1). Merthyr Tydfil is the nearest town, four miles away to the north.

Merthyr Mountain rises above Aberfan with a slope of one in four at first, steepening to one in three and levelling out when some 800 feet above the river. The area receives a high rainfall, and while the sandstone core of the mountain is only slightly porous itself, cracks and fissures within it, accentuated by mining subsidences, allow surface water to percolate down until it reaches bands of coal or impervious clay sandwiched between layers of sandstone. These bands incline towards the valley at a slope of only 1:12, so water intercepted by each band runs down along the clay until it reaches the surface of the mountain, there to appear as readily visible springs and streams. If this surface water had been noticed and avoided when mine waste was tipped on the hillside, the Aberfan disaster would not have occurred.

Figure 1 Aberfan and Merthyr Mountain, 1919

TIPPING

A coal mine generates a large quantity of what can only be called rubbish. Some is the result of cutting and widening shafts and tunnels, not only to reach the coal but also to provide workshop and storage areas, airways and drainage shafts. At the coalface itself coal and other material must be dug away and laboriously transported to the surface. There the saleable coal is separated from worthless material. Together with boiler-house ash and discarded equipment all this must be disposed of.

At Merthyr Vale Colliery the waste went up the mountain in 'trams' on railway tracks. A stationary engine hauled the trams up in groups by cable until on arrival at the engine house they were allowed to run back to where a fork in the track directed the trams to the next operation. This usually involved a crane which lifted and inverted each tram, tipping the contents down on to the hillside. The crane ran on its own short length of track, while incoming and outgoing trams each had their own separate tracks, all on top of previously tipped material. By discharging the rubbish forwards as well as sideways the tip would advance. By tipping down the hillside a greater amount of material can be disposed of than on flat ground, and the practice had been endorsed in a Technical Advisory Committee report of 1945. In South Wales, hillsides are cheap and abundant but on Merthyr Mountain such tips were to become too high for safety on the wet ground, and would moreover be poised over the village and its schools.

Five of the seven tips on Merthyr Mountain operated in the fashion just described. The other two tips each began with the erection of a lattice-work steel tower. Containers on a short aerial ropeway carried the rubbish to the top of the tower; there it was released to form the tip as a cone around the tower. (Figures 2–5 taken together show these and other features.) Whatever the method adopted, the ground to be covered would not be in doubt.

It is clear that mining officials would be reluctant to abandon a tipping site prematurely. Indeed it was suggested at the disaster inquiry that local fears of pit closure (if expensive changes to tipping arrangements were found to be necessary) silenced cries of alarm at the state of Merthyr Vale's tips.

Again, the whole purpose of a coal mine was to produce coal: disposal of waste was a chore. The attention of officials on the production side was understandably concentrated on events underground. Likewise in respect of safety: work underground is dangerous, but on the surface no one had been killed by an unstable rubbish tip. Spoil heaps were either symbols of industry or eyesores in the environment; they were not regarded as potentially dangerous.

TIP CHRONOLOGY

The Merthyr Vale Colliery shafts were sunk a century ago, but tipping on the hillside was unnecessary until 1914–1918, when the 85 feet high Tip 1 began the sequence (Figures 2–4), followed by Tips 2 and 3, 90 feet and 130 feet high respectively. The conical Tip 4 had risen to 147 feet in eleven years when in November 1944 a large part of it slipped down the hillside. So in 1945 Tip 5 was started. Its cone rose to 171 feet. Tip 6 began to deal with the colliery's rubbish in 1956, but two years later became unusable as it encroached on farm land when only 56 feet high.

The fatal Tip 7 was born at Easter 1958 and had risen to 111 feet by the time of the disaster in 1966. Unlike previous tips it contained 'tailings', the slimy residue from the froth-flotation process designed to get the last ounce of usable fuel out of the material brought to the surface by the pit. Tailings set rock-hard when dry, and the tipping gang took to wetting them before tipping.

Tips 1, 3 and 6 lay between streams; they gave no trouble. Lying like Tip 7 across springs and streams, Tip 4 slipped and Tip 5 bulged, to the alarm not

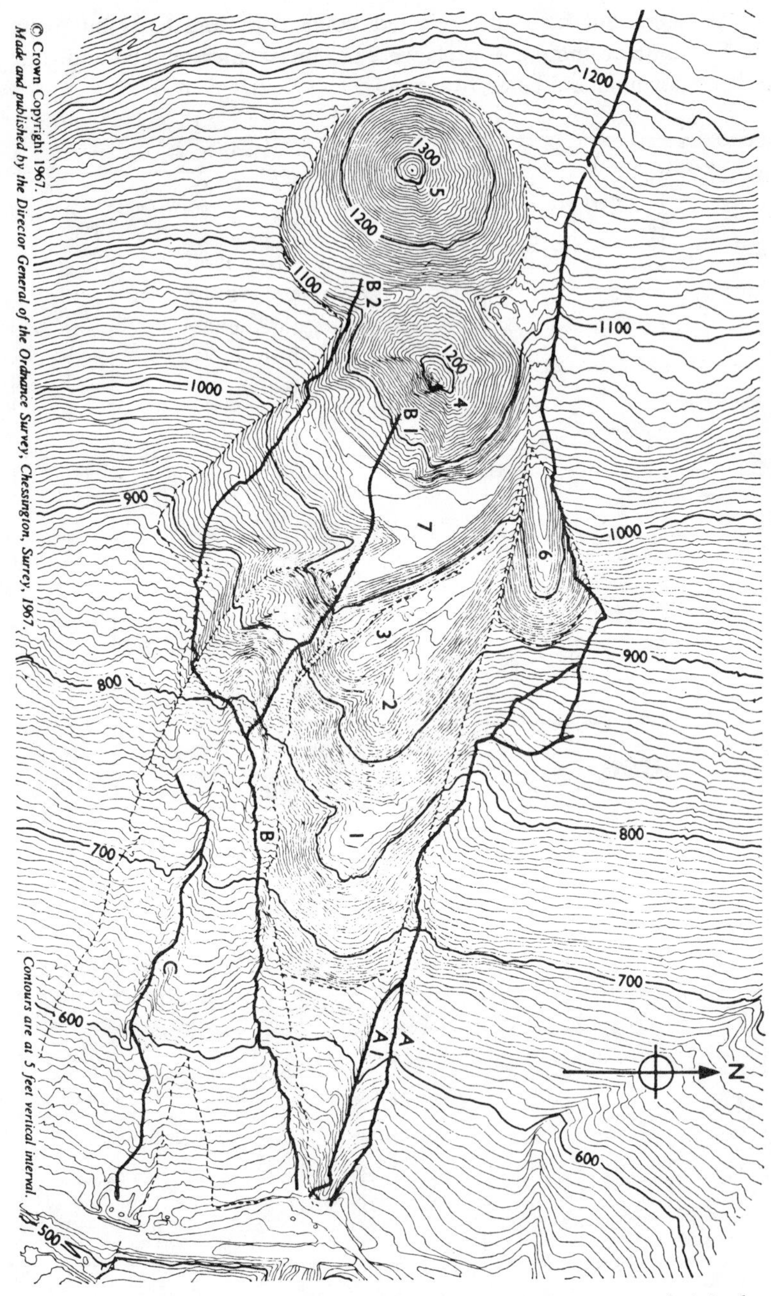

Figure 2 Contours of the tips and mountain, after the disaster (original streams shown in heavy black)

only of villagers but also their elected councillors and local authority officers. By contrast, mining officials were to remain unconcerned until part of Tip 7 slid downhill and killed 144 people.

Table 1 Involvement of NCB officials

	Merthyr Vale Colliery		No. 4 Group		No. 4 Area		South Western Division		
	Mech Engr 1952–	Manager 1962–	Mech Engr 1947–64	Manager 1961–	Civil Engr 1958–65	Mech Engr 1960–	Mech Engr 1958–	Chief Engr 1961–	Prodn Dir 1952–
1927 Paper by Prof. Knox									Saw it, and studied it since
1939 Slip at Cilfynydd			Mechanic at colliery				Assisted in clearance		Witnessed the aftermath
1939 Memorandum							Received copy from father		
1944 Slip of Tip 4									Gave orders for drainage trenches
1958 Site for Tip 7			Chose site	Chose site					
1960 Flood in Aberfan			Met with borough			Met with borough			
1963 Tailings discussions		Visited head of tip, promised remedy				Visited tail of tip, saw no solution			
1963 Slip at Tip 7		Saw it, action insufficient							
1965 Slip at Tymawr								Saw aftermath	
1965 Memorandum					Received	Received	Unearthed copy of 1939 memo	Issued with instruction	Learned of it
1965 Report on tips	Not consulted	Not consulted	Not consulted	No knowledge	No report made	Reported tip safe	Took no action to see reports	Insufficient attention to reports	Received summaries
1966 Sinkings of Tip 7	Reports denied	Reports denied							

OFFICIALDOM

In 1966 Merthyr Vale Colliery was one of five collieries making up No. 4 Group in No. 4 Area of the South Western Division of the National Coal Board. The Colliery Manager had his office near the pithead; the Group Manager's office was half a mile from the mine; the Area Manager's office was only a few miles from Aberfan. The Divisional office operating 75 collieries and employing 60,000 men was twenty miles away near Cardiff and the NCB Headquarters was, of course, in London. Officials at Colliery and Group levels had passed statutory examinations and were additionally qualified by experience. Officials at Area and Divisional levels were qualified academically and professionally.

Table 1 links men and events in the history of the Aberfan disaster. Each man included is referred to by the title of the position he held in late 1964, while the period each man held that position is also quoted. An entry in the table connects an individual with an event, on the basis of the evidence in the report of the disaster tribunal. Where he was involved in an early event, the individual would, of course, have held a more lowly position, but this degree of detail is not included in Table 1.

To a greater extent than in any other industry the senior posts in mining are held by men experienced in that industry. They would even stay in the same locality to the extent that certain Welsh surnames are common among the individuals in the Aberfan story. This is one reason for not using names here.

PROFESSOR KNOX'S WARNING

The connection between events and individuals in the Aberfan chronology begins in 1927 when a Professor Knox gave to a meeting of the South Wales Institute of Engineers, in Cardiff, a paper on landslides in South Wales valleys. The Professor warned of the menace of allowing water in a tip. He added that if collieries did not pay for drainage they would have to pay for the effects of landslides. After hearing the paper a contributor to the discussion warned that to neglect investigation of so-called suitable ground might land colliery companies in litigation and compensation that would bankrupt them. Among mining engineers of South Wales the paper was a classic, but was none the less almost unheeded in the Aberfan story.

Even at this early date, 39 years before the Aberfan disaster, evidence for later neglect begins to accumulate, for the man destined to become Production Director of the South Western Division of the NCB had seen the paper in 1927 as a student, and had studied it.

CILFYNYDD SLIDE

Until nationalization in 1947, Merthyr Vale Colliery was owned by the Powell Duffryn Company, as was the Albion Colliery near Cilfynydd five miles away. There, at 1.40 p.m. on December 5th, 1939, some 180 000 tons of waste from a tip slid down a hillside to block a road, a canal and the River Taff. No one was killed, or even injured, but the incident made an impression on the colliery owners. Powell Duffryn had commissioned reports on previous incidents, and now asked a consultant engineer to investigate. He prepared an illustrated memorandum entitled 'The Sliding of Colliery Rubbish Tips'.

The Chief Engineer in one of the Powell Duffryn Areas gave a copy of the memorandum to his son who helped operate equipment to clear up the mess at Cilfynydd, and appears in the 1966 disaster twenty-seven years later as Divisional Mechanical Engineer. Further, the future Divisional Production Director, employed in 1939 at a nearby Powell Duffryn colliery, reckoned Cilfynydd the worst of the three tip slides he had then seen. Finally, a mechanic at Albion Colliery itself would by 1964 have become Mechanical Engineer to the Group of five collieries of which Merthyr Vale Colliery was one. But memories of Cilfynydd in 1939 did not warn of future troubles, while the memorandum lay forgotten in a drawer until 1965.

TIP 4 SLIPS

Begun in 1933, the conical Tip 4 suffered a minor slip early in its life, and the material from this formed a surface which when buried by later tipping encouraged a major slip in 1944. The events left a hole in the side of Tip 4 running up to the apex and still visible in 1966. Some of the material travelled 1800 feet, nearly reaching the disused canal.

Evidence for movement before 1944 comes from the text of a report by the then Borough Engineer. This report shows an appreciation of the danger of water under a tip, and led to a site meeting in February 1944 at which the later Production Director appeared as a Colliery Agent and company representative. The same man had been Manager at Merthyr Vale from 1940 until 1942. The Company officials reassured the local authority that there was no immediate danger, but arranged to have drainage trenches dug to the South and South-west of Tip 4. They also started laying foundations for the tipping apparatus of the future Tip 5.

But late in 1944 came the major slip of Tip 4. The same Colliery Agent was called in. He was greatly concerned, but no one sought the reason for the slip. He told the Borough the slip had been caused by rain, and that his drainage scheme had minimized it. In fact Tip 4 had covered 400 feet of a stream.

As well as showing the ill-effects of water under a tip, the events of 1944 should have made clear the interaction between the surface of earlier slipped material and a new slip. This same effect was to occur again some twenty years later, for when Tip 7 advanced on to the surface of the fallen material from the then disused Tip 4, a slide from Tip 7 soon followed.

TIP 5

The 1944 slip rendered the mechanical tipper at No. 4 unusable, so Tip 5 was started. Although its site had the blessing of the Colliery Agent, this tip began to cover the trenches he himself had ordered dug around No. 4. Corresponding to pattern, by 1951 No. 5 covered a stream for 900 feet and had slipped.

In 1950 the Borough was still worried about these tips on the wet hillside above the village. The NCB Estates Manager allayed these fears by pointing out that disposal was above the old tips, and would cease when underground storage of rubbish began in a year's time. He added that the position of the tips was under constant check. In fact no checks had been made; tipping at No. 5 went on for five years more, and underground storage never became feasible. Plans were made for tipping beyond No. 5, but all were more expensive than adapting existing equipment to start Tips 6 and 7.

TIP 7

Use of Site 6 was short-lived owing to encroachment on to farm land, so after 1957 a new site was needed. From among the possibilities, Site 7 required only that a few lengths of track be transferred from Tip 6 (Figures 3 and 4). The junction in the track remained where it was but instead of the rubbish trams being directed to the North of the main track and on to Tip 6 they went to the South on to the site for Tip 7.

The choice of site for the new tip was made at Easter 1958 by the then Colliery Manager (later Group Manager) and the Group Mechanical Engineer; neither can be considered as qualified to select a site. No survey was made, no boreholes sunk, no tipping limits determined except to note the limits of NCB property. No other official was consulted (the Colliery Surveyor makes no appearance in the story).

A plan of the tip complex had been drawn, to help avoid encroachment. The

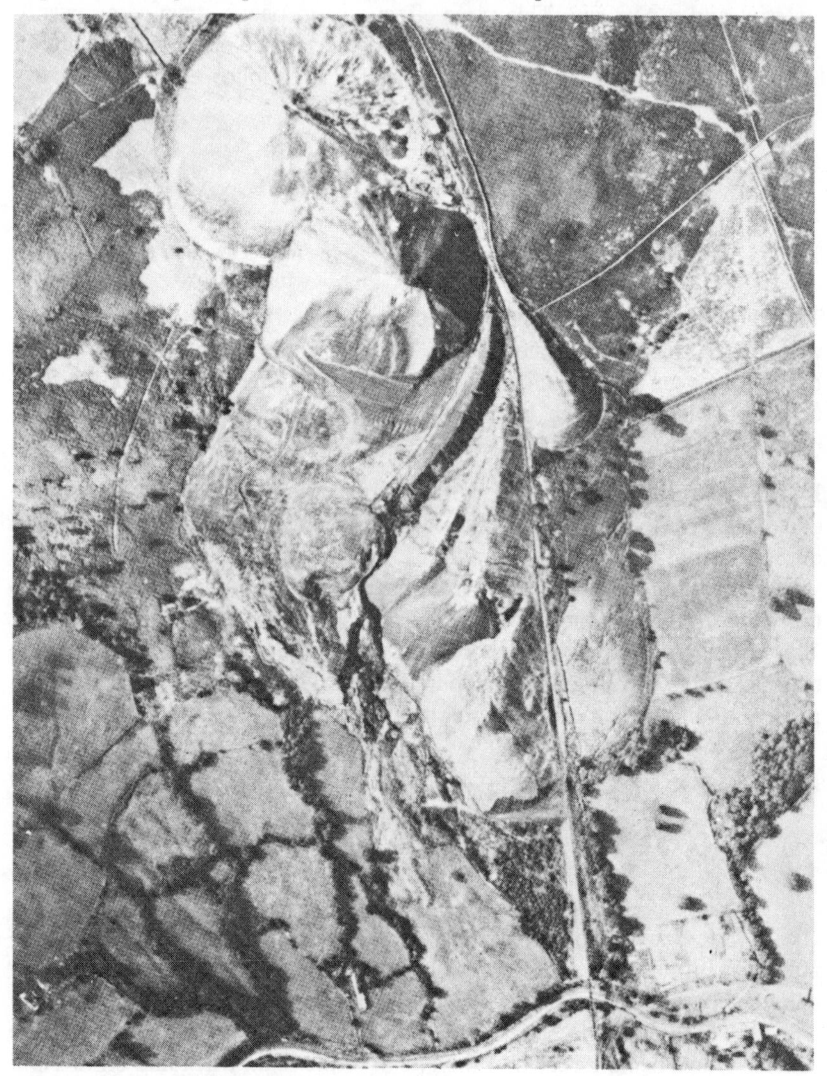

Figure 3 The tips in May 1963 (see key opposite)

Group Planning Engineer had it prepared by his staff from a sketch supplied by the Area Mechanical Engineer. The sketch was based in turn on a Powell Duffryn map of 1919. Although he could see the complex from his office, the Group Planning Engineer had never visited the tips and would later concede after the disaster that his plan was utter nonsense. It is not known whether the plan misled any officials, some of whom knew it was based on inaccurate information. That this was the best diagram of the area is an indication of the status of tip planning.

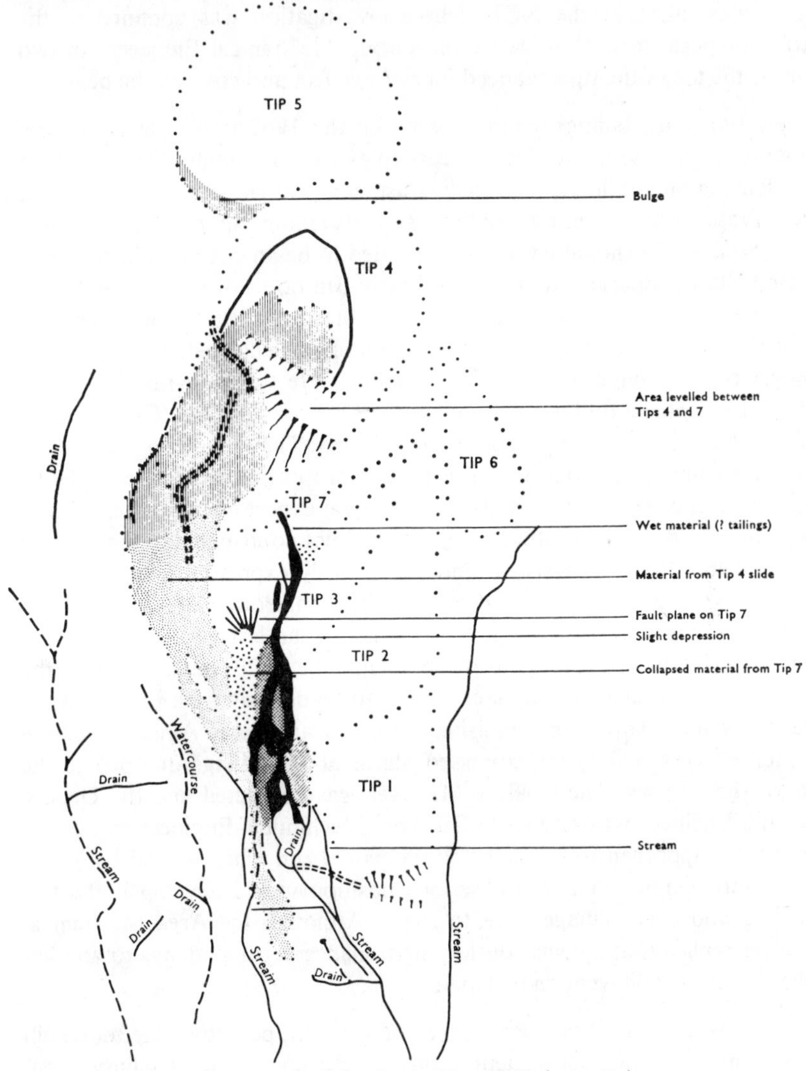

Figure 4 Key to photograph of the tips in May 1963 (opposite)

FLOODING AND TAILINGS

Ever since tipping began on the Mountain, disturbance of natural drainage and blocking of man-made water courses by fine waste had caused flooding in Aberfan. But, in their repeated complaints to the NCB in 1959 and 1960, the Council and its special sub-committee dealing with Aberfan tips not only protested about the flooding, it also expressed fears of tip-slides brought on by heavy rain. The Merthyr Vale Labour Party backed them up but no action was taken in the NCB, where investigation was confined to the setting of pegs in the hillside by the Group Mechanical Engineer. In two months the toe of the tip advanced four or five feet and covered the pegs.

A new pollutant, tailings, came down with the 1962 floods. Modern coal filtration plants use a chemical process to extract the smallest fragments of coal, leaving only tailings, a fine ashy dust, slimy when wet, rock hard when dried. Water, added to assist handling, spreads tailings almost flat when they are tipped. At Divisional level it was decided to begin putting tailings down disused shafts, separate from other rubbish. But no steps were taken to circulate this decision to No. 4 Group or to Merthyr Vale Colliery, and the NCB Director-General of Production had no knowledge before the Aberfan disaster of any dangerous qualities in tailings. He subsequently found that tailings had caused difficulty in four of the Divisions of the NCB. So Tip 7 continued to receive tailings from 1962 to 1965. They made up 10 per cent of the tip volume but contributed in greater proportion to local complaints of flooding and fears of instability. Independent expert opinion after the disaster concluded that the nature of tailings had not contributed to the disaster slide of 1966. But the persistent and vociferously expressed fear of tailings should have brought senior and expert attention from the National Coal Board. Perhaps then the more general danger of careless tipping would have been seen. Be that as it may, to those outside the NCB, tailings caused the most concern. When tailings later ceased to be deposited on the mountain local fears and complaints diminished. In the meantime, in August 1963 the Council officers had again expressed alarm about tailings dumped to the rear of the schools. The Colliery Manager was contacted and the Deputy Borough Engineer wrote to the NCB Area Mechanical Engineer expressing the current apprehension that the slurry would run when wetted by storm water, and pointing out that a serious position would develop if the tips towering above the village were to move. Although the Area Mechanical Engineer replied that he was considering transporting the tailings to another colliery, tailings still went on to Tip 7.

As will be seen in the next section, part of Tip 7 slipped down the mountain in November 1963. Subsequently on 26 November the Colliery Consultative Committee, attended by miners' representatives and by non-mining interests, listened to local fears of a further slide. On the next day the Colliery Manager visited the tip and decided the tipping of tailings must stop. It continued, although in reduced quantity. On that same day, but independently of the Colliery Manager and accompanied by the Deputy Borough Engineer, the Area Mechanical Engineer visited the areas subject to flooding.

Two months later this last officer wrote that a satisfactory and suitable plan for tailings disposal eluded him and caused him great concern, while in reply to letters complaining about flooding he wrote in March 1964 that the tipping of tailings would cease. He claimed to be taking great care in disposing of the material so as not to inconvenience anyone. He said he would not like to continue tipping on the mountainside for more than two months where it was likely to be a source of danger to the school. By way of reply the Deputy Borough Engineer reminded the Coal Board of the liability that would fall on it if the tip moved. The Colliery Manager and Area General Manager claimed to be unaware of this correspondence when examined at the Tribunal's Inquiry after the disaster.

1963 SLIP OF TIP 7

One particular spring continually washed away the foot of Tip 7, leaving a steepish face 70–80 feet high. Around November 1963, after several smaller movements, a substantial portion of the working end of the tip moved; 7–8 yards of the point slid part of the way down the face; some ran on down the hillside. Whilst tipping on No. 4 had ceased in 1944 when that tip slipped, Tip 7 in 1963 continued to grow. NCB archives show no record of this 1963 slide; several officers at Divisional, Group and Area levels denied knowledge of it. The problems of Tip 7 and the complaints from the village should have reached their ears.

If the mining officials were ignorant or calmly confident, not so a local councillor reported in the *Merthyr Express* of 11 January 1964 as declaring at a Town Planning meeting:

> If the tip moved it could threaten the whole school.

At the Consultative Committee meeting already referred to, an Alderman voiced fears of tip instability. The Chairman (the Colliery Manager) stated that the existing banking would protect the houses, and tenders were out for

Figure 5 View of tips in 1964

an aerial ropeway to carry waste to the top of the Mountain. At a meeting the following month he said the new ropeway would be installed, starting in May 1964.

THE AERIAL ROPEWAY

Those who feared for tip stability and suffered from the flooding sought help outside the valley when, in January 1964, a Town Planning Committee resolution was passed . . . 'that the Member of Parliament and the Association of Municipal Corporations be informed of the concern and alarm of the Committee at the excessive amount of tipping by the National Coal Board taking place in this area'. However, this resolution was regarded as linked to the Planning Officer's recommendation that an application by the NCB for planning permission in respect of an aerial ropeway for tipping above Tip 5 be approved. So, when the NCB withdrew the planning application, the resolution itself was dropped. A previous scheme for aerial ropeway tipping had been decided upon by the Area General Manager and submitted for planning permission but had been withdrawn in favour of the January 1964 scheme. As it was not until July 1966 that NCB Headquarters approved the expenditure of some £330,000 for an aerial ropeway, the Colliery Manager was incorrect to refer (as he did in late 1963) to tenders being out and work starting in May 1964.

On 11 March 1964 the NCB No. 4 Area Deputy Estates Manager and the Area Planning Engineer attended a Town Planning Committee meeting to discuss the aerial ropeway plan. The Council representatives were apprehensive that tipping higher up the mountain would put pressure on existing tips and lead to slipping. In reply the Area Planning Engineer explained that tipping would proceed in steps or tiers, starting from the canal. It seems that under this scheme the rubbish would cover the hillside and the top of the Mountain regardless of streams, existing tips, displaced material and a group of cottages on the slope. Dissatisfied, the Council deferred approval of the scheme so that, although the aerial ropeway was never completely abandoned, it remained dormant.

This same Engineer had seen the result of the Cilfynydd slide of 1939. Yet he made no protest when in 1957 he was invited to comment on the site chosen for Tip 7. His attendance at the meeting of 11 March 1964 (referred to in the previous paragraph) was as a last minute deputy. Unfamiliar with the situation and unbriefed, he advanced his tier-tipping scheme without premeditation, and although he presented it with an air of authority, it was not an official NCB view. Never again did the fear of tip stability feature in Council or Committee minutes, the Borough having accepted the persistent reassurances from the NCB officials, who were after all legally responsible and presumably expertly qualified. As it was, a Local Authority could well have civil engineers on its staff, and could have access to soil mechanics consultants better able to judge spoil heap safety than the mining mechanical engineers on whom tipping management problems fell.

TAILINGS AT TYMAWR

The difficulty of stowing tailings led to the use of lagoon storage at some collieries. On a gentle slope a bank of rubbish was pushed up. Behind it the semi-liquid tailings were placed, where they could level out as a lagoon. In this way, at Tymawr in No. 3 Area, a lagoon was formed at the base of a tip. On 29 March 1965 the pressure on the bank breached it and tailings ran down the hillside to cross a railway and flood the main road for hundreds of yards. Cars in the car park were smashed and the flow could well have gone down the colliery shafts. The incident cost the NCB £20,000 but nothing was known of it at NCB Headquarters in London.

For some time the failure was regarded as due to a slide of the tip behind the lagoon, and this false impression impelled the Divisional Chief Engineer to consider issuing a warning on dangerous tipping. He mentioned this to his Mechanical Engineer, who recalled the Powell Duffryn memorandum of 1939 and produced the copy given him by his father. As modified and re-issued in 1965 it could have saved Aberfan.

THE 1965 MEMORANDUM

The Divisional Chief Engineer adopted the form of the 1939 memorandum, and reissued it in 1965 complete with additions referring to tailings. Extract 1 reproduces part of the 1965 version. The memorandum reads as a pre-cognition of conditions at Aberfan, but both the original version and the new one were both prompted by events not far away, so this is perhaps not surprising. Extract 2 reproduces the letter accompanying the 1965 memorandum, and addressed to Area Chief Engineers, Area Mechanical Engineers and Area Civil Engineers, but not to Area General Managers or Area Production Managers. In No. 3 Area, where there had been previous trouble at Tymawr itself in 1961, the 1965 incident led to the local Member of Parliament contacting the Chairman of South Western Division. The Area General Manager set up a scheme under the direction of his Civil Engineer to examine the tips in No. 3 Area. In No. 4 Area the memorandum never reached the Area General Manager or the Merthyr Vale Manager. At the London Headquarters of the NCB nothing was heard of the Tymawr in-cident.

The Divisional Chief Engineer had in mind that in each Area officials would collaborate to examine every active tip. In No. 4 Area he expected the Civil Engineer to take a leading part, owing to the absence of a Chief Engineer. In the event the Area Mechanical Engineer reported, in the brief statement reproduced here as Extract 3. This last individual was to thwart the only serious attempt by higher authority to effect an inspection of tips.

The Area Civil Engineer and the Area Mechanical Engineer had visited the Mountain on April 13th. But we have only the latter's word that he made a special inspection on May 4th, for he neither informed the Colliery Man-ager, nor took along the Mechanical Engineers responsible at the various levels of authority. He took no plans, made no notes. If he did visit the tip he sought no information from the tipping gang. At the time of his visit the remains of the 1944 slip and of the 1963 incident on Tip 7 were all visible. If he observed these features he makes no reference to them in his report (Ex-tract 3).

The Area Civil Engineer and the Area Mechanical Engineer occupied key positions in the Aberfan story. When told to report on tips they put up a dismal performance which must be attributed in part to a clash of personalities. This aspect was probed by the Tribunal after the disaster, and Table 2 uses the results.

Table 2 Two engineers at Area level

Area Civil Engineer (C)	**Area Mechanical Engineer (M)**
Appointed 1958	Appointed 1960
Extract from Statutory Notices defining duties:	
responsible for 'technical engineering control of all surface buildings and structures at mines in the No. 4 Area' (May 1961).	responsible for 'technical engineering control of all mechanical apparatus and of all surface buildings and structures at mines in the No. 4 Area' (August 1960).
When examined by the disaster Tribunal:	
C denied any estrangement with M	M admitted that at times he and C were at loggerheads.
C claimed M told him he would see to the report himself.	M asserted he assumed that he and C would submit independent reports.
The Tribunal concluded:	
C never consulted M, C taking it for granted that M would not welcome his assistance. C overshadowed by M	As tips were traditionally the responsibility of mechanical engineers, M ignored the addressing of the letter to C. M the dominant character
When told to report on tips in 1965:	
No report made	Report made – see Extract 3

Extract 1

The 1965 memorandum (1965 additions to the 1939 text are printed bold).

1. Introduction

The stability of a colliery rubbish tip is dependent on:

1.1. Nature and strength of the ground which supports it;

1.2. Inclination of the surface of the supporting ground and of the underlying rock beds;

1.3. Presence of water;

1.4. Composition of tip material.

. . .

4. Action of Water

In South Wales the action of water has been the most important factor in causing both landslides and slides of rubbish tips.

A foundation of soil and subsoil, of clay or of sand is weakened considerably if water has access to it, and a supporting bed initially of sufficient strength may rapidly deteriorate.

The amount of water which falls annually upon the hills in South Wales is enormous. If the rainfall is 60 inches in a year, and this is the average value, the weight of water deposited upon a surface 100 yards square is about 12,500 tons. All of this water must flow from the surface or soak into the ground, and the greatest danger of sliding exists when a tip is so placed and aligned on a sloping surface that its presence interferes with the drainage.

Rain water which penetrates a permeable rock such as Pennant sandstone, sinks until it is stopped by a bed of impermeable rock, usually a fireclay or a shale. When such a bed crops out on the slope of a hill, the water issues from the ground and a line of springs is formed. These springs may flow continuously, or intermittently following a period of wet weather. If a rubbish tip is extended so as to cover such an outcrop, the issuing water may be checked or dammed, and a slide may result.

Springs of water may also occur where the lower slopes of a hill are formed of impermeable beds overlying the permeable rock.

The tendency of a rubbish tip to prevent the drainage of water through it increases as the material composing it is weathered. In addition to water drained from the hillside, an immense amount of rain falls directly upon the surface of a large tip, and washes down to its base the fine clay products of weathering. It is then more liable to dam back water.

A slide is usually the result of a combination of these circumstances:

4.1. Silting of the lower portion of the tip.
4.2 Water-logging and softening of the supporting ground.
4.3. Accumulation of water drained from the tip and the hillside above it after a period of heavy rain.

5. Composition of Tip Material

The material to be tipped differs greatly in both size and composition. This results in variation in the angle of repose that it takes up, and this must be taken into account when deciding on the location and subsequent management of the tip.

The inclusion of such materials as "tailings" in the general run of rubbish for disposal can result in a marked lowering in the angle of repose from as high as 27° to as low as 4–5°. The tip then becomes completely unmanageable.

6. Precautions to Prevent Sliding

6.1. The height of a tip should be limited to avoid overloading the supporting ground.

6.2 Where a slide would cause damage to property, no tip over 20 feet high should be placed on a hillside unless the ground is a compact gravel or of better quality than this.

6.3. The advancing tip should be so aligned, along a sloping surface, that water draining off the ground above it can be collected, if necessary, by a system of drains cut in the ground, and led past and clear of the tip. Along the uphill edge of the advancing tip, no bays or recesses should be formed in which water can collect.

6.4. On the dip side of the tip, deep drains (not less than 18 inches) should be cut leading downhill to prevent water accumulating and to keep the ground dry. A herringbone system is illustrated as well as the method of packing the drains with flat stones placed on edge.

6.5. Tipping should never be extended over springs of water, whether continuous or intermittent, or over bogged and water-logged ground.

6.6. The composition of the tip material must be carefully watched for variation and the disposal of materials, such as "tailings" must be carried out separately, preferably into redundant shafts or similar enclosures where the failure to maintain a good angle of repose is of no consequence.

. . .

Extract 2

Letter accompanying the 1965 memorandum

Date: 12th April, 1965

SUBJECT: Control and Management of Colliery Rubbish Tips

An incident occurred recently within a Colliery of this Division involving the slipping of the rubbish tip resulting in severe financial loss. I should be pleased, therefore, if you would arrange with your colleagues, for a detailed examination of every tip within your Area, and to take the necessary action for its immediate safety and ultimate good management.

A copy of a report is attached, indicating certain conditions that should be borne in mind during this examination, and I should be pleased if you would let me have a report by Friday, the 30th April, 1965.

I would like to draw your attention specifically to the dangers of including materials such as "tailings" in the general rubbish for disposal, and in particular, to the serious adverse effect this type of material has on the angle of repose that can be expected.

Signed Chief Engineer
South Western Division

Extract 3

Report by Area Mechanical Engineer in reply to 1965 letter.

Merthyr Vale

Rubbish disposal is both by lorry and tram – the lorry disposal is to the old flat site at Plymouth Colliery, where no slipping is likely to take place, and by tram to the old tip on the mountainside – a certain amount of slip has taken place at this point with the taking of tailings to the tip over the past three years. Tailings disposal at this site has ceased and are now being disposed of at Plymouth Colliery site, otherwise the tip remains stable.

THE LAST YEAR

A search for every available source of fuel prompted an industrial fuel company outside the NCB to investigate reclamation of coal from Aberfan's tips. To this end, on the first of his three visits to the complex the Managing Director of the Company was accompanied on 7 July 1965 by the Colliery Manager, the Area Mechanical Engineer and the Group Mechanical Engineer. Although the evidence was there to be seen, these NCB officials were to tell the Tribunal they saw nothing unusual then, and no indication of instability. The date of this inspection comes shortly after two of the officials had learned yet again of local fears.

OTHER PARTIES

Before recounting the last days of Tip 7 it is necessary to balance the evidence somewhat, in that absence of attention to safe tipping was not confined to the persons mentioned so far. In 1938 the Royal Commission on Safety in Mines made no mention of tips or tipping in its 500 page report. The 1954 Mines and Quarries Act confined its reference on tips to declaring them part of each mine. The 1945 Coal Mining Report of the Technical Advisory Committee perhaps indicated the attitude of the industry to its tips –

> Very little choice usually exists in the selection of the dumping site, but where possible a site with falling ground in front of the direction of advance, or sidelong sloping ground, should be chosen. In such circumstances a greater amount of material can be dealt with at no greater cost.

The Mining Qualification Board, the Mining Research Advisory Board and legislation on Town and County Planning did not treat the subject of tipping. Unlike dams and other earthworks no Code of Practice for the construction of mine tips existed. Departmental instructions of Her Majesty's Inspectorate of Mines and Quarries contained no reference to colliery tips: only the mechanical equipment could be held to be their responsibility. Proper legislation for safety would include, indeed often began with, a statutory requirement that accidents be reported. Yet for mines, notification was required only for accidents to employees. As the Aberfan disaster did not involve injury to any person employed at the mine there was no obligation on the colliery to report the disaster, let alone the many previous slides of tip material.

The situation was little different abroad, where searches on behalf of the Inquiry tribunal found enactments on tipping in two places only. The Dortmund Mines Inspectorate issued an order in 1964 governing the construction (but not the siting) of colliery spoil-heaps, while in South Africa a Mines and Works Act required a manager to ensure the safety of any 'slime dam' near a public area.

LAST MOMENTS

In the final six months of tip 7's existence its toe advanced 20–30 feet downhill while the point sank frequently. Sinkings of 10–12 feet occurred exactly where the 1963 slip had been. The tipping gang chargehand claimed to have reported many of the sinkings to his foreman or the Colliery Mechanical Engineer. Both denied this, but an event one hour before the disaster suggested to the Tribunal that reports were not only made but had led to a decision to finish with Tip 7.

For after starting work at 8 a.m. on the day of the disaster the chargehand descended the tip to make his Friday report to the Colliery Mechanical Engineer (the telephone had been removed because the wire had been repeatedly stolen). He reported the tip sinking badly. In reply he was told in effect 'go to the tip, get the crane back as far as you can; we will start another tipping site on Monday'. This saved the lives of the tipping gang, who moved the crane back but decided to have a cup of tea in their hut before doing more.

The haunting feature of the instruction, made at a low level of hierarchy, is that it implies a prior higher-level decision to cease tipping when necessary on No. 7, it being left to the man on the spot to decide just when. Indeed a new site for a conical tip between No. 4 and No. 7 had been discussed over a year before, but the reason given for delay in starting was that new equipment delivered had the wrong gauge of rails. All concerned were to deny

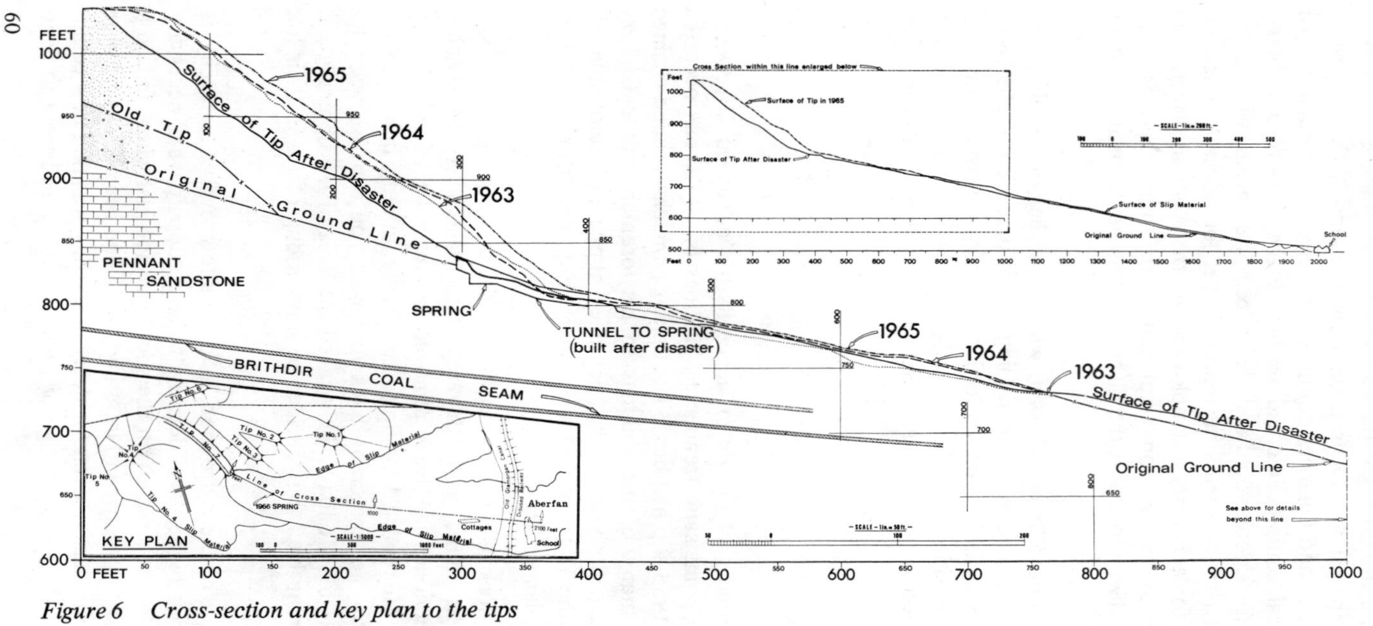

Figure 6 Cross-section and key plan to the tips

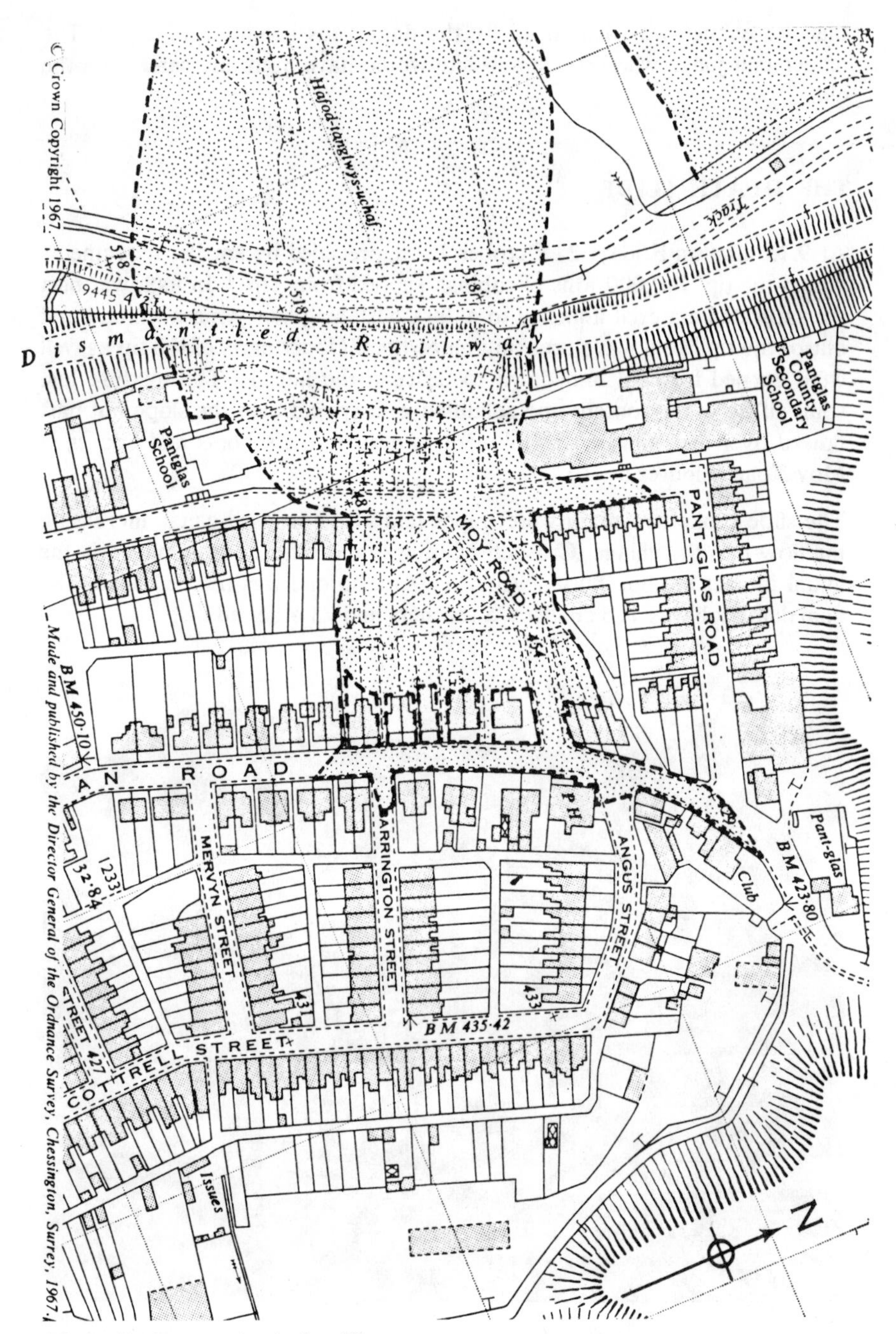

Figure 7 Destruction in the village

that the change was demanded by the dangerous condition of Tip 7. The reader can judge whether the new site would have been any safer than the old.

THE DEATH SLIDE

At 9.15 a.m. on Friday, 21 October 1966, preceded by smaller movements within the tip, 140,000 tons of rubbish slipped from Tip 7. In its lower part the saturated material liquefied to a dark glistening heavy mass which burst out of the tip like a wave breaking on a shore. Upper parts of the tip as well were carried forward and down to descend the hillside. The mixture lost some of its water content and solidified as it spread over the slope but part flowed over the railway embankment to destroy the schools and houses in Moy Road (Figures 6–10).

The slide broke two main water pipes laid in the disused canal, increasing the flow into the village. Crushed buildings, and others not damaged in the initial impact became buried. After 11 a.m. no one was rescued alive. The final death toll was 116 children, 5 teachers and 23 other adults.

Figure 8 Tips after the disaster

RECKONING AND AFTERMATH

After hearing and considering evidence the Inquiry Tribunal sought to make clear in their report their strong and unanimous view that the Aberfan disaster could and should have been prevented. They observed that their report told not of wickedness but of ignorance, ineptitude, and a failure in communications. Ignorance was found amongst those charged at all levels with the siting, control and daily management of tips; bungling ineptitude was displayed by those supervising and directing; the failure was that those having knowledge of the factors affecting tip safety failed to communicate that knowledge and see that it was applied.

In 1948 the NCB appointed a Committee to review the Board's organization. The Board endorsed the Committee's considered view that there should be . . . 'as much devolution of responsibility as possible; the creation of a clear channel of command; and the maintenance of a clear distinction between policy making and execution, but not so as to prevent the association with policy making of those responsible for execution . . .' The Committee went on to point out that efficiency could not be guaranteed merely by setting up a sound system of organization. It takes time to select and train suitable people for management, while those appointed to managerial positions would only gradually acquire the habit of working together.

At the time of the Aberfan disaster the NCB organizational structure still involved five tiers of management. But in 1963 discussions had begun on a new structure, and by autumn 1965 the main principles had already been decided. Early in 1967 the new organization came into being, with only three tiers of management – Colliery, Area and Headquarters. We can only speculate what effect this change might have had on tipping policy had the Aberfan disaster not occurred, for the critical remarks of the 1948 Committee just referred to would operate each time an organizational change is made.

At Aberfan itself now, the tips have been removed from the Mountain, but a special hillside cemetery and memorial commemorate the victims. Below in the valley new buildings bring new life and new problems to a village that like many others had been forgotten. Like no other it will always be remembered now.

Figure 9 The tips, two days after the disaster (see key opposite)

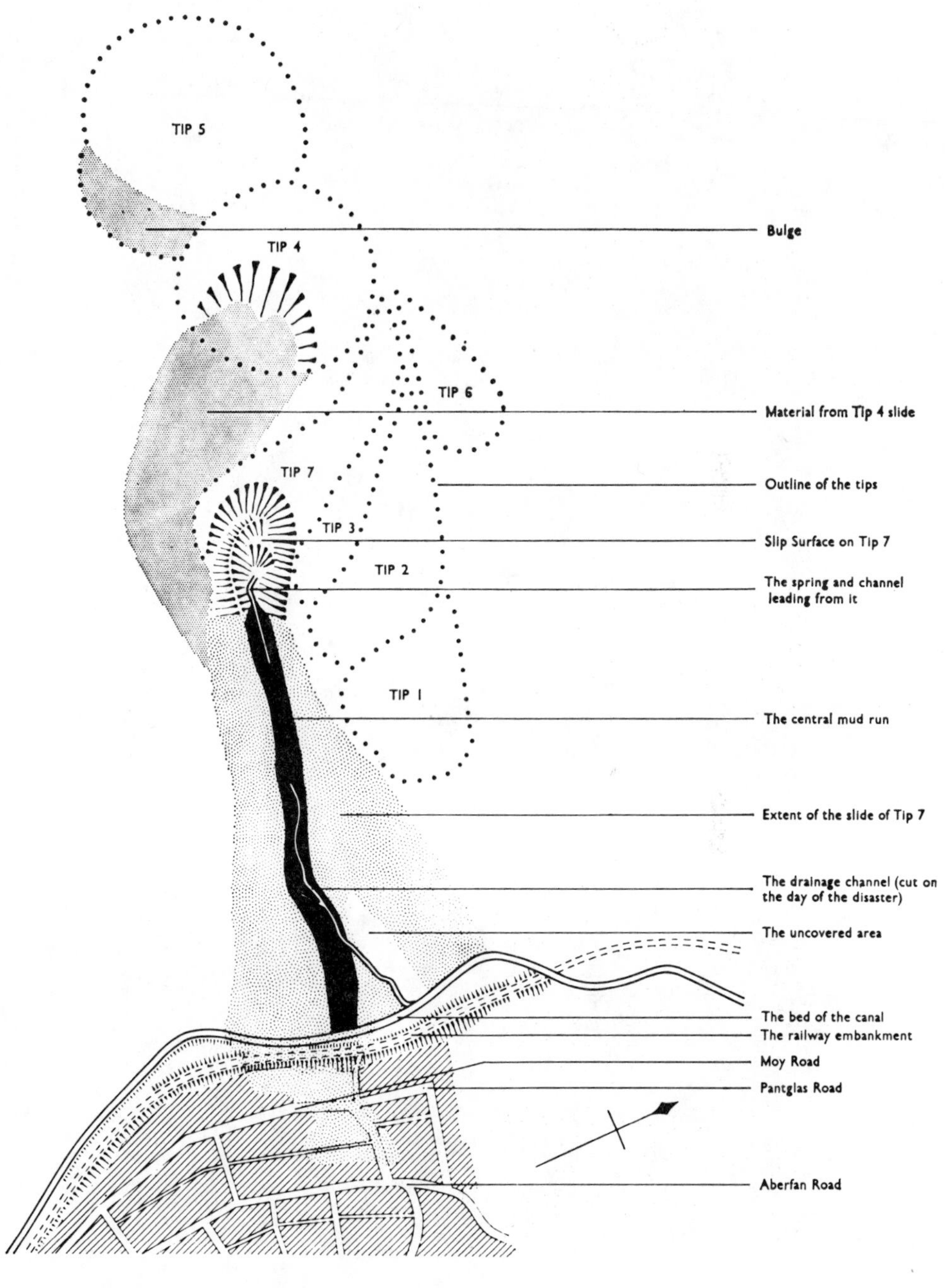

Figure 10 Key to photograph of tips, two days after the disaster (opposite)

Case Study 3
The Summerland Fire Disaster

by Christopher Pym

CONTENTS Page

THE SUMMERLAND FIRE DISASTER

On the evening of 2 August 1973, The Summerland Leisure Centre in Douglas, Isle of Man caught fire and, within an extremely short time, it was reduced to a burnt-out wreck with all floors at and above entrance level (level 4) completely destroyed, 50 men, women and children dead and an equal number of people being treated in hospital.

This account is based on 'Report of the Summerland Fire Commission' published in 1974 by the Isle of Man Government Office. Sections 2.5 and 7.0 utilize press reports. Section 1.3 refers to an advertising leaflet which is not mentioned in the report. The use made of the following two articles is gratefully acknowledged: 'Summerland: the anatomy of disaster', *RIBA Journal,* Vol. 81, No. 7, July 1974, and 'Summerland: the reckoning', *The Architect's Journal,* Vol. 159, No. 22, May 1974.

BACKGROUND

The Summerland Project

The Derby Castle, situated at the northern end of Douglas promenade, was very much a landmark of the Isle of Man in Edwardian and Victorian times. It became an entertainment centre early in the twentieth century, but by the 1960s its buildings were outmoded and its appeal out-of-date. Cheap travel attracted tourists, who might otherwise have come to Douglas, towards the Mediterranean. The great attraction of the Mediterranean was its reliably warm climate.

In the world of architecture and building, designers were experimenting with glass and concrete. Huge leisure complexes were being thought of, and the Montreal Expo (1967) showed some exciting new structures. Already in the early 1960s the architect J. Philipps Lomas was developing the Summerland idea: he planned to replace the old Derby Castle with an artificially heated Cornish or Mediterranean village. The village would include terrace levels suggesting the slopes of steep streets giving access to shops, kiosks, pub and amusements, and with a bathing pool, sand, trees and shrubs. In order to simulate a Mediterranean climate the architect intended to enclose the whole village in a transparent skin so that the holidaymakers would be protected from the worst weather of an Isle of Man summer. The temperature inside the skin would be suitably high.

The concept of Summerland was new, but Douglas Corporation in a serious attempt to attract tourists decided to give it a chance. The programme for the scheme was on the basis of Douglas Corporation developing its own site with financial assistance from the Government of the Isle of Man and on completion continuing to run and maintain the premises. There would be three phases: (1) the Aquadrome (swimming pool), (2) Summerland (the village), and (3) a multi-storey car park. However, the concept of Summerland gradually changed. Instead of the idealized Cornish or Mediterranean village it deteriorated into a vast assembly area into which bands, bars, bingo, and amusement arcades could easily be incorporated. When the shell of Summerland was completed, Trust Houses Forte leased the building and turned it into a fun palace. Summerland had the capacity for about 5000 people and offered a wide variety of entertainment including music, singing, dancing, eating and drinking, sun-bathing, bingo, pin-table games and table tennis. The cost was about £2 million and the result proved to be a big tourist attraction on the Isle of Man.

Appointment of the Architects

J. Philipps Lomas and Brian Gelling accepted the appointment as principal architects to the Aquadrome and Summerland project in April 1965. Mr Lomas recommended that the firm of Gillinson Barnett and Partners of Leeds should act as associate architects for the project because of their established expertise on leisure buildings and enclosed shopping precincts, and this recommendation was accepted in May. It was understood, however, that Mr Lomas remained totally responsible to his client. A letter dated May 24th, 1965, defined the relationship as follows:

> J. Philipps Lomas is the architect employed by, and is directly responsible to, the Douglas Corporation. Gillinson Barnett & Partners will act in association with and be responsible to J. Philipps Lomas. It is presumed that Gillinson Barnett & Partners will be generally responsible for the preparation of all drawings and details, and J. Philipps Lomas will be generally responsible for site supervision. The preparation of contract documents to be the responsibility of J. Philipps Lomas. Generally, all correspondence and discussion with specialists and any appointed consultants will be the responsibility of Gillinson Barnett, after prior agreement with J. Philipps Lomas.

Mr Lomas's firm on the Isle of Man was small and had rarely involved more than six technical staff, of whom Mr Lomas and his partner Mr Gelling were the only two qualified architects. The firm had undertaken no work outside the island at the date of their appointment.

The firm of Gillinson Barnett was a fairly young firm, with the two named principals, Basil Gillinson and Clifford Barnett, still in their middle forties. The firm was formed about 1954, and had grown rapidly until it was well over 100 strong, and had, by 1973, four offices in various parts of Britain.

The Design

The site at the northern end of Douglas Promenade imposed constraints. The available land was limited North–South by a rock cliff on the North and by a railway line running next to the main road on the South. The East–West dimension was longer, being bounded by the railway depot on the East side and by the railway terminus on the West. The two acre site rose from West to East along the road, though the cliff top on the north side was roughly level with a mean height from the site centre of 90 ft. Because of these obstacles access to the site was difficult.

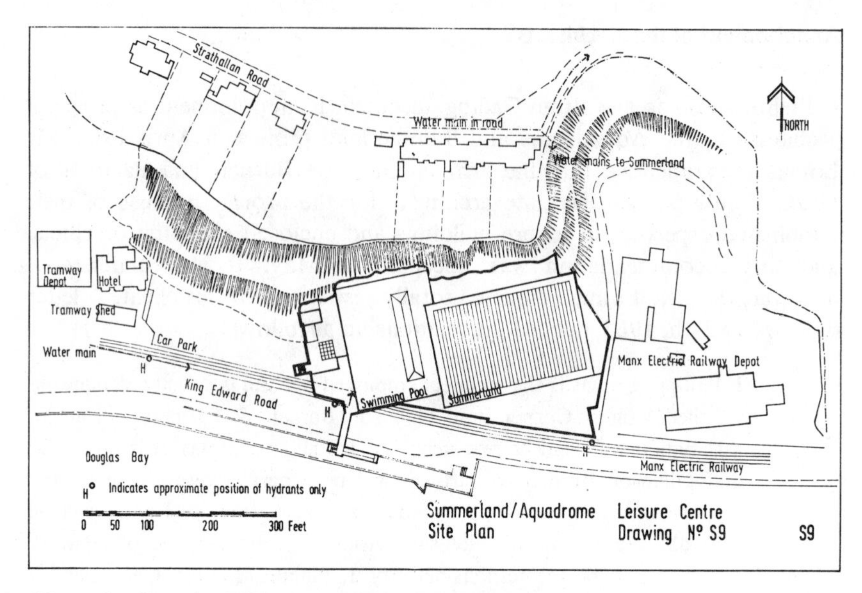

Figure 1 Site plan of Summerland and the Aquadrome

The Aquadrome, built *first* on the west section of the site, constrained the design of Summerland by its own design. The construction of the Aquadrome was of reinforced concrete, including walls and floors. There were few windows and at the swimming bath most of the natural light was obtained from a west wall and a large acrylic roof light. The main service control areas for the future Summerland (main boiler house, heating plant, electrical switchgear and emergency lighting control) were placed in the ground floor of the Aquadrome. A staircase (No. 6) gave access to this plant (see Figures 3 and 4).

The siting of the Aquadrome constrained access to Summerland even more. The Summerland design solution was an entrance floor platform at the fourth floor (solarium) level, to which all patrons (except of the lower ground floor discotheque) had to climb. This was built in reinforced concrete. The basic design had seven main floor levels: Level 1 (discotheque), Level 2 (children's play area known as 'lower downstairs'), Level 3 (large balcony, known as 'upper downstairs'), Level 4 (solarium), Level 5 (Marquee showbar terrace and pool bar), Level 6 (Leisure terrace), and Level 7 (Cruise deck terrace).

Rock formed the north wall both of Summerland and the Aquadrome. The basic structure of Summerland was formed of large steel V sections rising from the reinforced concrete structure of the lower floors and forming a strong V pattern grid. The final structure of the terraces was steel supporting wood floors.

The structural levels and staircases of Summerland are illustrated in Figures 3 and 4. The staircases at Level 4 are tabulated on p90. All the staircases leading from Level 4 (solarium) down to Level 3 (Upper downstairs) were reinforced concrete. Two of them came from above and were enclosed. The north-east service stair (No. 2) came down from Level 6 (TV viewing area and sunbathing) to the east service yard, thus serving all floors except Level 7. The administration stair (No. 6) descended from Level 5 (pool bar), served three levels, and opened into the service accommodation of the Aquadrome. The other two stairs which had open access from the solarium were also constructed in reinforced concrete. Both descended only to Level 3. The main 'flying' stair (No. 1) rose from the solarium to Levels 5 and 6. This was a completely open stair constructed of hardwood open treads on steel bearers. Two similar stairs led from Level 6 up to Level 7, where there was no enclosed stair. A wooden stair, known as the rustic stair and approached by a wooden gangway from Level 5, descended to the solarium just west of the north 'carousel' stair (No. 3). This 'rustic' stair was added at a very late stage of the fitting out. The details of all these stairs (and of the escalator linking Levels 4 and 5) are particularly relevant to the loss of life in the Summerland fire disaster.

The main south face of Summerland was formed of acrylic dome panels 6 ft square with a diamond profile, patented as Coxdomes and made from Oroglas by Williaam J. Cox Ltd. The entire roof was glazed with Oroglas too, but none of the eastern elevation was glazed. The close association of the architect Clifford Barnett with Williaam J. Cox Ltd is indicated in the advertising leaflet issued by Cox after a symposium in London on October 20th, 1970. Mr Barnett had acted as consultant to the symposium on *Thermoplastic Glazing for Space Structures* organized jointly by Williaam Cox Ltd, Lennig Chemicals Ltd, ICI Plastics Division and Vickers Ltd. During the symposium Mr Hazelwood of ICI Plastics Division stated that none of the acrylic-glazed space structures in North America (e.g. at the Montreal Expo 1967) had caught fire. During the discussion a Ministry Research scientist asked: 'Is there a problem when fire causes the destruction of the complete structure including the metal work? Have any fire tests been carried out on a completed glazed structure?' The reply to these questions was not given in the leaflet, but interested readers were invited to write to Cox for copies of the symposium papers (£2). In any case Mr Barnett had been convinced long before 1970 that Oroglas was the right material for the transparent roof and south face of Summerland. The west face of the solarium, where it joined the Aquadrome and above its roof level, was also of Oroglas. But where this wall was shared with the actual swimming pool, it was of glass to allow a good view of the pool. The Oroglas areas appear in the view of Summerland shown in Figure 2.

There remained the need to choose a material for the eastern elevation. Reinforced concrete was chosen, but this choice was changed to coated corrugated steel sheet supplied by H. H. Robertson (UK) Ltd. It was specified as Colour Galbestos, coated both sides, because at the time of the order it was expected that some walls would be left as a single sheet and uncovered. The sheets were supported on steel angle rails, which were in turn supported on the main steelwork. During fitting out, a considerable amount of partitioning was carried out, some of which was parallel to the inner face of the Galbestos. The roof immediately over the Galbestos walling on the eastern end, and at a slightly lower level than the Oroglas roof, was covered with three-ply bituminous felt on boarding.

Permissions and Approvals

Building by-laws in the Isle of Man were made under an act which conferred power on the authority, in any particular case, to 'suspend, alter, or relax (them) or dispense with compliance therewith' with the consent of the Local

Figure 2 Summerland showing the use of Oroglas for the south face

Government Board. The local authority had to give notice of the proposed waiver in such manner and to such persons as the Local Government Board might direct, and the board could not give consent to the waiver before the expiration of one month from the notice.

By-laws 39, 50 (1) and 47 were significant in the context of the Summerland fire. By-law 39 required that the external walls of any building should be *noncombustible* throughout *and* have a *fire resistance of two hours.* By-law 50 (1) required that in every public building the roof be 'so covered as to afford adequate protection against the spread of fire into the building or to adjoining buildings'. By-law 47 provided that the cavity between any leaves of a wall formed of or containing combustible material should be fire-stopped at the junction of the wall with any other wall or with any floor, ceiling, or roof, and at intervals of not more than 15 ft.

In October 1967, J. Philipps Lomas submitted the first of three applications for by-law approval. It showed reinforced concrete for the eastern elevation, and Oroglas for the roof and south wall. The Borough Engineer advised the works committee of Douglas Corporation that Oroglas in the walls of Summerland would not comply with By-law 39, but that it was a proper case for a waiver. A letter from Mr Lomas to the Borough Engineer stated that 'the enveloping structure is, in fact, an acrylic glazed space frame, no part of which is combustible, but both the acrylic sheets and the alloy framing cannot be regarded as fire resistant.' The committee obtained the views of the chief fire officer, who made it clear that Oroglas afforded no fire resistance. But he concluded: 'Since the complex does not present an exposure hazard to any other building and since there is unlikely to be any interference with the means of escape, I raise no objection to the suggested construction'. A waiver of By-law 39 was approved for the Oroglas walls in respect of the two-hour fire resistance requirement. But the actual wording of the standard document concluded with these words: 'This approval shall have the effect of suspending By-law 39 . . . to the extent necessary to give effect to this approval.' Unintentionally Douglas Corporation had waived the noncombustible requirement of By-law 39 too. There was no proposed waiver in respect of the Oroglas roof since the Borough Engineer believed it did not contravene By-law 50.

In July 1968, J. Philipps Lomas submitted the second of the three applications for by-law approval. These plans showed Galbestos in place of reinforced concrete in the external walls of the solarium and terrace at the east end of the building. The Borough Engineer was aware that Colour Galbestos would not comply with the requirements of By-law 39 neither as to fire resistance nor noncombustibility, but he considered it an adequate material in all the circumstances. The plans were approved and the waiver of 1967 repeated in exactly the same words as before.

In February 1971 Trust Houses Forte Leisure Ltd, the lessees of Summerland, submitted the third of the three applications for by-law approval. These plans were essentially concerned with the fitting out and subdivision of the premises. By this time the structural work and shell of Summerland were already complete.

The only general fire safety regulations applicable to Summerland were the Theatre Regulations of 1923. Regulation 1 required an application for a certificate to be accompanied by plans of every part of the proposed 'theatre', and by a statement of the respective number of persons proposed to be accommodated in the various portions of the building. The lessees applied for a 'theatre' licence in June 1971. No plans were submitted with the application which did not say how many people were to be accommodated. The chief fire officer had inspected the shell several times, but did not know how these conventional regulations could be applied to a building which was not strictly a theatre. He wrote to the administrator and secretary of the Local Government Board as follows (July 8th, 1971):

> There is a good deal of work still to be done before it can be said that all safety requirements have been met. However, urgent steps are being taken to ensure completion, and in order that the opening of the complex should be legalized, I recommend that the certificate of fitness be issued now. I recommend that this be accompanied by a letter making it clear that its issue is conditional on all safety requirements being completed without delay.

The Board then issued a certificate saying that the building known as Summerland complied with the Theatre Regulations of 1923.

The Timetable of Events

1	Appointment of J. Philipps Lomas as Architects	14th April, 1965
2	Agreement to the appointment of Gillinson Barnett and Partners of Leeds as Associate Architects	24th May, 1965
3	The first design report presented to the Douglas Corporation	July, 1965
4	First By-law and Town Planning submission .	11th October, 1967
5	Visits to Expo. '67 Montreal	May, 1967

6	Second By-law and Town Planning submission	9th July, 1968
7	Work on site began	25th October, 1968
8	Sub-contract tender for steelwork by Wright Anderson accepted	20th November, 1968
9	Sub-contract tender for Oroglas by Lennig Chemicals through Williaam Cox Ltd. accepted	14th July, 1969
10	Sub-contract tender for Galbestos by H. H. Robertson (U.K.) Ltd. accepted	3rd February, 1970
11	Completion of structural and shell work	December, 1970
12	Design and tenders for shop fittings	early months 1971
13	Submission of third By-law plans	15th February, 1971
14	Opening of Summerland........................	25th May, 1971
15	Completion of shop fittings....................	March, 1972

The Grand Plan Achieved

J. Philipps Lomas was responsible for supervising the building of the structure and carcass of Summerland. Then Douglas Corporation leased Summerland to Trust Houses Forte Leisure Ltd., and Gillinson Barnett became principal architects for Trust Houses Forte. The lessees wanted the interiors designed quickly so that Summerland could open in May 1971. All this work was done in a hurry. Contractors used the following combustible materials: plasterboard or plywood on softwood studding, exposed timber and plywood, Decalin wall linings, decorative ceilings, a hardwood and perspex sliding partition, and a polythene curtain.

The brochure for Summerland claimed that the design had 'Set the architectural world alight'. The brochure also stated:

> In an entertainments centre of such a size, the question of fire prevention was another major factor. Nothing could be left to chance. The main structure was ideal, solid concrete and non-combustible acrylic sheets. ... any outbreak of fire in the future had to be one which could be localized to one room or one machine without any risk of spreading. Again the problems were overcome ....

Although acclaimed by the non-technical public, Summerland was received with lukewarm enthusiasm by technicians in the building industry. They felt that architecturally the building was uninspiring and catered for the lowest

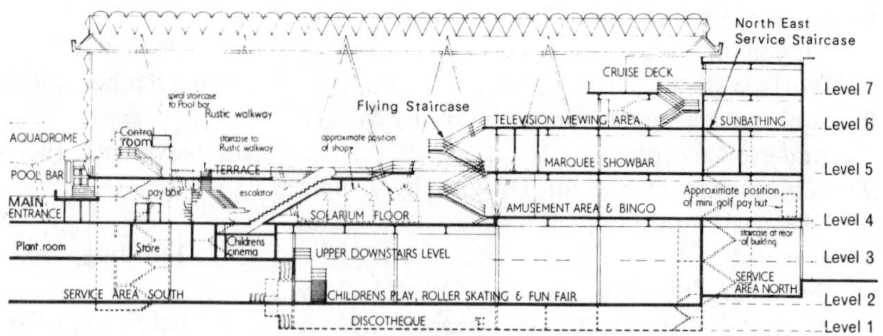

Figure 3 Long section: fire did not penetrate below Level 4

common denominator of the public's taste in entertainment. However, they granted that Summerland was the first attempt in Britain to build a habitable microclimate and what it lacked in sophistication it made up for in originality.

The grand plan had been achieved. Summerland was the biggest Isle of Man building of the century, and a very considerable undertaking for a small community. The idea of setting up a fun palace under a huge transparent skin had been carried to a successful conclusion. The fun palace, an immediate success, had its first full season in 1972 providing 13 per cent of the Isle of Man's tourist revenue.

NARRATIVE OF THE FIRE

The fire starts

A fibreglass kiosk had been used during the early summer of 1973 as a ticket office in connection with the minigolf course on the outside terrace which extended along the seaward side of Summerland. About two months before the fire, it had been damaged by storm and was dismantled. Most of it had been taken away, but, for some reason, one section was left lying on its side at the eastern end of the terrace close to the Galbestos wall. It contained a roll of wire netting covered in some combustible plastic, and possibly some litter.

On the evening of 2 August 1973 the remains of the kiosk and its contents were set alight by three Liverpool schoolboys. Within a matter of minutes, the kiosk was burning fiercely and the flames were impinging on the Galbestos wall.

The remains of the kiosk then collapsed, still burning, against the Galbestos wall. By this time, the combustible coating on the outside of the Galbestos had ignited. Because of the high conductivity of the sheet metal in the Galbestos, inflammable vapours quickly issued from the coating on the inside of the Galbestos and became ignited so that there was fire within the void between the sheeting and the fibreboard lining of the Amusement Arcade (Level 4).

The fire spreads

The fire spread within the void, igniting the fibreboard lining and its wooden supports and increasing the quantity of combustible gas. The Decalin lining gave way as it became charred or burnt, and fire massively invaded the Amusement Arcade (Level 4), then the terrace restaurant (Level 4). First the fire spread upwards over the front edges of the terraces (Levels 5, 6 and 7) successively. Second, smoke and inflammable vapours went up a nest of voids between the Galbestos wall and interior partitioning. Third, flames from the Amusement Arcade (Level 4) ran up a void or 'chimney' between the south Oroglas wall and the ceiling/floor edges of successive terrace levels (5, 6 and 7).

When the south Oroglas wall and the east end of the Oroglas roof caught fire, a huge conflagration rapidly developed on the whole height of the building at the east end. The fire spread westward quickly until almost everything combustible at and above the solarium (Level 4) was destroyed. But the fire could not penetrate below the reinforced concrete floor of Level 4 itself (see Figure 3).

Attempts to deal with the fire

Unsuccessful attempts to extinguish the fire in its early stages were made by members of the Summerland staff. They brought extinguishers and a hose through a window of the Amusement Arcade (Level 4) and tried also to remove the burning kiosk. Two members of staff, Mrs Bisson in the Discotheque (Level 1) and Mr Harding in the service area of the Marquee Showbar (Level 5), set off the fire alarm. The alarm did not sound in Summerland, but it did sound in the local Fire Station. Mr Shaffer, the House Manager, switched off the main electricity supply, and also telephoned the fire brigade from a public call-box. But he did not notice that the automatic emergency generator had failed to start. The north-east staircase (No. 2) was plunged into darkness. The fire brigade duly arrived. The

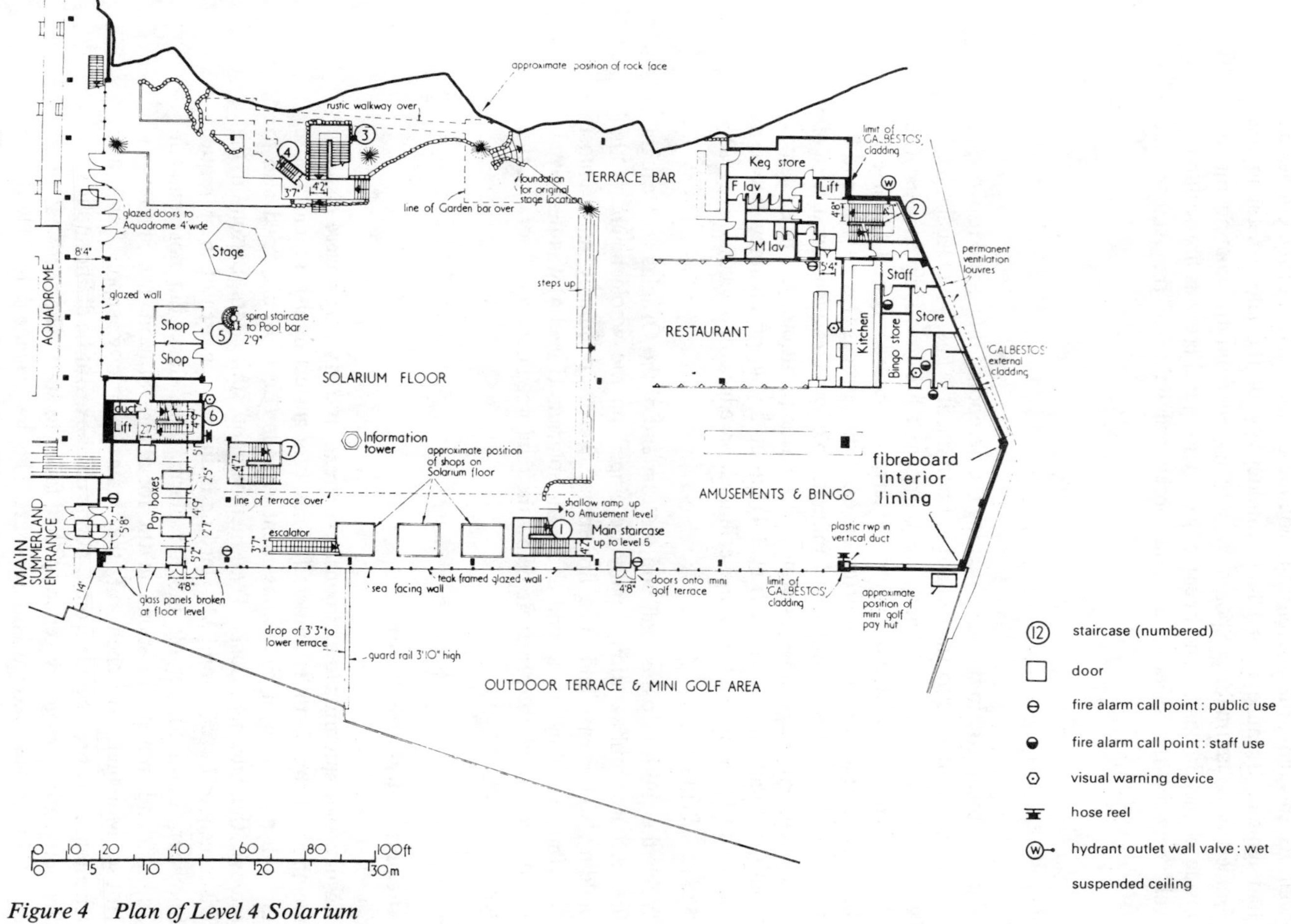

Figure 4 Plan of Level 4 Solarium

Chief Fire Staff Officer decided that no fire brigade could save Summerland at that point. So a concentrated effort was made to save the Aquadrome. This was successful since the firemen were able to stop the fire at the western boundary of Summerland.

Attempts to escape

Mr Mannion, the organist who was just about to conclude his recital, was asked by the compere to continue playing because there was a small fire and the compere did not want anybody to panic. Mr Harding told Mrs Wynne Smythe, Manageress of the Marquee Showbar, to evacuate the patrons. He also stopped an escalator which was moving upwards while people tried to escape down it, and unlocked the door of an emergency exit. Mr Mannion, the organist, shouted 'everybody out' while Mr De Lorka, the General Manager, tried to break open the locked emergency doors leading to the Aquadrome. Mr Shaffer ran to the Manager's office to find some duplicate keys. Smoke, followed quickly by flames, swept through the building. Later, many eye-witnesses spoke of panic as the holidaymakers screamed and tried to find an exit from the inferno. Many people fell over and were crushed. Parents rushed from one level to another looking for their children. Within a few minutes everybody who had not found an unblocked exit was dead, and many people who did find an unblocked exit became severely injured as they fell over each other in the darkness.

The aftermath of the fire

On the day after the fire Mr Cyril Pearson, the chief fire officer, said:

> Every aspect of fire protection was considered by me; it would not have got a licence if it had not met with my approval (*The Times*, 4 August 1973).

In the same report the fire brigade was quoted as saying that all exit signs were clearly marked. Two days later (*Guardian,* 6 August 1973), Mr Pearson complained about being treated as a scapegoat. At the same time the Department of the Environment said:

> It is unlikely that a building of that type could be built in England or Wales under our regulations without a number of relaxations of those regulations (*The Times*, 4 August 1973).

Figure 5 The Solarium (Level 4) showing the flying staircase (right) leading to Levels 5 and 6

When asked about Oroglas just after the fire one of the architects, Mr Basil Gillinson, said: 'I would rather not discuss the safety properties of the material. We want to go into this with the manufacturers. I feel a bit sick about tonight' (*Guardian,* 3 August 1973). The next day he said that he was not sure whether tests had been carried out on any particular materials used in the building (*Guardian*, 4 August 1973). He had not doubted the safety of Oroglas in use until the previous night.

On the day after the fire the sales manager of Rohm and Hass Ltd said that Oroglas might possibly have had something to do with the rapid spread of the fire (*Guardian*, 4 August 1973). He was commenting on a statement by the Fire Research Station that under no circumstances would it have recommended the use of 2000 four foot square sheets of Oroglas in Summerland. The Agrément Board said that it had so far been unable to discover to whom it had sent the plastic for flammability tests or whether it was also examined for its fire propagation properties.

Three days after the fire (*Guardian*, 6 August 1973), Mr Gillinson had to deny reports that he had said Oroglas was fireproof. An earlier statement of Chief Fire Officer Pearson was also recalled. Four days before the

Figure 6 An entertainment in the Solarium

Summerland fire he had warned local residents that fire precautions on the island were pitiful (*The Times*, 6 August 1973). 'We have been running incredibly serious risks,' he had said, 'but there does not seem to be a lot of action to do anything about it.' This statement probably referred to hotels on the island. Mr Pearson said on 6 August that he had been told to stop making statements (*Guardian*, 7 August 1973).

The press publicized questionable reasons as to how the fire started and spread. For example, Mr Trevor Castree, a milkman who fled with his family to safety, said he believed an electrical fault in a fruit machine could have started the fire (*Guardian*, 9 August 1973). Eight days after the fire (*Daily Telegraph*, 11 August 1973) Home Office experts were quoted as saying that the acrylic walls and roof did not catch fire until the floor of the Marquee Showbar was well ablaze and after fire was spreading to other parts of the terraced structure. This statement was assumed to contradict the general belief that the acrylic was ignited by a fire lit by boys around the dismantled kiosk, though various theories were advanced.

On 15 August the Agrément Board agreed to renew its certificate for Oroglas, which was due to expire at the end of the month. Its spokesman

Figure 7 Burning Galbestos (the big flame in the foreground) and burning Oroglas (left)

said the certificate stated clearly that Oroglas acrylic sheeting was not fire resistant and its use was restricted to vertical glazing and in-fill panels (*Guardian*, 16 August 1973). Meanwhile an inquiry set in motion by Bletchley UDC (*Surveyor*, 17 August 1973) revealed that the ignition temperature of Oroglas varied according to the way in which the sheeting was used and fixed. Ken Taylor writing in the *New Civil Engineer* (9 August 1973) reckoned that Oroglas as supplied by Williaam Cox Ltd was 'clearly very combustible'. On 10 October Lancashire County Council staged a fire demonstration during which three buildings made of different materials were simultaneously set on fire. The Oroglas building was destroyed the soonest (*Guardian,* 11 October 1973).

The guilt of Oroglas was presumed by a cartoonist of the *Daily Express.* His cartoon showed President Nixon standing in the doorway of a blazing White House. The caption stated 'It's rumoured that the President has panelled the building with Oroglas . . .'. Later on the Press Council agreed that the cartoon was 'undoubtedly offensive to some readers'. Into this welter of argument, speculation, contradiction and suggestion came The Summerland Fire Commission.

THE WORK OF THE SUMMERLAND FIRE COMMISSION

Operations

On 3 September 1973, the Lieutenant Governor of the Isle of Man appointed the Summerland Fire Commission. Its members were a judge, a fire service inspector, and a professor of building with an official from the Isle of Man Government office acting as secretary. The public hearing lasted from 19 November 1973 until 13 February 1974. The Commission sat for forty-nine days, watched films of the disaster, visited the site, and took evidence from more than ninety witnesses. The Commission was assisted by three advocates, by an independent architect, and by the assistant chief fire officer of the Kent Fire Brigade. Other parties were represented by twenty-four advocates, eighteen of whom had to be licensed specially to practise at the Manx Bar.

Organizations involved

There were four main types of organizations involved in the Summerland project: public authorities, private professional firms, commercial companies and research organizations:

Public Authorities

The Isle of Man is a self-governing dependency of the British Crown. Any Act of the British Parliament could apply to the Isle of Man if the island was specified in the statute. Many acts of the Westminster Parliament were virtually rubber-stamped by Tynwald, the Isle of Man legislature. But in fire regulations, for example, the differences which had grown up over the years were considerable. At the time of the Summerland fire an equivalent bill to Britain's Fire Precautions Act 1972 was being drafted.

The Executive Council of the Lieutenant Governor, the Local Government Board of the Isle of Man, and Douglas Corporation (the local Council) were all involved in the appointment of the architects. The different responsibilities of the Local Government Board and Douglas Corporation are shown on page 96.

Private Professional Firms

Two firms of architects were involved, J. Philipps Lomas and Gillinson Barnett.

Commercial Companies

Rohm and Haas, an American Company, authorized Lennig Chemicals Ltd to market in Britain the acrylic material known as Oroglas from which Williaam J. Cox Ltd supplied diamond-shaped panels patented as Cox-domes.

Wright Anderson Ltd were subcontractors for the steelwork. H. H. Robertson Ltd supplied the Galbestos.

Trust Houses Forte Leisure Ltd leased Summerland from Douglas Corporation, and insured the building with Commercial Union.

Research Organizations

The Agrément Board, a non-statutory body that carries out voluntary tests on new materials, is run with a grant in aid from the Department of the Environment as an offshoot of the building industry's Building Research Station. The Government-sponsored Fire Research Station carries out its own research into new materials.

The report

The conclusions and recommendations of the Summerland Fire Commission have been summarized below (5 and 6). The Commission analysed at length the factors leading to the spread of the fire (below) and the factors contributing to the loss of life (p89). The report itself, copiously illustrated with photographs, tables and plans, is 35 000 words long.

ANALYSIS BY THE SUMMERLAND FIRE COMMISSION

Factors in the spread of the fire

The Commission tried to ascertain some relevant times in the development of the fire, but had difficulty in doing so. However, it concluded that the fire was started by three boys on the mini-golf terrace shortly before 7.40 p.m. and first entered the Amusement Arcade (Level 4) from the void in the wall at about 8 p.m. The automatic fire alarm from Summerland sounded in the fire station at 8.05, and the first fire appliance arrived one or two minutes

Figure 8 The fire brigade halts the fire at the west facade and saves the Aquadrome

later. At 8.11 p.m. when the mains electricity was switched off, there was extensive fire on all three terraces (Levels 5, 6 and 7) above the Amusement Arcade (Level 4), and the solarium (Level 4) could not be entered from the floor below. The rapid spread of the fire was caused in part by the design and construction of the building; and in part by the failure of the Summerland staff to take prompt and appropriate action. After considering the second cause, the Commission concluded that, had the fire brigade been called in time, the building might have been saved.

If Galbestos had not been substituted for reinforced concrete at the eastern end, and had the wall possessed the two-hour fire resistance required by By-law 39, the disaster would not have occurred. The Commission felt that the waiver of a safety provision is always a responsible decision and that the design should incorporate some compensatory measure to restore the standard of safety to that which would have existed without the waiver.

The combustible components of Galbestos accelerated the growth of the fire in the early stages. Things were made worse by the creation of a concealed void. An interior designer, employed by Gillinson Barnett, substituted

Figure 9 Gutted Oroglas panels on the south and west faces

Decalin for plasterboard as the material for an interior wall. This error might well have been the biggest single structural contribution to the disaster of the fire. The designer did not know the properties of Decalin, and did not know that it was combustible. He had seen it for the first time the previous day, when a trade representative produced a sample. The Commission did not accept a suggestion that even had the interior wall been of plasterboard (which is virtually noncombustible) the fire would have broken into the Amusement Arcade (Level 4) nearly as quickly. Fire stopping would have delayed the fire, but the void had not been effectively stopped.

There were several reasons why the fire would progress rapidly once it had broken out of the void. One half of Summerland was, in effect, a multi-storey building. All the upper floors were open on one side, part of another side was exposed to a narrow chimney-like opening between the edge of the floor and the external wall, and the remainder of the sides, at least on one floor, were exposed to holes in a void enclosed by combustible surfaces. The other half of the building was completely exposed to the effects of a fire in any part of it, and the roof was made of a material that would fail at once and fully vent a fire below. In short, there was no compartmentation, which is what modern fire regulating systems rely on for defence against rapid spread of fire. Although the floors were correctly classified as 'low fire load' and the fittings were not chosen irresponsibly, the fire was so violent as to consume immediately everything combustible in its path. One way of protecting this type of building would have been to provide sprinklers.

The evidence suggested that the Oroglas wall caught fire inside from the flames passing up from the burning Amusement Arcade (Level 4). Very soon after that the fire penetrated the first Coxdomes to the outside. The evidence could not be established definitely whether the Oroglas roof caught fire before the Oroglas wall. Once the roof caught fire, it burned out in an astonishingly short time perhaps in as little as ten minutes. It was obvious that the rate at which the Oroglas burned had increased rapidly as it had been heated by other material near to it. The 'experts' and manufacturers giving evidence about Oroglas had not foreseen this. The designers had neglected to protect the exposed edges of the Oroglas even though this protection had been strongly recommended. Rapid consumption of the roof domes permitted venting very quickly, and this released great heat and smoke. There was no suggestion, however, that any domelights from the roof or Coxdomes from the south wall fell out *before* igniting. Venting increased the speed and ferocity of the fire. Although fire tests had been carried out on acrylic sheeting, there was no sound philosophy of the effects of scaling up the results in size.

The advertising literature of H. H. Robertson Ltd had been so unclear that the architects thought Galbestos was virtually noncombustible. They had not known what questions to ask about Galbestos, and Robertsons had not volunteered their assessment of the risk. It was believed that Galbestos had not been used before to clad a multi-storey assembly building. Robertson's were praised for the investigations which had been carried out since the fire. Beyond the Amusement Arcade (Level 4) and the back of the Marquee Showbar (Level 5), the external Galbestos sheeting itself probably did not contribute much to the extension of the fire, which was predominantly fed from the combustibles on the internal wood floors. The designers were responsible for not assessing these risks.

Factors in the loss of life

The high number of casualties was attributed by the Commission to two causes: the very rapid development of the fire, and the fact that the evacuation of the building was delayed. The defective evacuation was the result of faults in management and faults in the design or construction. First there was a bad bottleneck between the foot of the escalator and the main entrance to the Solarium floor (Level 4). Second, three important escape routes were defective:

(a) the flying staircase (No. 1),

(b) the north-east service staircase (No. 2) and

(c) the main entrance itself.

As a means of escape, the flying staircase (No. 1) was wrong in type, position, and dimensions. Since it was unsuitable for escape purposes, a second protected staircase was essential. But the alternative escape, the north-east service staircase (No. 2), was not wide enough to accommodate the full number of persons who might have needed to escape. As the north-east staircase (No. 2) could only accommodate about half the escaping occupants, the fire officer should not have issued the theatre certificate and the designers should have appreciated the danger. However, the inadequacy of this stairway had probably not led to any deaths there. Overcrowding and exposure to the flames on the flying staircase had caused fatalities. Another hazard had been parents looking for their children and bumping into people trying to escape.

Staircase directions at Level 4 (Solarium)

Staircase Number	Description	Up	Down
1	Flying staircase	Yes	—
2	North-east service staircase	Yes	Yes
3	North Carousel stair	—	Yes
4	Rustic stair	Yes	—
5	Spiral staircase to Pool Bar	Yes	—
6	Administration staircase	Yes	Yes
7	Children's Cinema staircase	—	Yes

There were six unsatisfactory features in the arrangements for exit from the Solarium floor (Level 4) through the main entrance. These were:

1 Locked doors at the main entrance (Level 4) caused a bottleneck. The main entrance was badly designed. It was made narrow by pay-boxes and barriers. Glass doors in the south wall were at a right angle to the entrance.

2 Doors on the Solarium floor (Level 4) were secured not by panic bolts but by mortice locks with keys in glass fronted boxes.

3 The glass doors leading to the Aquadrome (Level 4) were at the end of a long open escape route and did not give access to a place of safety, but into another building which was not fire-separated from the Solarium. (See Figure 1 for a site plan of Summerland and the Aquadrome.)

4 The pair of doors leading on to the mini-golf course (Level 4) did not lead to a place of safety. A railing had been substituted for steps without reference to the fire officer. (See Figures 3 and 4 for the approximate position of the mini-golf pay hut.)

5 Of the three staircases leading downward from the Solarium floor (Level 4), one (No. 6, the administration staircase) had narrow access, its doorway was marked 'private', and at the end of the staircase was an encloseable yard. The north 'carousel' staircase (No. 3) and the children's cinema staircase (No. 7) were wide enough, but led to the basement, which was far from ideal. (See Figure 4 for location of the staircases.)

6 Most exits from the Solarium (Level 4) were at the same end of the building. There was, however, no evidence that any deaths were caused by congestion at these exits.

A proper evacuation procedure would have provided, among other things, for doors to be unlocked by staff, but there was no such procedure established at Summerland. Mr De Lorka (General Manager) thought it was for Mr Harding (Technical Services Manager) to organize an evacuation procedure, but he never discussed it with him. He told the Commission that it was the height of the season and they were busy. A girl operated sound, lighting, announcements and recorded music from a control room. Although this room had an important function in a fire emergency, the girl said in evidence that she had no idea of anything to do with the alarm system. There probably were, or had been, notices about the alarm system posted in the building. But the Commission noted that a proper evacuation system is not established or mentioned merely by putting up notices.

The doors at the foot of the covered stairway in the north-east corner (No. 2) were fitted with panic bolts, but one pair was padlocked and also obstructed by a parked motor-car. Twice previously the fire service had complained to the management on finding exit doors padlocked. It was difficult to find one's way about Summerland, and there were no proper signs guiding the public towards exits.

Though the north-east service stairway (No. 2) was a service stairway, the architects (other than Mr Lomas) were positive that it was at all times designed and intended as a protected emergency escape route. It is undesirable to combine the functions of a service stairway and an emergency staircase in a building of this type. Because of its service function, this staircase had many defects in its design as an emergency exit. A number of doors leading from accommodation on to the stairway were not self-closing or fire-resistant. The worst feature, however, was the open doorway between the landing and the Marquee Showbar (Level 5). This doorway, which was used for moving goods in and out of the bar, had been cut without permission from authority. The unprotected opening must have been responsible for a lot of smoke entering the staircase. When the fire reached the north side of the Marquee Showbar (Level 5) at about 8.11 p.m., the conditions on the stairway (No. 2) at that level would have been lethal. Twelve bodies were found on the stairs, some only eight feet from the exit.

When the main electricity supply was switched off, the emergency lighting system failed to come on automatically, either because the starter batteries were not adequately maintained by Douglas Corporation, or because the switch for isolating the generator had been left in the 'off' position, or because the fire had by that time attacked the wiring of the emergency circuit. The darkness added to the chaos.

CONCLUSIONS OF THE SUMMERLAND FIRE COMMISSION

The Architect's relationship with his client

When the Summerland project was put into the hands of J. Philipps Lomas, it seemed that the Local Government Board and Douglas Corporation concluded that he had also taken over nearly total responsibility for the design development, its management, and eventually its success in performance. Too often the Commission was told that 'we relied on the architects' for correct decisions and solutions. The selection of J. Philipps Lomas was criticized on the grounds of inexperience. It did not, in the Commission's view, materially improve this choice that a firm in Leeds with a large organization and more resources was appointed as associate architects.

Even with the best possible choice of architect, the clients must continue to examine critically the conceptual ideas as they develop, and test them against a practical background of proposed usage and management of the completed building. They must remain in control of capital expenditure, costs in use, and the likely budget appropriate to the intended use of the building. The Commission obtained no evidence, though it was sought, to show that these particular controls were ever applied. If they had been, it was considered that some serious design mistakes might have been brought to light.

A critical analysis at the time of the scrutiny of the plans and completed building, would, it was believed, have revealed: the inaccessibility of the main entrance, deficient access for fire fighting, extreme expanses of acrylic on walls and roof beyond the needs of transparency, softwood structural floors, haphazard arrangement of stairs and exits, and the vast multi-storey space above the entrance floor (Level 4).

The Architect's service to his client

No efficient design control was imposed by the architect. It was the design team's responsibility to consider carefully the functions of the building, particularly from the point of view of its efficient usage, comfort, maintenance and safety. Neither Mr Lomas nor Mr Barnett ever stood back and looked at the project as a whole. Significant decisions were taken successively by two 'job' architects, neither of whom had the right experience. Communications between the two firms were poor. Mr Lomas told the Commission that he acted as a 'post box or conduit' between Gillinson Barnett and the participants on the island. But Mr Barnett denied this admission, and under cross-examination he agreed that it was necessary to watch Mr Lomas 'like a hawk'. Quotations from correspondence between the two firms included such phrases as 'we might get away with it' or 'I do not think we need worry unduly on this business of fire resistance'. Theatre regulations might be treated 'with a pinch of salt'.

The Commission concluded that acrylic was not essential to the design of Summerland, and that the architects had not carried out a proper analysis of alternative materials.

Architects could not be expected to have a very specialized knowledge of the chemical and physical attributes of materials, but they should seek advice. The suggestion that research establishments would be unable to say anything of real use was quite unacceptable. In the particular cases of both Galbestos and acrylic material, the Commission believed that the Building Research Establishment and the Fire Research Station could have said something useful.

There was no evidence offered to confirm that matters of occupancy and fire precautions and escape were discussed at any length among the architects during the critical periods of design development. A number of occupancy figures were given, but these had not been considered in proper detail before the fire. If a consensus of view had been established in the early stages between clients, authorities and architects, seven factors could have been envisaged very early in the project:

1 There could be high densities of people congregated in particular areas.

2 The building would be unfamiliar to the casual (once only) visitors.

3 A combination of the above could lead to panic in the event of fire.

4 There could be some relatively immobile people, such as the very young, the very old, and the disabled.

5 Some children would be unaccompanied by adults.

6 The possibility of vandalism was always present.

7 There would be much combustible material and some potential sources of fire outbreaks in such a building.

The Commission was not convinced that the north-east stair (No. 2) had been designed from the outset as an emergency (fire) exit. The architects could have designed it very satisfactorily (from known precedents) if they had regarded it as such, and they could not shift design responsibility on to local authorities and fire officers. The Commission was not impressed by the architects' repeated attempts to suggest that other people should have told them of any mistake or inadequacy in the plans.

Communications between public authorities

Various matters contributed to misunderstandings between Douglas Corporation and the Local Government Board (e.g. the wording of the waiver of By-law 39). These were:

1 The lack of communication between the two parties.

2 The carrying on concurrently by the planning committee of two quite different functions: viz, the consideration of planning applications and the exercise of the Local Government Board's functions under Section 3 of the Local Government (Building By-laws) Act 1950.

3 The absence of any clear and prescribed procedure for applications to the Local Government Board for consent under Section 3 of the Act.

4 The long established failure to observe the procedure under which

Douglas Corporation would have had to give notice of a proposed waiver, followed by a month's delay before the consent of the Local Government Board.

5 The practice of incorporating in a planning permission the waiver of a by-law which might have nothing to do with planning considerations.

The Commission considered that the plans offered for planning and by-laws approval were indifferent and should have been sent back to the architects for clarification. It might have been that detailed scrutiny of the plans by all the officials and committees concerned did not take place, each party perhaps believing that the other had already inspected the proposals properly.

Tests for judging the behaviour in fire of building materials

Tests for judging the behaviour in fire of building materials and structures, published by the British Standards Institution and by other organizations, were mentioned frequently during the inquiry. Their limitations needed to be understood and kept in mind. Where the performance of a material in a particular application could not safely be predicted from the standard tests, then specific *ad hoc* investigation and testing would need to be carried out by the manufacturer, the designer, or the user.

Official Inspections

The nature and character of official inspections of work in progress were not clearly understood. No official inspection of Summerland during the fitting-out stage was recorded or carried out by the building inspectorate of Douglas Corporation. The corporation believed that in the late stages the presence of a clerk of works and the periodic supervision by the architect were sufficient. If these had been the corporation's own appointments, there could possibly have been some formal delegation, but even this would not have been wise. No formal inspection was undertaken by anyone before the building was released for occupation, and no completion certificate was requested by the contractors nor issued by the local authority. No continuing inspections by the fire officer were made, though there may have been the occasional visit. The style of inspections and certificates associated with the Theatre Regulations needed to be improved, and the regulations themselves updated. It was wrong to vest the responsibility for the issuing of a theatre licence totally in the hands of the Chief Fire Staff Officer.

Trust Houses Forte (the lessees)

When Trust Houses Forte accepted the structure of Summerland as an enclosure for the proposed leisure facilities for which they were to provide all the fittings, equipment, furniture, and decoration, they made no technical inspection or assessment of the structure; the structure was obviously unusual, and they had entered into a full repairing lease and were going to complete the building with material in excess of £400,000 in value. If an inspection had been made, the need for additional safeguards would have been perceived. Trust Houses Forte seemed never to have been aware of how vulnerable Summerland was or might become. This was remarkable since in 1971 their experienced insurers had offered a very substantial reduction in premium if a sprinkler system was installed. The motive of Trust Houses Forte was to gain the earliest opening date for Summerland, but their procedures verged on the irresponsible. Given time and wise counsel, money could have been found for safe standards, sprinkler systems, and proper detailing, particularly of associated materials.

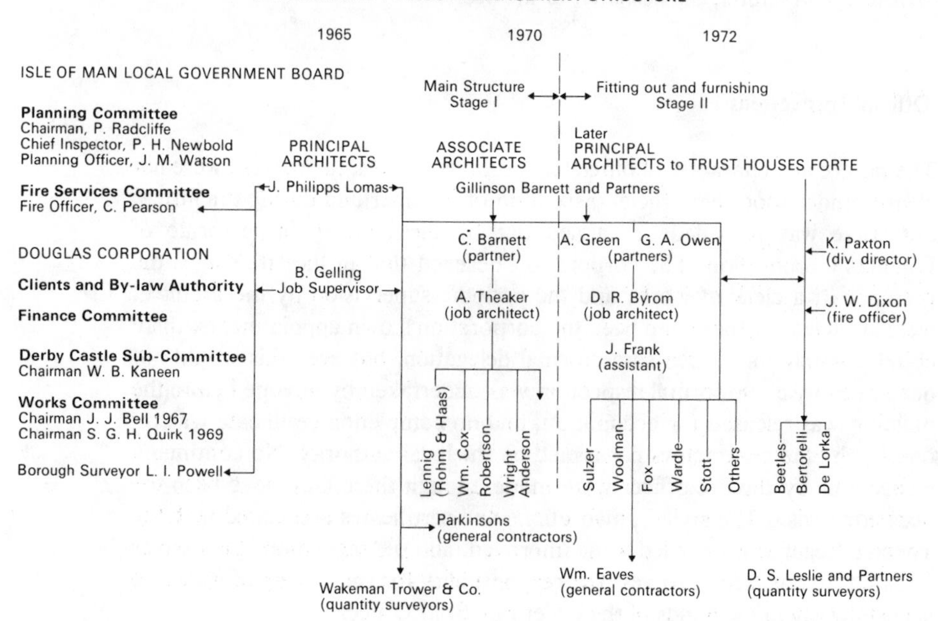

Oroglas and Galbestos

The application for a waiver of By-law 39 in respect of Oroglas walls, and its subsequent granting by Douglas Corporation and authorization by the Local Government Board, should only have followed exhaustive inquiries and some scientific investigation. The waiver of a by-law is only justifiable when no reduction in the standard of personal safety then occurs. Enough was known about Oroglas and Galbestos to permit a detailed study of safeguards against fire risks, including fire-stopping and fire barriers, and differential temperature movement. It had been stated by the manufacturers that exposed edges of acrylic sheets were relatively easily ignited, but this characteristic was not taken into account in the design of the Oroglas roof by the architects.

The stage at which Oroglas became involved in the fire deserved and received special attention, particularly as there was at one time a widespread public impression that Oroglas played the primary role in the development and spread of fire within the building. This was contrary to the evidence. The Commission was satisfied by clear and positive evidence of eye-witnesses that the Oroglas was ignited from fire within the building and was not ignited until there was a very substantial fire in the Amusement Arcade (Level 4). On the south wall the Oroglas was almost certainly ignited from flames spilled over the ceiling of the Amusement Arcade into the 'chimney'. As far as Galbestos was concerned, its plastic coating of polyester resin and the bitumen saturate of the material were highly combustible. The combination of burning Galbestos, combustible fibreboard linings and the floor–ceiling relationship was lethal.

Fire protection and precautions

The Chief Fire Staff Officer received the plans for the 1967 submission. He should have considered the problems of firefighting at that time in order to improve the conditions, which, he agreed, in the event, were very difficult. On matters of materials and escape, however, he was not consulted formally either by his committee or by the architects, and was not even sent the changed by-law plans of 1968 and 1971. There was no doubt that his opinion should have been sought on all these matters at the time of the deposit of the plans. In hindsight, he wished he had insisted on considerable modifications to the plans.

Final conclusions

In designing buildings architects must not rely on efficient management by the users, but neither must the users necessarily accept the building as safe, without studying the problems which might arise because of the usage. There was reason to believe that under a former general manager appointed by Trust Houses Forte a proper system of fire precautions was worked out, but in the summer of 1973 there was no such system. The Commission concluded that there were no villains – just human errors and failures, poor communications, and too much reliance on an 'old boy' network. A final comment stated: 'It would be unjust not to acknowledge that not every failure which is obvious now would be obvious before the disaster put structure and people to the test.'

RECOMMENDATIONS OF THE SUMMERLAND FIRE COMMISSION

The Summerland Fire Commission made thirty-four recommendations which have been summarized here under four headings.

Architects

In the designing of a building, a named person should be in charge from the outset and take, and be known to be taking, the major design decisions. Architects and clients together should carefully consider the requirements and performance of a building in use at the stage when conceptual designs are proposed, and before proceeding with the details of the design and the later submission of plans to the authorities. Early in the design stage, designers should consult the authorities concerned with by-laws, town planning, and fire regulations. Given this collaboration and advice, the designers must take responsibility for agreed decisions. Architectural training should include a much extended study of fire protection and precautions.

Full provision of escape and fire protection means should be included in the earliest designs with regard to the maximum foreseeable occupancy. When a large public assembly or entertainment building will contain a lot of flammable materials (notwithstanding any proposal for flame retardant treatment), the design should include installation of a sprinkler system unless special reasons apply (for example, in a museum). Voids with combustible interior surfaces should not be unnecessarily incorporated in public assembly buildings. If functionally necessary they should be provided with permanent and reliable fire-stopping, or with sprinklers.

In applying the results of fire tests on building materials and structures, the difference should be borne in mind between the standard test and the conditions of use in full size. If necessary, special investigations should be made on a suitable scale to supplement the tests. The use of sheet steel cladding materials for multistorey public buildings should be considered with regard to the instability which may result from thermal and vibratory movements and thus effect junctions with other materials. Planning should include a schedule of means of escape correctly designed. If the disposition of facilities means that children and parents will be separated, these facilities should be confined to one floor level. If parents and children are using different floor levels, there should be generous means of escape and arrangements for marshalling so as to give confidence.

Building Inspectors

Building inspections during construction should be conducted formally and precisely, both by architects and local authority inspectors. They should be recorded to confirm that the building is being built in accordance with the approved plans and the relevant by-laws and regulations. No public building should be occupied until a satisfactory official inspection has taken place and a completion certificate issued.

Public Authorities and Entertainment or Assembly Hall Managers

Detailed and up to date plans should be available in all occupied buildings. The (Manx) building by-laws and theatre regulations should be revised. An officer responsible for recommending the issue of licences or certificates relating to safety in public buildings should report to a properly constituted committee which will authorize the issue of the licence or certificate. Certificates under the theatre regulations should specify any exemption granted and any special conditions imposed. Before granting an application for waiver of a by-law or regulation, an authority should satisfy itself that the standard of safety for occupants which is set by the by-law or regulation will be maintained by some other means.

Full provision of means of escape and protection against spread of fire, with proper regard to maximum foreseeable occupancy, should be incorporated in the design from the start. Fire routines should be reviewed, regularly checked and practised. Staff should be trained. Inspections should be carried out while the public are present. Instruction in the use of fire-fighting equipment should be carried out. If a fire-fighting group cannot reach a required standard, the fire brigade should be called to every alarm of fire. Access to buildings for fire-fighting purposes must be satisfactory. Emergency lighting equipment should be tested regularly and a record kept of the tests. Diagrammatic plans showing escape routes should be publicly displayed, and there should be prominent signs showing the routes to be taken to emergency exits. Doors intended for use in an emergency should never be locked while the public are on the premises, even if keys for the locks are available in adjacent boxes. All exit doors should be readily openable from within, and advice as to suitable fastening should be sought, if necessary from the fire authority.

Manufacturers

If manufacturers are expected to take responsibility for some part of the performance of the building, these responsibilities should be clearly agreed in writing, and the client should be informed. The fullest possible information about the fire properties of building materials should be provided to intending users.

There were eight recommendations about the use of acrylic sheeting for cladding:

1 Until more information is available, its use should be confined to situations in which the hazard it might present is minimal.

2 It should not be placed within 3.5 m of any point which would normally be within reach of persons inside or outside the building.

3 It should not be placed within 6 m of any combustible material, or any point where combustible material may be put.

4 Its use should be limited in multistorey structures. Each area of acrylic roofing or cladding should be sufficiently separated by noncombustible material.

5 External exposure hazard to any occupied building roofed or clad with acrylic sheeting should be avoided by the provision of adequate separation distances between the building and its site boundaries as laid down by modern regulations or codes of practice.

6 If recommendation 5 is not followed, the roof and/or cladding should be protected by a reliable and effective water spray system.

7 Higher standards of means of escape should be provided when a building roofed or clad in acrylic is intended to be occupied by more than one person to every 3 m^2 of the net area.

8 When acrylic sheets are used for roofing or cladding, the edges should always be protected against ignition unless this risk is otherwise obviated.

Manufacturers should investigate the possibility of designing a fire alarm system so that the effect of fire on the building's wiring is always to sound the alarm and not to render the system inoperative. There should be investigation into the design of emergency generator sets so as to ensure that any set fitted with a cut-out switch is also provided with either an interlock or a buzzer or warning light to prevent the set being inadvertently left inoperative when unattended. Where a fire alarm system incorporates a mechanism whereby either the public warning signal or a call to the fire brigade can be placed on delay, the mechanism for this purpose should, if possible, be so designed that the period of delay cannot readily be altered without reference to the fire authority.

REACTIONS TO THE REPORT AND SUMMING UP

The architectural profession reacted promptly to the Report of the Summerland Fire Commission. In June 1974 an editorial comment in the *RIBA Journal* spoke of the report being 'of great concern to the architectural profession' and having 'serious implications not only for architects as designers, but also for public authorities, developers, and the managers of public buildings'. The Royal Institute of British Architects felt that it must take, and be seen to take, prompt action in response to the report. Its Policy Committee started an immediate review of all relevant aspects of education and practice. Meanwhile the Institute advised all its members to read the report.

In July 1974 the *RIBA Journal* carried a digest of the report illustrated with plans and photographs. The editorial comments showed that the architectural profession was acutely aware of its role in the Summerland disaster. Although the Commission had decided that there were 'no villains', the architectural contribution to the disaster might have seemed prominent.

Some early press criticism thought that the report was too severe. It was certainly not a whitewash job. Meanwhile the Institute's Policy Committee carried on with its extensive review of the Commission's report.

David Barclay, Secretary of the Institute's Practice Board, summarized the review as follows. First, the Institute was reviewing its own activities in the light of the report, and second it was examining current regulations which affected or controlled building. About the recommendation that architectural training should include a much extended study of fire protection and fire precautions, Barclay wrote: 'This is by no means a new subject for the board because, for the past two years, a joint working group set up by the Fire Protection Association and the RIBA has been appraising fire education in the schools of architecture, and a booklet *Fire and the architect* has now been published.' This booklet (price 75p) would now be promoted in Schools of Architecture and the Summerland report itself perhaps included on standard reading lists for students.

The first recommendation of the Commission (that in the designing of a building a named person should be in charge from the start, and should take and be known to be taking the major design decisions) posed the RIBA with a problem. If adopted, this recommendation would radically affect the role of the project or 'job' architect. It appeared from the Institute's initial response that this recommendation was not acceptable. On other matters the Institute seemed reasonably happy that its procedures and publications were adequate though improvements would probably be made. In concluding his summary Barclay exhorted every RIBA member 'however he is employed in the design of buildings, to try to ensure that disasters like Summerland cannot recur'. *And so say all of us* was the instinctive reply of architects, architectural students and the general public. On the subject of fire prevention David Barclay wrote:

> The building control panel has drawn attention to the *Fire prevention design guide,* an earlier publication by the Fire Protection Association. This is a handbook for architects which is based on the RIBA plan of work and allows for information on fire protection to be collected, analysed, and fed into the early stages of building projects. Though not an RIBA publication, it was produced by the FPA with the Institute's co-operation and, like the plan of work, it deserves to be more widely used.

The Architects' Journal (29 May 1974) was more forthright than the official *RIBA Journal.* In a leading editorial article the *AJ* referred to the Summerland errors as 'so ordinary and casual that many of them could have occurred in any architect's office'. A worse indictment followed –

> . . . it is the ignorance and cynicism of the (Summerland) architects and the chaotic communications within the design team that are most frightening. Which of us has not sometimes felt that the building regulations are too onerous, that all the fuss and expense is really a waste of time because the building we are designing will never catch fire? Who has not specified a new material – even on occasion a whole string of untried components – without being fully aware of all the problems that are likely to ensue? What architect has not delegated design to inexperienced assistants or accepted work for which he was not qualified? Who has not forgotten to tell the other members of the design team that materials have been changed with the result that the building cannot be fully understood as a whole?

The most serious fire in a single building in British history killed 183 people at the Victoria Hall, Sunderland in 1883. In 1927 a Glasgow cinema fire killed 70 children, and 49 people died in a fire at a Huddersfield clothing factory in 1941. But the world's worst fire in one building was in 1845, when 1670 people died in a Chinese theatre at Canton. The Summerland (Isle of Man) fire, in which 50 men, women and children died was added to the list in 1973. This terrible disaster left (in the words of the Commission) 'not only . . . a temporary ruin on the Island but a permanent scar in the minds of Manxmen'.

Case Study 4

The Ronan Point Tower Block Collapse

by Victor Bignell

Contents Page

At Canning Town in East London on 16 May 1968 a small domestic gas leak led to an explosion in a flat on the eighteenth floor of a twenty-two storey system-built tower block called Ronan Point. Floor panels, walls and contents of the damaged flat fell to the ground; more than twenty other flats on the same corner of the block followed.

Luckily only a few people died in the accident, but the cost of remedial work on tower blocks has been estimated at £18 million. To this must be added the delay to local authority housing programmes.

The following description of the incident is based on the official 'Report of the Inquiry into the Collapse of Flats at Ronan Point, Canning Town', published by Her Majesty's Stationery Office, 1968.

HOMES AND HOUSING

Tower Blocks

The London Borough of Newham was formed in 1965, mainly from the former Metropolitan Boroughs of East and West Ham. The new authority inherited a massive housing problem; over a quarter of the dwellings in West Ham had been destroyed in the Second World War, while the majority of the remainder dated from before 1914. In 1968 they included 9000 classed as slums; despite great efforts 8000 names remained on the waiting list for homes.

In the early 1950s the housing problem had been tackled by constructing blocks of flats, two or three stories high, at a density of some seventy persons to the acre. A change of national policy allowed the density to rise in the 1950s to about 140 persons to the acre. With the change of policy came a new solution: to build tall blocks of flats. Office blocks in cities already rivalled church spires, now homes in tower blocks ('high-rise housing') joined them on the skyline, as a major part of local authority housing programmes.

There is still a common misconception that tower blocks automatically allow more people to dwell on each acre than do 'low-rise housing' developments, although architects have demonstrated this to be false by devising low-rise layouts at high density. Of course, if tower blocks were built high enough and close enough together the density of accommodation could even exceed the figure of 500 persons to the acre achieved in Glasgow tenements in the last century. But regulations now restrict densities to levels based on the needs of daylighting, recreational open space, car parking, fire engine access, etc., so the major reasons for the rash of high rise flats must be sought elsewhere than in density.

At the same time as tower blocks were being examined for land-saving economies, novel building techniques were becoming more feasible, which, by solving a general problem in the building industry, favoured widespread use of high rise flats by local authorities. Traditionally a labour-intensive activity, building was losing its labour force. Unpleasant, difficult and dangerous working conditions on most building sites drove men to seek the warm security of factory production lines. Large building firms ingeniously exploited this drift by following their former employees into factories, and transferring to these factories as many building operations as possible. This new factory industry came to be called 'Industrialized Building'. The techniques of 'System Building' were a part of it, and seemed ideal for constructing tall blocks of flats.

System Building

'System Building' may be used for all kinds of structure from schools and offices to barracks and factories. Whatever is to be built, systems principles dominate the project right from the earliest stages of design drafting, when as much attention is given to problems of construction as to the needs of the user. A variety of materials can be used, from timber to the latest novelty; even using traditional bricks, mortar, timber and tiles, systematic planning early on will reduce the time taken to build a house, but economy of labour, and particularly site labour, will not be achieved unless the materials are chosen with systems objectives in mind.

After a comprehensive planning stage actual construction of a system building might commence many miles from the site. Factories prepare their production lines, and for a block of flats similar to Ronan Point they cast room-width floor panels and room-height wall panels in reinforced concrete. Complete with as many fittings as possible the panels travel to the site. There a team of civil engineers has prepared a concrete foundation and the ground floor. The panels and other parts arrive according to a schedule, so without delay erectors can sling each panel into place by crane, using some dozen panels for each small flat. Each flat resembles its neighbours and the work proceeds apace.

System Building for High-Rise Flats

Having set a crane on a building site, it is an obvious economy to continue building upwards without repositioning the crane. A tower crane dominates the skyline like the towers it builds, and indeed it has been claimed that positioning the crane has fixed the position of tower blocks on awkwardly shaped sites.

High-rise system building promised rapid progress towards housing targets. It demanded fewer site workers but would cost much more: the higher the block, the more each flat would cost. To offset this the Government gave larger grants to local authorities for their tall blocks.

Building in this fashion lends itself to tight organization and modern methods of business. It became difficult for small firms of builders to take on the large projects offered by local authorities, so large firms of contractors moved in with offers of complete package deals competitive in unit costs. This accelerated the switch to system building.

Another reason quoted for the new shape of housing is the prestige then accruing to the Councils, Borough Officers and architects responsible for a tower. Thrusting upwards vigorously, isolated from the miserable terraces it replaced, a tower could be christened with the name of a local Councillor, as was Ronan Point.

THE RISE OF RONAN POINT

Newham and the Larsen–Neilsen System

The report of the Inquiry into the collapse of Ronan Point gives as the reason for Newham's decision to adopt high-rise housing by systems methods the shortage of skilled labour. Seeking a solution to their Borough's problem, Newham's officials had already been looking at available designs and chose the Larsen–Neilsen system from Denmark. Apart from the emergency 'prefabs' of the late 1940s, development of system building had been pioneered on the continent of Europe. The Larsen–Neilsen system had been initiated in 1948, and had come to be used by 22 licencees in 12 countries.

The British group Taylor Woodrow–Anglian held the UK licence. This large contractor possessed, in a single group of companies, wide experience beyond mere building of houses and flats. The firm of Phillips Consultants contained the group's experts on the Larsen–Neilsen system, which comprised not only patterns for panels and joints, but included methods of producing and assembling the panels. Thus colleagues such as Anglian Building Products could make the panels, while another member of the group, Myton Ltd, had been experienced in prefabrication since 1946.

Newham's Borough Architect prepared an outline scheme for Ronan Point and three other tower blocks in Canning Town. Taylor Woodrow–Anglian assured the Borough that the designs were feasible for the height proposed. In preparing working drawings for room layouts the Borough Architect's department kept in close touch with Taylor Woodrow–Anglian in order to reduce costs by further standardization of precast units. The final relationship to include the Borough as client was complex, with Phillips Consultants being employed by Newham as consultants for the foundation, and also by the building side of their own group when it came to the superstructure. This system of relationships came in for gentle criticism after the Ronan Point disaster. Phillips Consultants checked the strength and stability of the towers, but, as these twenty-two storey blocks were higher than any yet built by this system, the structural proposals were referred to Larsen–Neilsen in Denmark. They were approved.

Statutory Approval of the Building

Plans for the building had to comply with local by-laws, dealt with by the Chief Building Surveyor using staff of the Borough Engineer's Department. The Council's Chief Building Surveyor questioned the contractors on loads in the lowermost walls, fire resistances of internal walls, loadings allowed on floors and wind loading on the structure. On this last point, using his experience of local conditions, the Surveyor insisted that the figure taken for wind loading be raised.

Phillips Consultants supplied details, drawings and copies of their own calculations for checking by a structural engineer in the department. In particular, he looked at conditions at the tower base, where the weight of the building and accumulated wind force have greatest effect. The checks followed normal practice in consisting of reference to specific existing regulations. As there were none especially appropriate to the assembly of precast panels into tall blocks of flats by system methods, no checks were made on the strength of joints between panels. The detailed structural calculations were not considered or checked by any other engineer, and indeed the Borough Architect did not expect the Borough Engineer to assess safety except within the requirements of existing by-laws and Codes of Practice. We shall see that, as well as ignoring the new way of building, the regulations did not allow for the long-standing hazards of wind and fire.

Before recommending Exchequer subsidy and sanctioning the raising of a loan by the Borough, the Minister of Housing and Local Government required formal assurance from the local authority in respect of certain matters. These included layout and density of development, standards of accommodation, of health and of safety, structural strength and stability. To this end the Borough Architect wrote out a certificate which read in part:

> I certify that the buildings to be built are not inconsistent with the building by-laws in force in the district and the materials and construction are of a type appropriate to a building which is to have a life of sixty years or more.

This certificate was issued before the engineers had finished their calculations on the structure.

THE FALL OF RONAN POINT

The Explosion

Formalities complete, building operations were set in hand for nine tower blocks. Construction of Ronan Point started in July 1966 and proceeded without a hitch, so that tenants were able to begin moving into the completed flats in March 1968. Many were eager to do so, and had looked forward to the amenities which their new flats offered.

The tenant of Flat 90, a single lady living alone, moved in on 15 April 1968. Like eighty per cent of the other tenants she chose gas for cooking. A

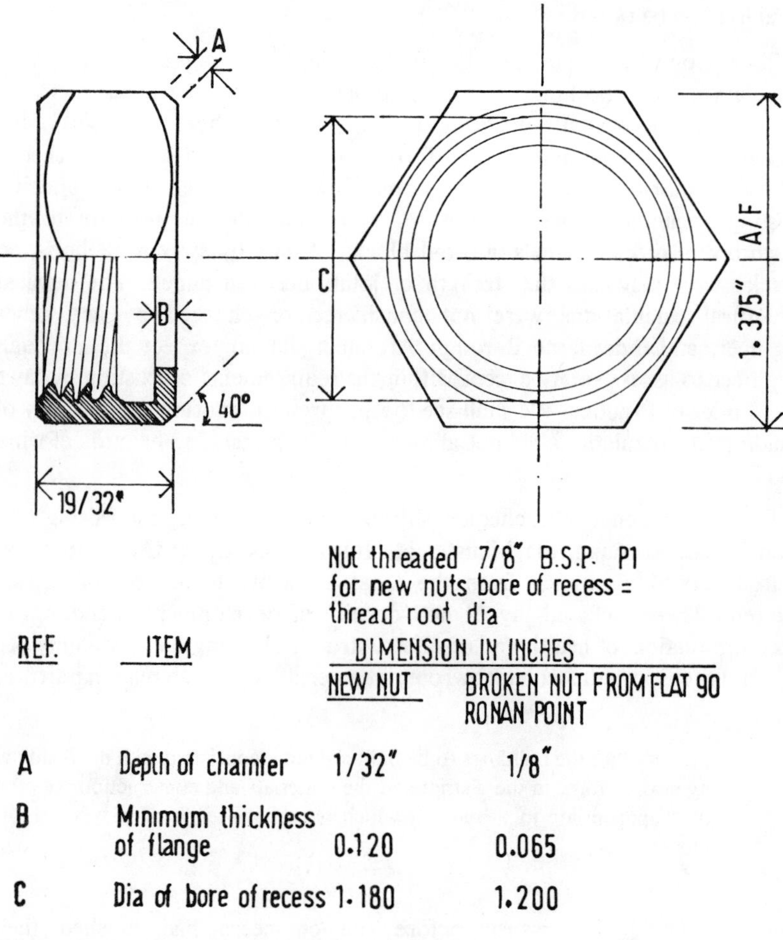

REF.	ITEM	DIMENSION IN INCHES	
		NEW NUT	BROKEN NUT FROM FLAT 90 RONAN POINT
A	Depth of chamfer	1/32"	1/8"
B	Minimum thickness of flange	0.120	0.065
C	Dia of bore of recess	1.180	1.200

Figure 1 Brass nut, showing standard and substandard dimensions

neighbour arranged to install her cooker, which had done duty elsewhere for three years, as also had a brass nut which was to connect a flexible hose on the back of the cooker to the gas supply stand pipe on the kitchen wall. The neighbour reported to the Gas Board his intention to install the cooker, and connected it to the gas supply system using the correct tools and techniques. But someone had cut the brass nut incorrectly during manufacture (Figure 1). At a critical section it was too thin, so that even without the use of excessive force it must have begun to give way when tightened.

It finally split during the night of 15–16 May, to fill the flat with a mixture of gas and air (Figure 2). The previous evening neither the occupier nor visitors to the flat smelt gas. Indeed the tenant could not even remember smelling gas when at 5.45 on the morning of 16 May she got up and crossed the gas laden hall to her kitchen. There she filled a kettle to make some early morning tea and struck a match for the gas. She remembered nothing from after filling the kettle until she found herself lying on the floor in a pool of water from the kettle, looking up at the flames on the ceiling. The match had ignited the gas in the flat.

The explosion in the kitchen threw the refrigerator, sink unit and water heater to the floor. The cooker was overturned and the gas which issued forth freely from the now fully broken nut (Figure 2) caught fire. But being at the point of ignition the kitchen and its occupant escaped lightly compared with the rest of the flat, for as the advancing flame moved out of the kitchen it heated the mixture of gas and air in front of it and the combustion accelerated, becoming an explosion. It vented itself on reaching the living room and bedroom by blowing out the walls.

The Collapse

Before examining the sequel to what was so far a localized incident, it is important to realize that the explosion was not of exceptional magnitude, nor

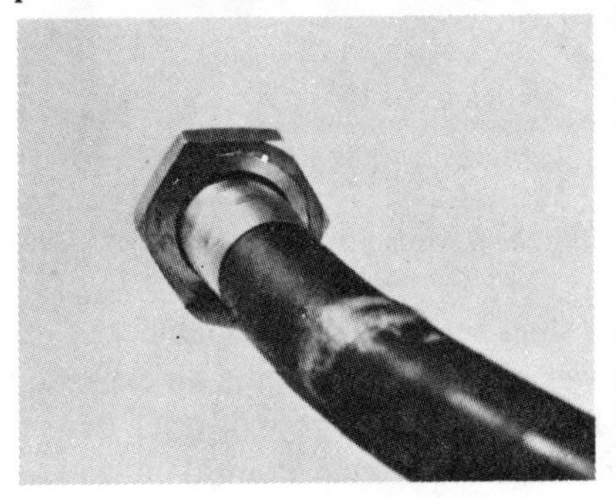

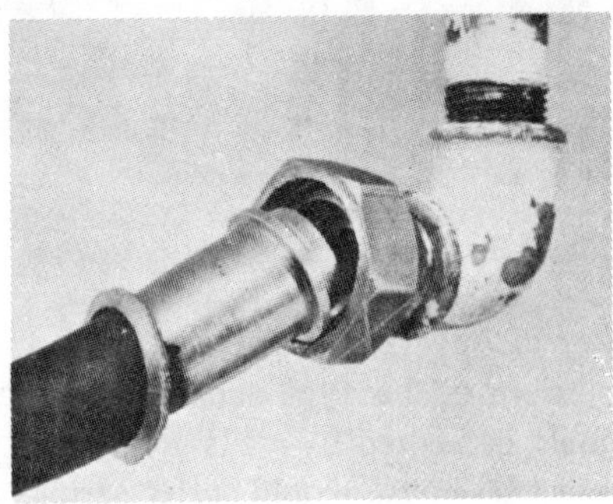

Figure 2 Brass nut showing (a) Deformation, (b) breakage

Figure 3 The gas cooker in Flat 90, showing the flexible hose

was its occurrence unlikely. Indeed we shall see later the probability of explosions of this type occurring in a tower block. In any home an explosion could be vented by walls giving way. But in a terraced row of brick houses only one house would suffer serious damage. At Ronan Point damage was to be more than local, it would progress to destroy twenty-one more homes.

Figure 4 Close-up of damage

The incident became a disaster because the walls of Flat 90 on the eighteenth floor were the sole supports for the floors and walls of the flat immediately above. These now fell, and floors and walls of flats higher up, deprived of support, joined the falling debris. This first phase of collapse ended only at roof level.

Figure 5 Aerial view showing Ronan Point

The panels detached from above Flat 90, together with the human and inanimate contents of the flats, fell on to the floor of Flat 90. The impact smashed this floor, and in the second stage of progressive collapse it was the turn of flats below to suffer. The accumulated mass proceeded down through the remaining seventeen flats on that corner of the block, breaking or detaching more panels as it went (Figures 4 and 5).

The human toll was remarkably small, only four persons dead and seventeen injured, thanks to a fortunate combination of circumstances. Of the eight flats unoccupied in the whole block, four were situated at the fatal corner. Of the four flats above Flat 90, all of whose bedrooms and living rooms were destroyed, only one was occupied. Below Flat 90 the living rooms had the contents spilled to street level but at 5.45 a.m. most people were in their bedrooms. If the incident had occurred one evening, the loss of life in twenty-two living rooms would have been far greater.

THE STRUCTURE OF RONAN POINT

The Philosophy

To see why Ronan Point collapsed progressively at one corner it is necessary to recognize that there are several ways of building tall blocks. One way is to erect a continuous framework of steel girders firmly bolted together and clothed with walls of brick, stone or concrete slabs. The steel frame can support each floor and each set of walls individually so that a wall of one room need not depend for support on the presence of a wall below. Together with reinforced concrete framing as an alternative, this is how the skyscrapers of New York were built, so that when in 1945 a bomber aircraft flew into the side of the 102 storey Empire State Building the eleven people killed in the building died not from falling seventy-eight floors, but from fires started by blazing fuel. The frame, walls and floors remained intact except for a neat aircraft-shaped hole. At Ronan Point each element of structure relied entirely on the presence of another just below. Removal of one brought down many more.

Structural Details

Unlike the upper part of the Ronan Point tower the base was of heavy reinforced concrete cast on site. Above the base each storey conformed to a pattern, with prefabricated panels making up small flats on each side of a central corridor, served at its mid point by a lift and stairs. The grouping around a central core and the compact layout of the plan gave the title 'Point' to the block. Inside Flat 90 (Figure 6) the bedroom, living room, bathroom and kitchen all led off a small central hall.

The walls of the corridor and the thick flank walls and cross walls at right angles to the corridor carried the weight of flats above. Other walls such as between the bedroom and hall, together with exterior walls on the East of Flat 90 were light in construction. They carried their own weight, wind loads and minor loads from those furnishings and fittings directly attached. Each floor panel did duty as the ceiling of the flat below, and rested on the load-bearing walls.

Assembly

The sequence of assembly of the load bearing panels can be followed in Figures 7–10. Starting with the flank wall and cross walls of the flat below

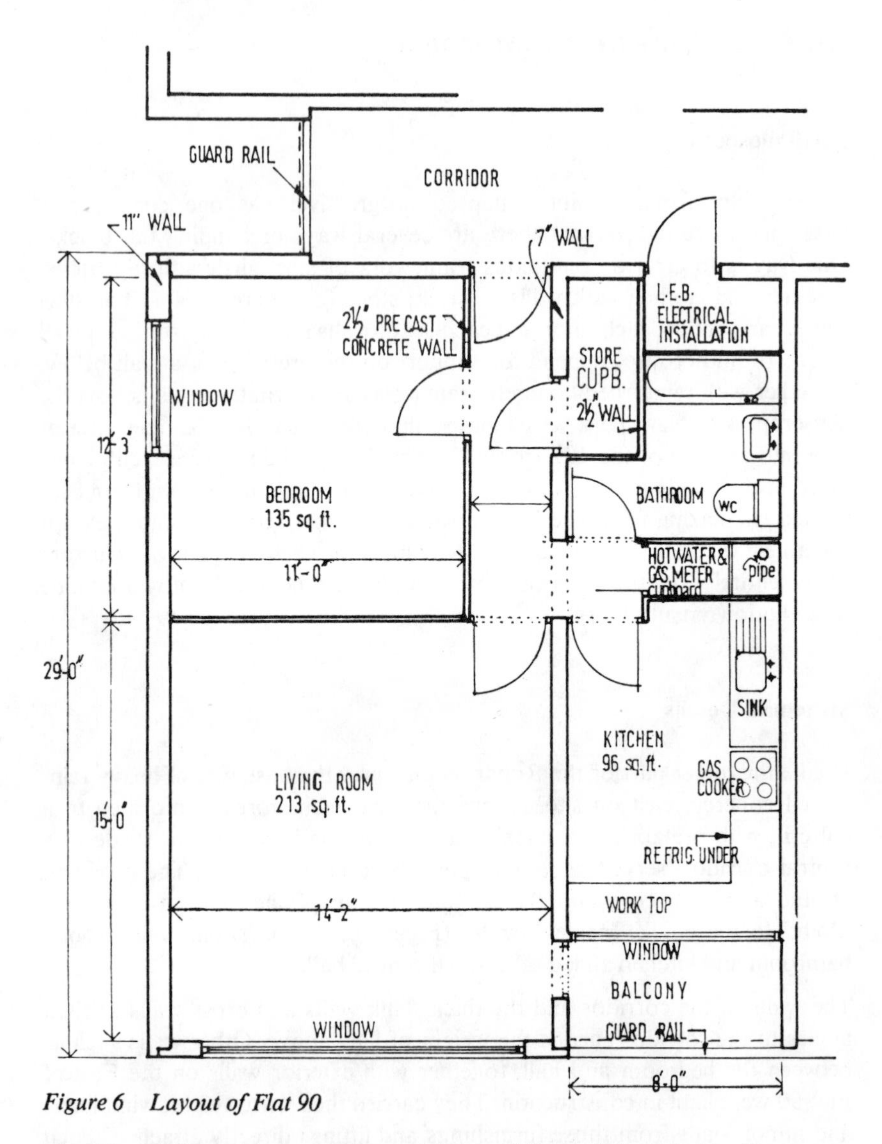

Figure 6 Layout of Flat 90

Flat 90 standing erect, a tower crane placed floor slabs side by side on top of the walls. Hardboard pads evened out small irregularities.

At the flank wall joint H2 (Figure 7) each floor slab had two steel tie straps. A hole at one end of each strap located it on two vertical lifting rods precast into each flank wall slab, while through a hole at the other end of the strap a stud passed, to be screwed into the floor panel and fitted with a nut. However, at the corresponding joint H4 where the floor slabs and cross wall

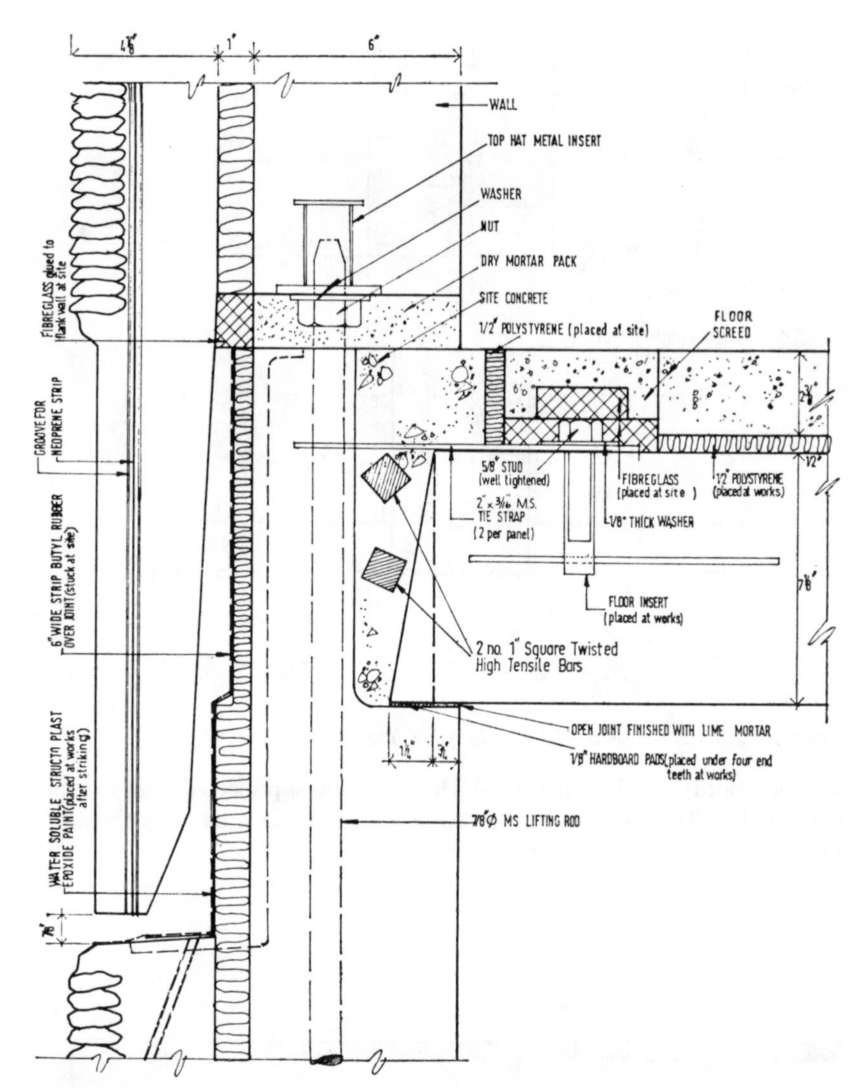

Figure 7 Joint H2. Horizontal joint between floor slab and flank wall

met no straps were used (Figure 8). Steel bars were laid in each joint and the remaining gap filled with concrete. Where adjacent floor slabs touched as they lay side by side, joint H3 (Figure 9) was made. The floor of Flat 90 could now be finished off smooth, leaving only the lifting rods projecting.

The tower crane next lowered on to these rods the wall panels for Flat 90; the erectors used the nuts on the lifting rods to adjust the positions of these wall panels. Joints H2 and H4 were finished off smooth. Where wall slabs

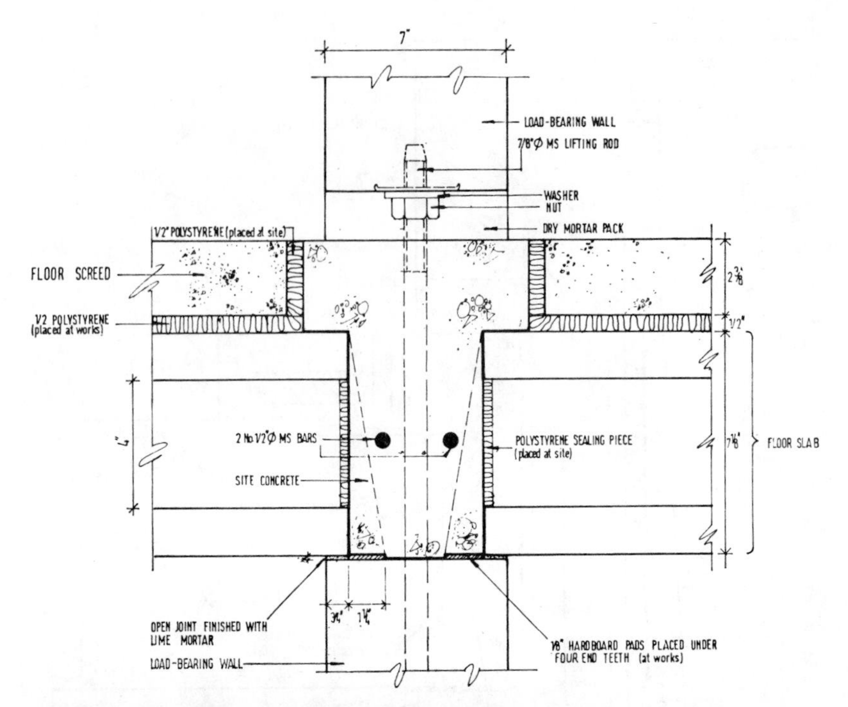

Figure 8 Joint H4. Horizontal joint between floor slabs and cross wall

met was joint type V13 (Figure 10). Here steel loops projected from the end of each slab. The loops overlapped and to lock them a bar was threaded through. Concrete filled the gap again.

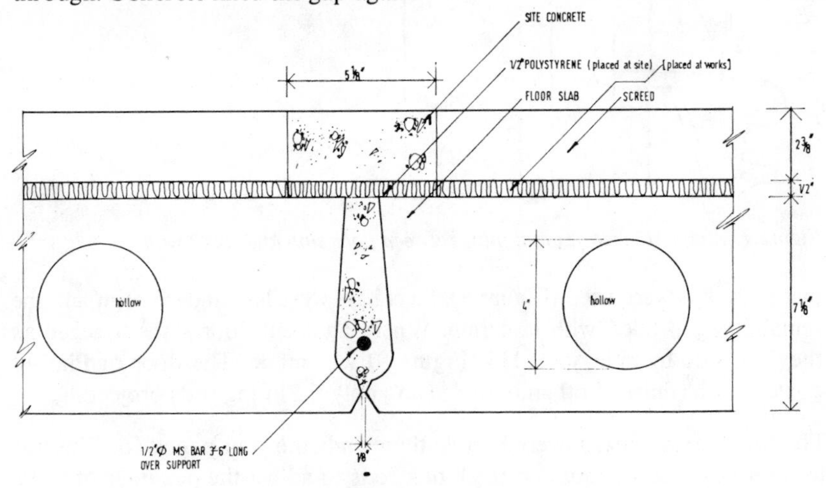

Figure 9 Joint H3. Horizontal joint between adjoining floor slabs

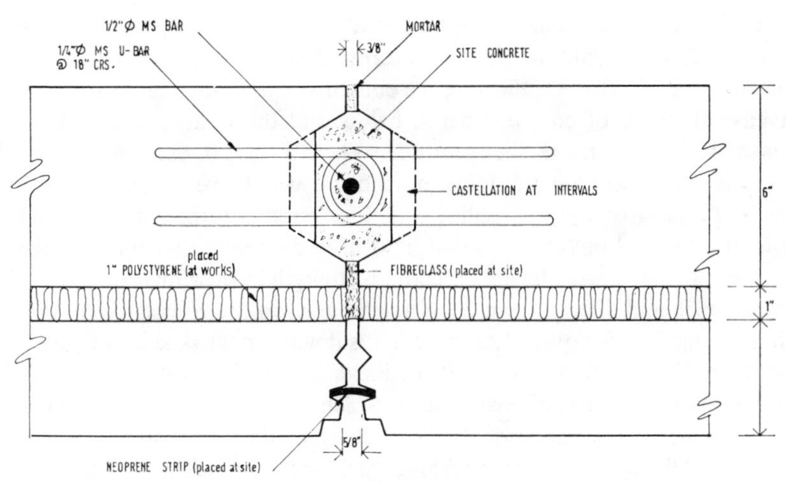

Figure 10 Joint V13. Vertical joint between adjoining wall panels

The Effect of an Explosion

Having seen how Ronan Point was put together, we can reconstruct the aftermath of the explosion in Flat 90. Outward movement of flank wall panels was prevented only by friction where the floor panels rested and by the tie straps. The concrete fill contributed little strength, nor did the laid-in bars, which ran the wrong way for the purpose. It has been calculated that a pressure of only 2.78 pounds per square inch could break the joint at ceiling level. Damage to small articles in the flat suggested pressures in the region of 12 pounds per square inch from the explosion, so it is no surprise that the flank wall slabs of Flat 90 were forced out. With the flank wall blown out and floor panels now falling at one end, the flank wall above Flat 90 was unsupported, and it fell too. Alternatively the projecting lifting rods carried this flank wall away in the first stage of collapse. Behaviour at the cross wall was even worse; here only the friction at the hardboard pads stopped the components separating. The reader can judge the strength of the floor panel joints H3. The best of the joints was V13 between wall panels, but even this allowed these panels to hinge about the locking bar, and no matter how good these vertical joints were, the building also needed horizontal joints to tie the parts together.

The foregoing presents a neat explanation of how the structure became separated into the same set of parts as had been brought to the site during two years' construction. A further possibility was considered and tested for the Inquiry. It was found that an upward pressure of 2.22 pounds per square inch could bend and break the ceiling of a flat. This is what happens when gas explodes in the kitchen of a two-storey terraced house: the ceiling and floor above are destroyed, allowing the contents of the room above to fall. In this case there is, of course, no flat below and the houses each side are supported directly from the ground. When Flat 90 exploded it was reasonable to expect severe damage inside; it was to be expected that its walls might blow out and its ceiling and floor burst into the flats above and below. But beyond this there should have been no severe damage. The flats above and below should have had enough strength in their own structure to remain entire and should have been able to rely on the resistance of joints with adjacent flats for overall support. Thus it was not weakness of the components in Flat 90 that converted an incident into a disaster but lack of integrity in the structure of nearby flats, which themselves relied on the continual presence of the panels of Flat 90. The slab and joint system of Ronan Point lacked the continuity of the frame used for the Empire State Building.

GAS

The only explosive substance in Flat 90 was gas, and apart from the mystery that the occupant smelt no gas as she went into the kitchen it is clear that a gas–air mixture was responsible for the explosion. Immediately after the disaster public reaction was guided by the Press and other media into blaming gas for the whole catastrophe. Although tower blocks had been criticized previously as socially undesirable eyesores, they had not gained a reputation of being unsafe. On the other hand the image of gas as a fuel was under scrutiny in the public eye as a result of difficulties in converting domestic gas from a town gas system to natural gas. An immediate cry after Ronan Point was that gas was dangerous and should be banned, at least in tower blocks. The false story was circulated that this was already so in France.

For the purposes of the Ronan Point Inquiry and a later report on the safety of natural gas, investigations were made of gas fuels. Statistics showed that the risk of a town gas explosion causing structural damage in a dwelling was of the order of 3.5 in a million. The score is low but it means that in a set of 50 blocks, each comprising 110 flats, town gas may cause structural damage once in the 60 year lifetime of the set. This risk is acceptable provided damage is confined to one or two flats. What is unacceptable is that a considerable part of a block should collapse. A block like Ronan Point could and should be designed from the outset to be proof against collapsing after the statistically predictable explosion of gas. If this is done then gas can be used, even in tall blocks.

Attention was focused on gas explosions, but there are other ways in which a panel of a tower block could become detached. Other explosive substances, such as petrol, liquefied gas, lighter fuel, might be in a flat. Even dust will explode. From outside, the block could be struck by aircraft, road vehicles, or cranes working nearby. Civil strife could cause deliberate or accidental explosions inside the flats or outside. Furthermore, at Ronan Point, and possibly in other tower blocks, we shall see that not only was the explosion risk ignored, two other factors – fire and wind pressure – were inadequately catered for. These could have damaged a panel and triggered collapse. Having seen now so many ways in which a panel could be damaged, how was it that a structural system was used in which the loss of *one* component caused the system to separate and the components to fall? Where were the watchdogs?

WATCHDOGS

The National Building Agency

This independent advisory body having fifty architects and five engineers on its staff was set up by the Ministry of Public Building and Works in 1964 to promote the use of improved techniques of design, management and site operation in building. The Agency became the responsibility of the Ministry of Housing and Local Government in 1966, in which year it was asked to concentrate on housing. The Agency issued appraisal certificates for approved systems of building, but was still examining the Larsen–Neilsen system when Ronan Point collapsed. When questioned at the Public Inquiry the Agency's Chief Engineer expressed little doubt that a certificate would have been granted.

A Ministry circular in 1965 made it clear that the Agency would not cover the structural stability of buildings over four storeys high, and that analysis of systems would only go as far as application of existing codes and regulations. As none referred specifically to explosions or progressive collapse, the Agency did not carry the responsibility of forestalling this disastrous combination.

The Building Research Station

This Government organization had no specific brief to conduct system building research, and had no direct role in the approval chain. The Station had conducted some research early in the history of system building, and scientists there were, of course, aware of the techniques. One senior member of staff was an English representative on the European Committee on Concrete, but not until July 1968 was an English translation available of the Committee's document of March 1967: *International Recommendations for the Design and Construction of Large Panel Structures*. An extract from this says:

> One can hardly over-emphasize the absolute necessity of effectively joining the various components of the structure together in order to obviate any possible tendency for it to behave like a 'house of cards' and of organizing the structure accordingly. In this respect it would appear to be of major importance to install mechanically continuous steel ties interconnecting opposite walls or facades and providing safeguards for all the vertical panels.

Building Standards

We have seen how the structure of Ronan Point complied with the standards in force, and now must ask how they failed to guard against progressive collapse of system-built blocks following a statistically probable explosion. For a century the Government has issued model by-laws, latterly replaced by national Building Regulations. As well as basic functional requirements the by-laws and Regulations came to quote details of the British Standards Institution's British Standards and Codes of Practice, which were 'deemed to satisfy' the by-laws and Regulations. An independent body, but in receipt of Government grant, the Institution works through Technical Committees to produce and update its Standards and Codes. Each committee seeks to represent all the interests concerned with the design, manufacture and use of the subject referred to it. The Ronan Point Inquiry heard no evidence from the Institution but commended the work it undertook. However, the Inquiry report criticized arrangements for initiating codes on new forms of construction and in particular the lack of attention to system building and to progressive collapse of tall buildings. Although it is agreed that preparation of a new Code must take a considerable time, Ronan Point was being designed in 1964 and yet no code was available for it, even in 1968.

So progressive collapse was not proscribed, but neither were two conventional agents of disaster: wind and fire. We have already seen that the Borough Surveyor insisted the design wind pressure be raised; the change was from the 17 pounds per square foot allowed by the Code, to 24 pounds. This last figure represents a design wind speed of 63 miles per hour. But meteorological records showed that for Canning Town the wind speed will rise to 105 miles per hour once on average in 60 years, giving a wind pressure of 45 pounds per square foot and leaving the structure with little or no margin of safety. The Surveyor had checked the building panels against fire, as specified in the Building Regulations. But though a fire would not penetrate a panel, the effect of heat on one face of a floor panel could be to so bend it that the vital joint with the flank wall was endangered. Once again the new type of building had not been analysed as a system should be: links as well as components must be sound.

CONCLUSION

Tower blocks had already been criticized for social defects and ugliness. Then in 1968 an explosion of a popular fuel within a so-called system building sent more than twenty homes plummetting on to a car park. After the Ronan Point inquiry had shown that individual homes supplied with gas would occasionally explode, the question asked next of the civil engineering and building industries was whether so many homes innocent of fault should suffer from an accident in only one. Ronan Point showed that industrial builders and the authorities had not given the subject of progressive collapse enough attention.

Ronan Point and blocks like it have now been repaired and re-occupied; blocks not then started have been redesigned. But even while Ronan Point was falling, the passion for tall blocks was waning, hastened by removal of the special subsidy. Ronan Point became a rallying cry for the detractors of tall blocks. Low-rise developments can give back to housing the qualities unintentionally provided by 200 years of speculative building of terraced houses, without losing all the selling points of high rise. But the tall blocks of the 60s remain, and will be hard to remove.

It has been estimated that incorporation of safety features in new and existing blocks would add £18 million each year to the cost of housing, yet the deaths and injuries at Ronan Point amounted to no more than a few minutes national toll of road accidents. How much is each life worth? What should the numerical safety objectives be in a system?

Nevertheless, anyone whose system hurls Britishers' homes into the street must beware; his systems will be publicly dissected. How did it happen that so manifestly unsatisfactory a system came to be employed for local authority housing in receipt of government approval, encouragement and special subsidy? Did no one foresee a panel being lost from the system? Well no one had to: there was no Code of Practice. No one devised a Code of Practice as no one foresaw a panel being lost. No one foresaw a panel being lost because no one had to. Nobody in the industry broke this vicious circle, it was left to the neighbour who tightened the brass nut on the gas pipe in Flat 90.

Case Study 5
The West Gate Bridge Collapse

by Victor Bignell

CONTENTS Page

At midday on 15 October 1970 the collapse occurred of a 367 ft. long span of the partially completed West Gate Bridge over the River Yarra near Melbourne in the State of Victoria, Australia. Thirty-five workers on or beneath the bridge died.

A Royal Commission was initially set up to inquire into the circumstances and causes of the failure, but later the terms of reference were extended to cover 'whether any aspect of the design of the steel span between piers 10 and 11 is inadequate or undesirable'. Interest in the failure was heightened by two previous failures of box-girder spans.

The following account of the disaster is based on the official report:

> 'Report of the Royal Commission into the Failure of West Gate Bridge' (printed and published in Melbourne, 1971).

THE IMMEDIATE CAUSE

The failure of the West Gate Bridge resembled two previous failures of box-girder bridges (at Milford Haven and Vienna) in that it fell during construction when certain thin steel plates gave way. In other respects its collapse was different: it fell at the end of a morning during which some thirty bolts had been removed in an attempt to deal with a buckle in some of the plates. The buckle itself arose from the deliberate use of heavy blocks of concrete to correct the camber of the bridge. Incorrect camber sprang from the adoption of a novel erection sequence fraught with potential difficulties. This system was a compromise avoiding problems which had in fact been successfully overcome on other bridges. At the same time, the procedure created unique difficulties, which in the event would not be surmounted satisfactorily by the engineers, and would set the scene for a disaster.

DRAMATIS PERSONAE

The professional engineers building the bridge had been appointed by several organizations. These are listed below, together with their abbreviated titles. The names of selected individuals, and their positions in each organization, have been added (an asterisk denotes that the man died as a result of the bridge collapsing).

Unfortunately, it is not possible to relate the story of the bridge and its fall without naming these individuals and firms. This is much to be regretted for it focuses attention on blame for this particular failure, when really the purpose of our study is to use the failure of this one bridge as an example of deficiencies which are known to occur in systems which have not yet passed the threshold of disaster. Not until a system fails and a disaster has occurred is so much information made available on the operation of technology, and only then does systematic study become possible. Thus, the present writer does not seek to allocate individual blame for the loss of the lives of these thirty-five men, or the other losses. Any attempt to use this account in that way can lead to false conclusions, for the full story cannot be traced in complete detail, even now.

The Lower Yarra Crossing Authority (The Authority)

General Manager	C. V. Wilson

Maunsell and Partners, consulting engineers, Melbourne (Maunsell of Melbourne)

Managing Partner	E. M. Birkett (see also below)
On temporary secondment	A. Wallace (see below)

Freeman Fox and Partners, consulting engineers, of London (FF & P)

Partner	O. A. Kerensky
Partner	W. C. Brown
Partner	Sir G. Roberts
Resident Engineer	J. Hindshaw*
Site Engineer	D. F. McIntosh (later P. J. F. Crossley*)
Section Engineer (East Side)	C. V. J. Simpson
Section Engineer (West Side)	D. Ward
Senior Inspector of Steel Work	E. Enness

Werkspoor Utrecht NV, contractors of the Netherlands (Werkspoor)

Senior Representative in Melbourne	G. Hardenberg

World Services and Construction Co Ltd, contractors, of Melbourne (WSC)

Werkspoor Representative	G. Hardenberg
Managing Director	J. H. Schut
Area Supervisor	R. Schot
Chairman	J. Schroeder
Area Supervisor	J. Spee
Project Manager	A. Van Veldhuizen
On temporary secondment	A. Wallace (see below)

Maunsell and Partners, consulting engineers, of London (Maunsell of London)

Senior Engineer	A. Wallace (see secondment)

John Holland (Constructions) Pty Ltd, contractor, of Melbourne (JHC)

Chairman and Managing Director	C. V. Holland
General Manager, Engineering Division	B. D. Barmby
Construction Manager and Assistant Project Manager	I. H. Miller* (recent)
Section Engineer (East Side)	T. V. Burbury
General Manager, Southern Zone and Project Manager	T. R. Nixon
Section Engineer	J. T. Riggall
Planning Engineer	R. Rugless
Adviser (West Side)	R. Schot (of WSC)
Adviser (East Side)	J. Spee (of WSC)
Section Engineer (West Side)	W. F. Tracy*
On temporary secondment	A. Wallace (see above)

and it is convenient to add here:

The Royal Commission of Inquiry into the Failure (the Commission)

The Honourable E. H. E. Barber, Judge of the Supreme Court of Victoria.
Professor F. B. Bull, Professor of Civil Engineering, University of Adelaide.
Sir Hubert Shirley-Smith, bridge designer.

FINANCE FOR THE BRIDGE

The money to pay for building the bridge came from the Lower Yarra Crossing Authority, which in turn raised the funds by borrowing on debentures. Although the title 'Authority' implies that it is an arm of Government, the Authority is in fact a company, limited by guarantee and composed of representatives of private enterprise. The Authority came about as follows: in 1957 local industries had formed an association (later to be called a company and finally the Authority), among whose aims was the linking of activities on the left and right banks of the River Yarra by a tunnel or bridge. Government sources would not finance the union, so private enterprise found the cash for a road bridge.

Armed with the necessary powers, the Authority could raise debentures to pay for the necessary compulsory purchases of land, and then levy tolls on users of the completed bridge. The toll receipts would gradually pay off the debentures, and when all the loans were discharged the bridge would become the property of the Crown. This may seem to be an unnecessary detail, but it does suggest that a private company backed by shareholders is less able to accommodate expensive delays on a project than a government body would be.

The Authority received its powers in 1965, and in the following year the Government of Victoria guaranteed repayment of the debenture funds borrowed. The style of the bridge was to be the fashionable variety referred to as 'box-girder'. In this type of bridge, steel plates are assembled into a flattish tube having a trapezoidal cross-section. The tube is supported by steel cables running from the tops of towers erected on piers. The style was popular, for sound reasons as we shall see.

BRIDGE LAY-OUT

West Gate Bridge was to be more than a simple bank-to-bank span (Figure 1). Its 8 500 ft.* length (including approaches) took the ten lane, 70 mph

**Imperial units (i.e. feet and inches) were used in the original bridge design, and in the official Inquiry report. Their use is continued here for the sake of consistency.*

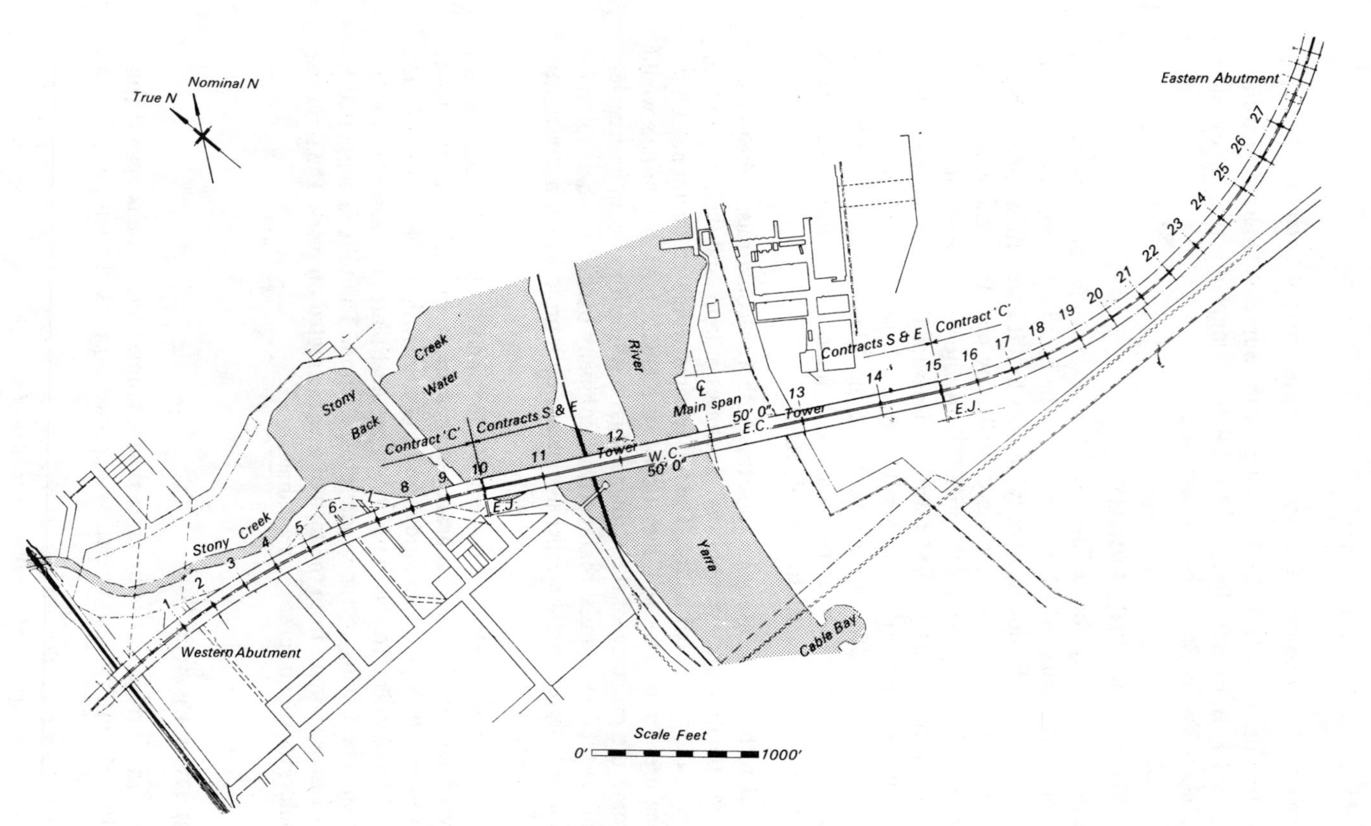

*Figure 1 West Gate Bridge site plan** E.C.=Eastbound carriageway W.C.=Westbound carriageway E.J.=Expansion joint

**Figures 1–7 and 9 are based on the tender drawings of the Joint Consulting Engineers.*

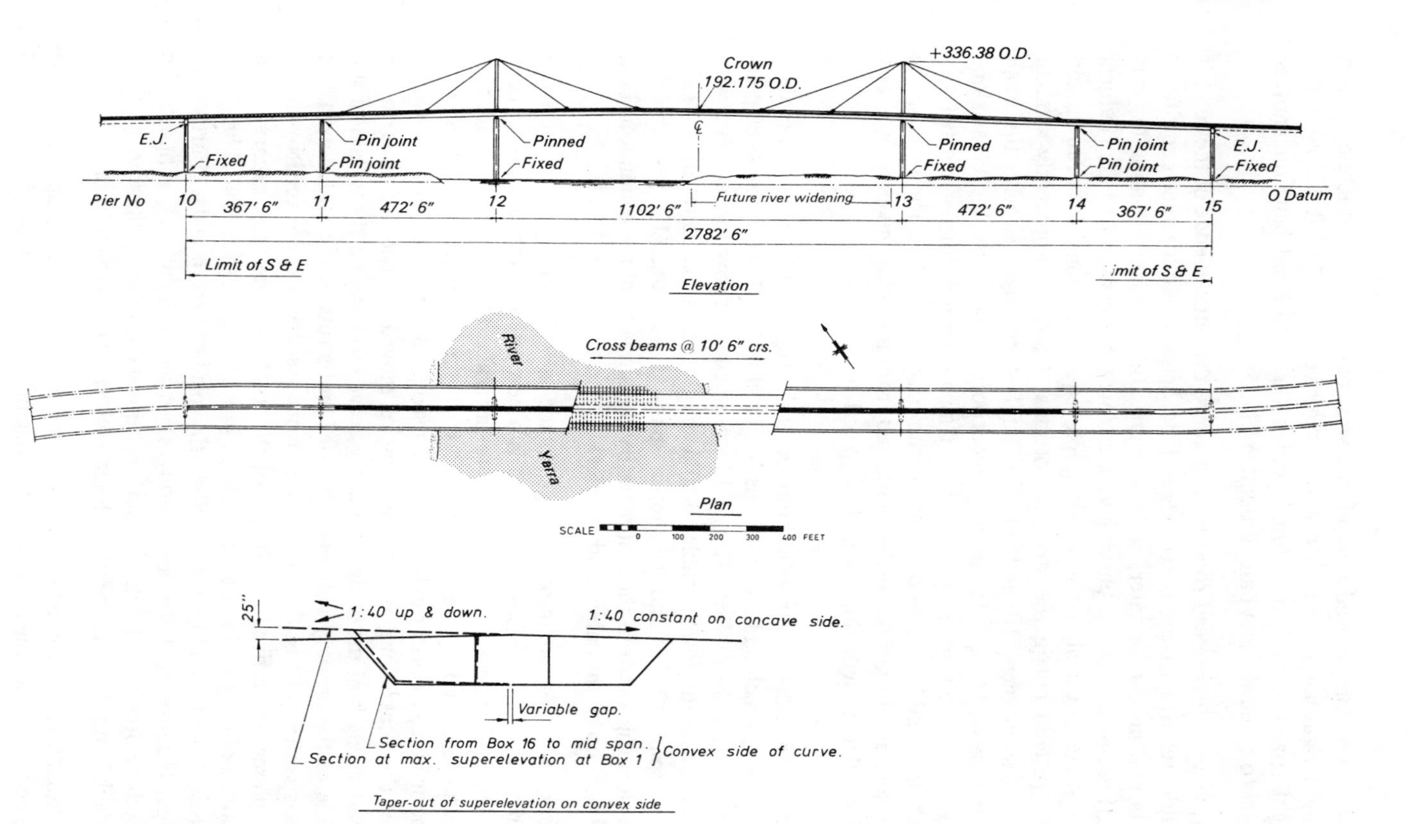

Figure 2 General arrangement of bridge E.J.=Expansion joint

roadway up from ground level on the west bank, on to a concrete viaduct having a right-hand bend, then across the river some 192 ft. below in five straight spans of steel, then finally down via a left-hand bend on another viaduct to reach the east bank ground level.

Now, when a high-speed road is on a curve the outside edge of the road is elevated relative to the inner edge. This helps to counteract centrifugal effects and makes for safer, easier driving. But the super-elevation (as it is called) necessary for the curving viaducts was not confined to the viaducts alone. As is universal, the super-elevation required for the curves ran on and finally petered out in the straight portions. Thus, the apparently straight span between piers 10 and 11 (the fatal span) together with the span between piers 14 and 15 actually incorporated not only the cross-slope necessary for rain water to run off but also a steadily increasing twist to match the viaducts. The diagram at the base of Figure 2 shows how the cross-section of the road surface changed from a shallow inverted V at box 1 (pier 10) to a single slope at box 16 (pier 12).

Vehicles using the bridge would run along the top surface of the trapezoidal section box, which had a continuous length of nearly 2 800 ft. between piers 10 and 15 (Figure 2). Piers 12 and 13 were built up above the box level with towers. From the towers cables would 'stay' (that is, partially support) the longest span (12–13) and the shorter spans (11–12) and (13–14). Vehicles were thus supported in the first place by the strength of the continuous box, itself held up by the cables and the piers.

Except for a few box-girder bridges made in wrought iron for nineteenth century railways, the box-girder idea is a new one for bridges, having been transferred from steel ships and metal aircraft. The box-girder bridge as adopted recently is to be distinguished from the lattice-girder type (Sydney harbour bridge, Forth rail bridge) often used in former times for railways. In these, the deck along which the vehicles moved contributed little to the overall strength of the bridge, it merely served to transmit the weight of the vehicle to the primary members, the ties and struts of the lattice work. In short-span railway bridges the lattice work tracery was replaced by heavy steel plates set vertically each side of the track, but the same separation of functions of deck and girders remained. More recently, the demand has been for road bridges, and the suspension principle has been popular (Forth road bridge, Humber and Bosporus bridges). Again a light deck supports the immediate presence of vehicles, and perhaps damps out oscillations. In turn, the deck hangs from graceful cables stretched between tall towers.

The box-girder bridge moves on from these ideas as did the ship when metal replaced wood as the material of construction, and rigging for sails and

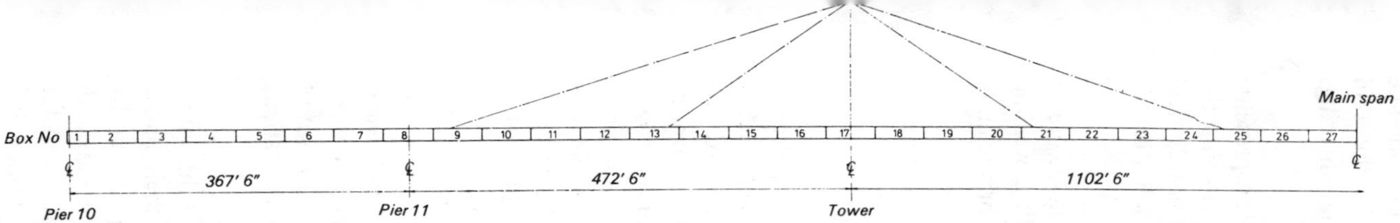

Table of Specifications——

Top Flange Panels	Plate	$\frac{3}{8}$″ M.S.; $\frac{3}{8}$″ H.Y.S.
	Stiffeners	3/No. Bulb Flats 6″ @ 7.42 H.Y.S.
Outer Web Panels	Plate	$\frac{3}{8}$″ thick
	Stiffeners	Vertical Stiffeners Bulb Flats 8″ @ 12.59 M.S. Longitudinal Stiffeners Bulb Flats 4″ @ 5.19 M.S.
Inner Web Panels	Plate	$\frac{3}{8}$″ M.S.; $\frac{1}{2}$″ H.Y.S.; $\frac{3}{8}$″ M.S.; $\frac{1}{2}$″ H.Y.S.; $\frac{3}{8}$″ M.S.; $\frac{3}{8}$″ H.Y.S.; $\frac{3}{8}$″ M.S.; $\frac{1}{2}$″ H.Y.S.; $\frac{3}{8}$″ M.S.; $\frac{1}{2}$″ H.Y.S.; $\frac{3}{8}$″ H.Y.S.
	Stiffeners	Vertical Stiffeners Bulb Flats 6″ @ 7.42 M.S. Longitudinal Stiffeners Bulb Flats 4″ @ 5.19 M.S.
Bottom Flange Panels	Plate	$\frac{3}{8}$″ M.S.; $\frac{1}{2}$″ H.Y.S.; $\frac{5}{8}$″ H.Y.S.; $\frac{1}{2}$″ H.Y.S.; $\frac{3}{8}$″ H.Y.S.; $\frac{5}{8}$″ H.Y.S.; $\frac{3}{8}$″ H.Y.S.; $\frac{3}{4}$″ H.Y.S.; $\frac{3}{8}$″ H.Y.S.; $\frac{5}{8}$″ H.Y.S.; $\frac{3}{8}$″ H.Y.S.; $\frac{1}{2}$″ H.Y.S.
	Stiffeners	7/No. Bulb Flats 6″ @ 7.42 H.Y.S.

TENDER DIMENSIONS

Top Flange Panels	Plate	$\frac{3}{8}$″ M.S.; $\frac{3}{8}$″ H.Y.S.; $\frac{1}{2}$″ H.Y.S.; $\frac{1}{2}$″ H.Y.S.; $\frac{3}{8}$″ H.Y.S.; $\frac{1}{2}$″ H.Y.S.; $\frac{1}{2}$″ H.Y.S.; $\frac{1}{2}$″ H.Y.S.
	Stiffeners	5/No. Bulbflats 6″×7.42 H.Y.S.; 3/No. Bulbflats 6″×7.42 H.Y.S.; 3/No. Bulbflats 6″×7.42 H.Y.S.
Outer Web Panels	Plate	$\frac{3}{8}$″ H.Y.S.
	Stiffeners	Vertical Stiffeners Bulbflats 8″×12.59 M.S. Longitudinal Stiffeners Bulbflats 4″×5.19 M.S.
Inner Web Panels	Plate	$\frac{3}{8}$″ M.S.; $\frac{1}{2}$″ H.Y.S.; $\frac{3}{8}$″ M.S.; $\frac{1}{2}$″ H.Y.S.; $\frac{3}{8}$″ M.S.; $\frac{3}{8}$″ H.Y.S.; $\frac{3}{8}$″ M.S.; $\frac{1}{2}$″ H.Y.S.; $\frac{3}{8}$″ M.S.; $\frac{1}{2}$″ H.Y.S.; $\frac{3}{8}$″ H.Y.S.
	Stiffeners	Vertical Stiffeners Bulbflats 6″×7.42 M.S. Longitudinal Stiffeners Bulbflats 4″×5.19 M.S.
Bottom Flange Panels	Plate	$\frac{3}{8}$″ M.S.; $\frac{3}{8}$″ H.Y.S.; $\frac{5}{8}$″ H.Y.S.; $\frac{1}{2}$″ H.Y.S.; $\frac{7}{8}$″ H.Y.S.; $\frac{3}{8}$″ H.Y.S.; $\frac{3}{4}$″ H.Y.S.; $\frac{5}{8}$″ H.Y.S.; $\frac{3}{8}$″ H.Y.S.; $\frac{3}{4}$″ H.Y.S.; $\frac{3}{8}$″ H.Y.S.; $\frac{5}{8}$″ H.Y.S.; $\frac{3}{4}$″ H.Y.S.; $\frac{3}{8}$″ H.Y.S.; $\frac{3}{4}$″ H.Y.S.; $\frac{1}{2}$″ H.Y.S.
	Stiffeners	7/No. Bulbflats 6″×7.42 H.Y.S.

SIZES ON WORKING DRAWINGS

Figure 3 Box-girder: make-up sheet Notes on Cover Plates: 1. All splice plates to be in same material as main plates. 2. Splice plates on both sides of plates on all flanges and webs. 3. Panel lengths shown on drawings may be reduced slightly to one standard length making allowance for variations due to deck curvature and erection camber provided cover plates are adjusted to suit.

masts disappeared. The aeroplane followed suit when the metal monoplane replaced the strutted and wired biplane. In all three systems the skin supports local loads while at the same time resisting bending, shearing, twisting and other wide-scale effects.

Technical advantages of the box-girder bridge are the low profile it presents to the wind, the control of aerodynamic stability by suitably shaping the box, and the inherent rigidity of box construction generally. Non-technical advantages more readily grasped are the sleek appearance of such a bridge and the ease of maintenance and painting.

A difficulty about the box-girder is that the plates of which it is made are so thin (Figure 3) that they are liable to distort during rolling, cutting, welding and bolting. Even more important, because of the unknowns it brings in, is the resistance to buckling, which is still a difficult matter to predict.

DESIGN BEFORE CONSTRUCTION

The Authority had received its powers by the Act of 1965, but had already started informal talks with Maunsell and Partners of Melbourne, consulting and civil engineers. In February 1966 Maunsell of Melbourne suggested that because of their own limited experience of major steel bridges the firm of Freeman Fox and Partners, consulting and civil engineers of world renown, be called in. The Authority agreed, and requested a report from both firms dealing with the general concept of the bridge. Acceptance of this was followed in July 1967 by the Authority formally appointing the firms as joint consultants. They were to prepare plans and estimates, which when approved would go back for development into detailed designs, working drawings, dimensions, bills of quantities, etc. The aim of this was to enable contractors to tender for the manufacture and erection of the bridge. The three sets of tender documents that went out in October 1967 were: Contract F for the foundation of the bridge, Contract C for concrete work and Contract S for steel bridge work. Early in 1968 Dr W. C. Brown of FF & P came out to Australia for a few weeks to discuss steel specifications and help evaluate tenders.

Senior spokesmen of FF & P were to admit after the collapse that this initial designing was done very quickly, and that for other jobs on their hands there would be more detail. However, the Commission was to point out by way of reply that an example of the tender drawings (Figure 4) includes full details and the location of every hole; a contractor could be forgiven for thinking that proper care and attention had been given to design and detailing, particularly when dealing with a firm like FF & P.

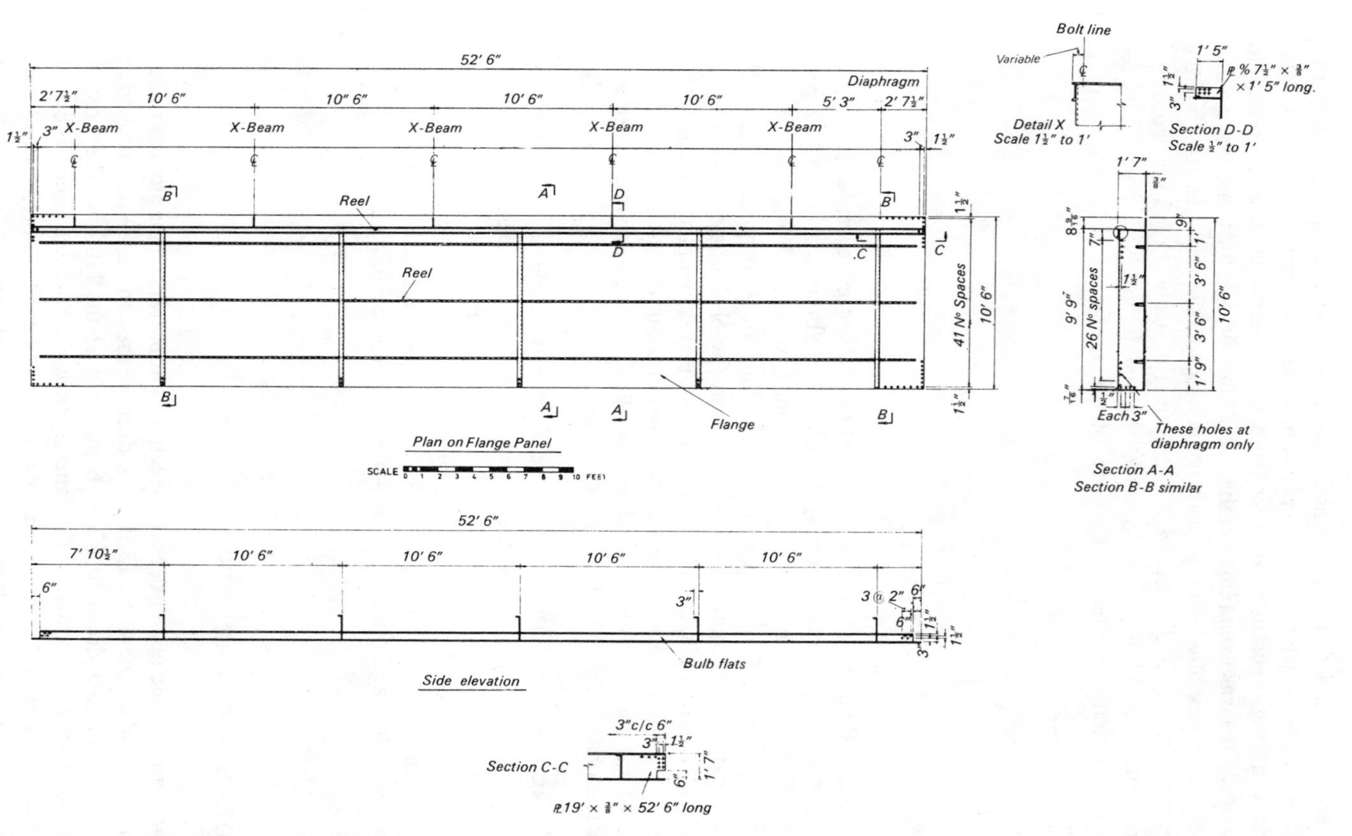

Figure 4 Typical panel: standard inner upper flange panel Note: All material to be mild steel unless marked H.Y.S. All material marked H.Y.S. to be High Yield Steel to ASA 151. All holes to be drilled $\frac{15}{16}$ in. diameter for $\frac{7}{8}$ in. diameter waisted grip bolts.

There is no hard and fast rule about which it should be, the consultants or the contractors, who work out procedures and strength calculations for a bridge during erection as distinct from the state of the finished bridge in service. This was exemplified in the West Gate Bridge, for while Maunsell of Melbourne specified the placement details of the prestressed concrete approaches they had designed, FF & P for the steelwork left the erectors a free hand in the choice of erection method and did not run a preliminary set of calculations to check the safety of the bridge at all stages of part-completion.

AWARD OF CONTRACTS

Contracts F and C, for foundation works and concreting, respectively, went to John Holland (Constructions) Pty Ltd, of Melbourne, a firm with a good deal of experience in concreting. Contract S went to World Services and Construction Co Ltd, an Australian subsidiary of Werkspoor Utrecht NV, a company of international repute based in the Netherlands. Construction started in April 1968, and work on Contract F was completed in September 1969. Contract C also went well, completion being expected early in 1971. But by the end of 1969 it was clear that WSC was behind with Contract S, for reasons which we shall consider later.

Aiming to avoid further delay, the Authority made a new contractual arrangement whereby WSC continued to make the steel parts for the bridge but JHC were to join the steelwork together under a new contract – E for erection – although JHC lacked experience in this specialized area of work. We shall examine the merits of this arrangement later, but first it is necessary to see how the steel parts were to become a bridge.

BOXES FOR A GIRDER

The layout of the box-girder cross-section is important to the story; Figure 5 shows the main member, 13 ft. 2 in. deep at the centre, 83 ft. 6 in. wide at the top, tapering down to 62 ft. 6 in. wide at the bottom. The box top provided space for three traffic lanes each way; brackets added each side would make extra lanes, but this stage was not reached before the failure. The basic subdivision of the 2 782 ft. long continuous girder was the box,

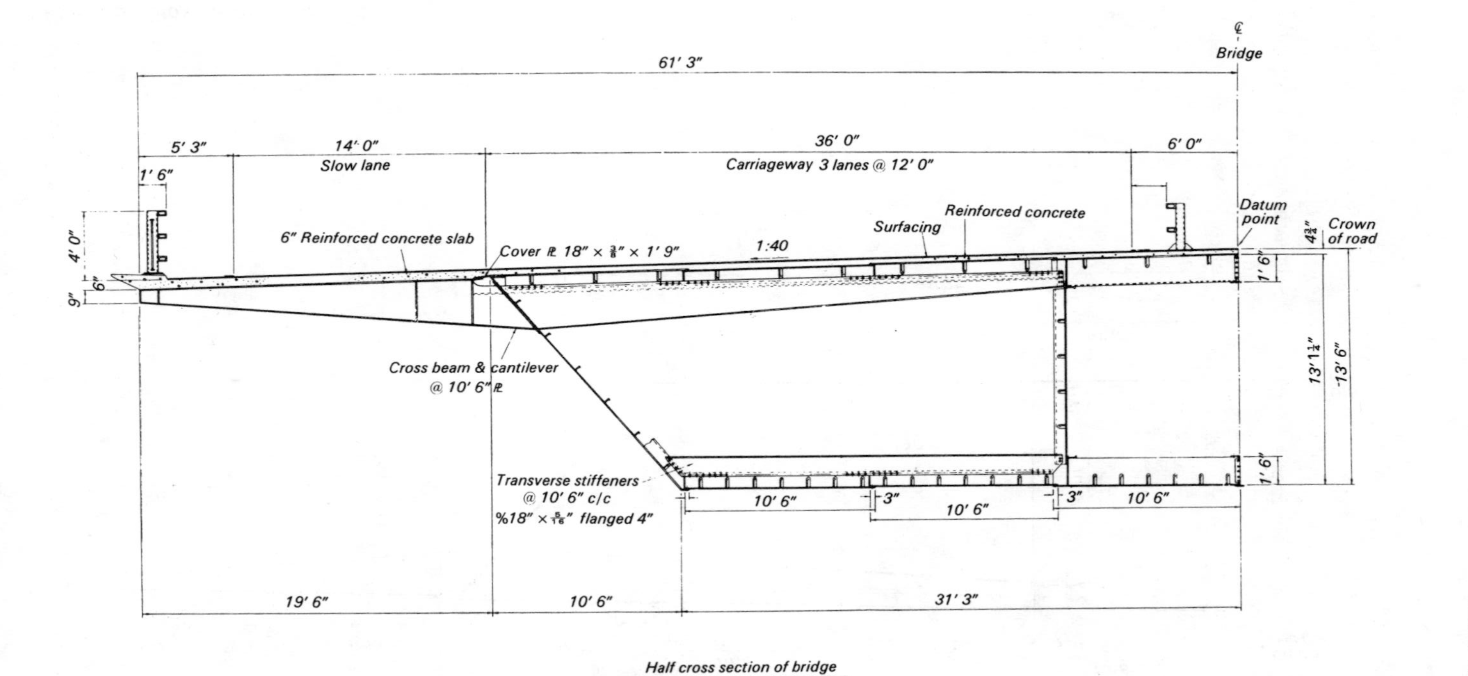

Figure 5 Main span; typical cross-section

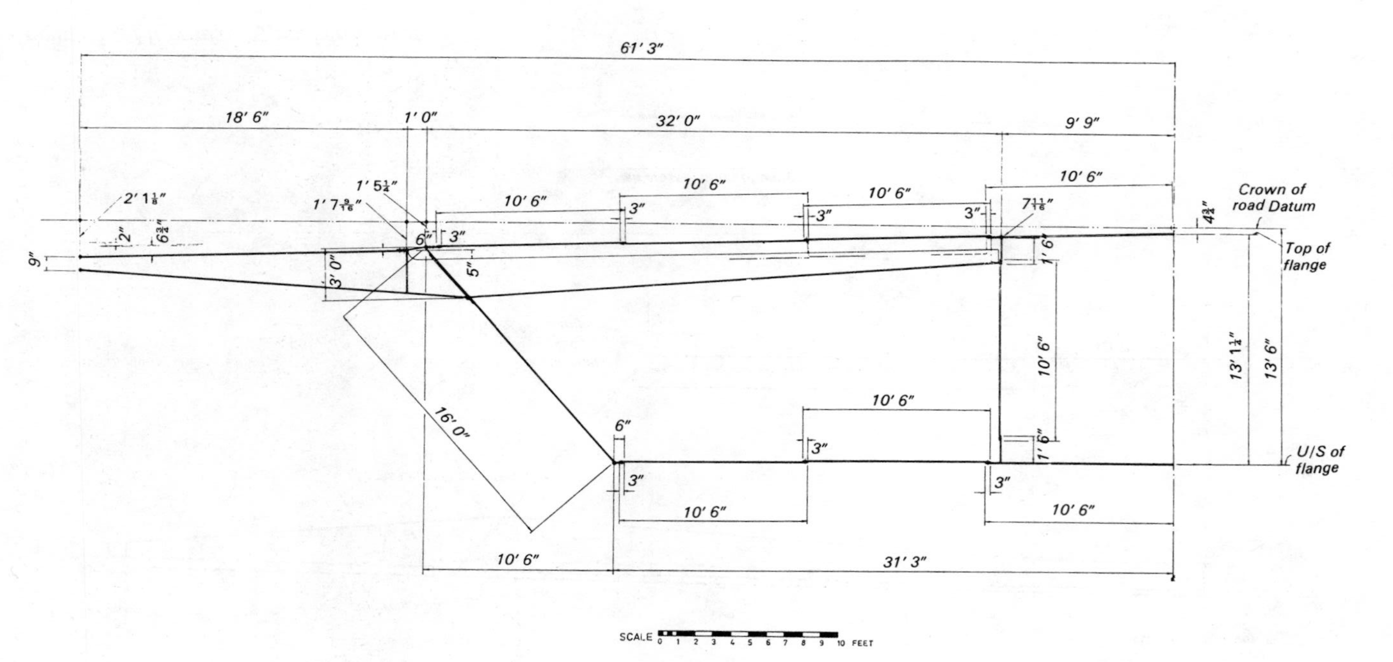

Figure 6 Box-girder setting out

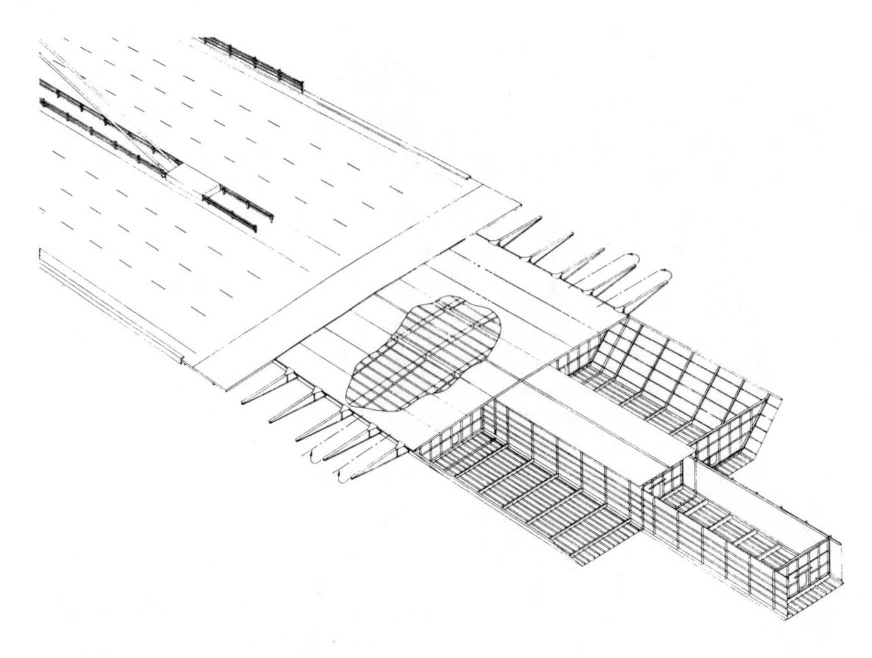

Figure 7 Box-girder assembly diagram

Figure 8 Typical half boxes shown ready for bolting into half span 10–11 north

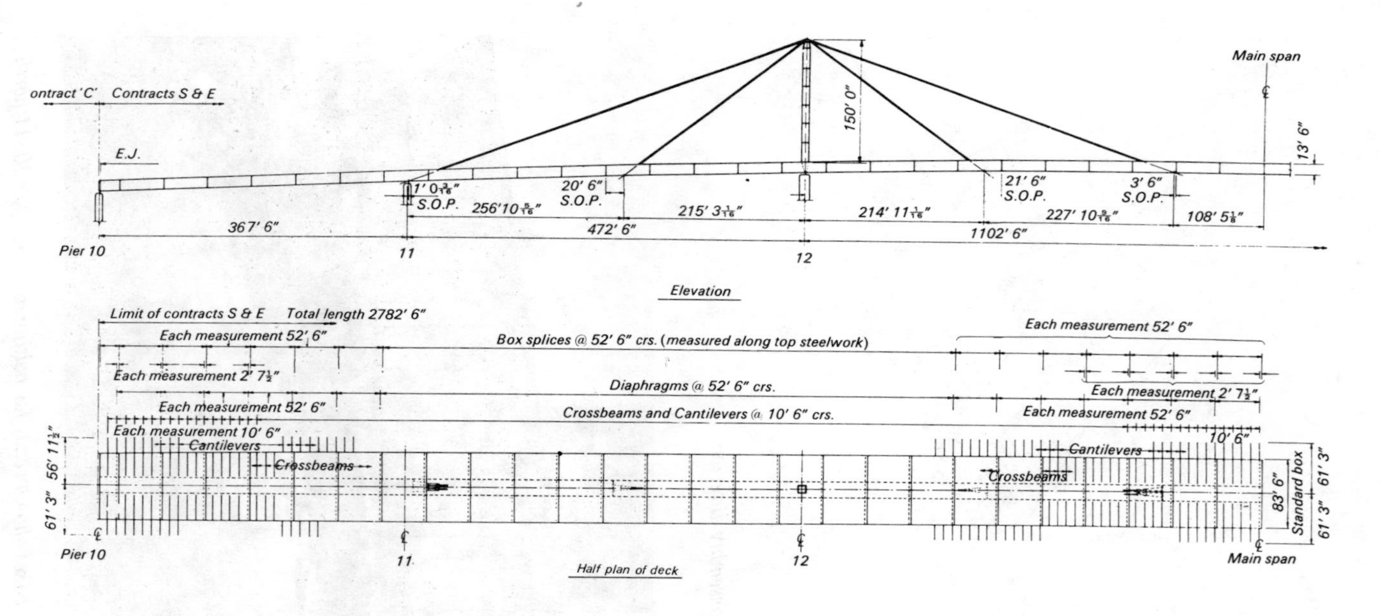

Figure 9 Main span: general arrangement of steelwork
E.J.=Expansion joint
Note: The positions of the crossbeams and cantilevers are as shown on the tender drawings. In fact they are incorrectly placed. As built, all the crossbeams and cantilevers shown were one half pitch (5 ft. 3 in.) from the positions shown.

Figure 10 Span 10–11 showing south half span being jacked up

Figure 11 Span 10–11 shortly before the collapse

which was 52 ft. 6 in. long and 83 ft. 6 in. wide. For convenience in shop handling each box was made as two half boxes, one for the upstream or northern carriageway, the other for the downstream or southern carriageway.

Arrangements were made for sets of half boxes to be made on the site, but how would the half boxes be assembled into spans some 200 ft. up in the air? Three methods were in common use in bridges of this type. The first began by putting up temporary staging along the entire length between adjacent piers. Boxes or half boxes would be lifted one at a time and joined in piecemeal fashion. As a second method the half boxes could be assembled in pairs to form single boxes. These were lifted in turn, starting at one end and allowing the bridge to grow outwards from a pier as an overhanging 'cantilever'. At some stage the cantilever would need a prop. Third of the proven techniques was to assemble each 1 200 ton span on the ground and jack it up on to the piers as a unit.

The scheme chosen for the span between piers 14 and 15, and repeated for the ill-fated span between piers 10 and 11 was an unhappy compromise, with ground assembly of the eight half boxes for the northern carriageway, followed by jacking to height of this half span (full length betwen piers but of half width) up to pier top height. Next the southern set of half boxes would be assembled into a half span and lifted complete. Then at pier top height the half spans could be brought together and the longitudinal splice made. The method did indeed combine two advantages; only a moderate weight had to be lifted and less joining needed to be done at height.

But there were also serious disadvantages in using such a scheme. The half boxes would need to be assembled with great care, so that corresponding parts for each carriageway met for the longitudinal splicing. In particular, the establishment of super-elevation (one side of the carriageway higher than the other) and camber (here used in the sense of the carriageway climbing or descending) demanded careful dimensioning of each half box and the way it fitted to its neighbours.

The super-elevation in particular led to complications. It was provided for by angular alignment of each half box relative to its opposite number on the other side of the central reservation strip of the roadway. There under the safety fence lay the longitudinal splice. It joined half box top-plates set with edges over seven inches apart at one spot; elsewhere in the span the half box top-plates approached each other until they almost met. This effected the super-elevation 'run-out'. Ensuring correct dimensions required precise calculation, accurate construction and proper checking at ground level of each row of half boxes separately. The success of such endeavours could only be gauged at a very late stage – the longitudinal splicing at height.

A less obvious difficulty is that whereas the completed girder cross-section is a 'closed section', a set of half boxes made into a half-width span leaves unsupported edges of top deck plating, underside plating and vertical diaphragms inside the box unsupported. In layman's terms these unsupported plate edges would flap about – and it is just these edges which must meet with precision later in the assembly.

Further, when lifted by its ends the untidy open section of half the box-girder not only bends, it twists and distorts in a peculiar fashion so that again the parts intended to join neatly will not meet up. This is a technical point of some complexity, best illustrated in the reader's mind by examining the behaviour of a long cardboard box, minus its lid, laid on one side and bent. It twists in response; so did the half-width spans of West Gate Bridge. Any discrepancy of more than an inch or so would cause difficulty. The prospect of snags had deterred others before. The Commission of Inquiry was to point out after the failure that no other bridge of this magnitude had been assembled in this way.

THE SPAN BETWEEN PIERS 14 AND 15

The span which failed (between piers 10 and 11) had its earlier counterpart on the other side of the river, the span between piers 14 and 15 (14–15). The chronicle of problems these two spans met justifies the cautions just expressed.

The boxes for the northern half of span 14–15 were placed on the ground side by side on low staging, adjusted to what was thought to be their correct relative positions and bolted together. On removal of the staging, leaving the half span supported at the ends only, the upper plates of the boxes became buckled at the unsupported edges (Figure 12). The buckle ran as a wave some fifteen inches high along the top plates. This effect had not been anticipated by FF & P or WSC.

Rather than separate the half span into its constituent half boxes, then brace the edges and re-assemble, WSC decided to go ahead and leave the buckles to be dealt with later. Roberts of FF & P saw the half span before lifting, and discussed its condition with WSC. Crossley of FF & P had made some calculations on the safety of the damaged half span, but he made an elementary mistake by using only the simplest bending formula, which was not appropriate to the complex open section before him; in fact a complicated piece of calculation was needed. The answers produced by Crossley's work gave figures for stress which came out not far from the truth—an arithmetical error had fortuitously corrected them. Possibly Crossley would have checked his calculations if an unfavourable state of stress had been revealed by them.

The half span was raised to bridge height, followed by its partner (this stage had been reached when JHC took over erection from WSC). As well as the buckling of the plate edges into a wavy shape the cambers differed by 3½ inches. This was dealt with ingeniously though crudely by raising one end of the sagging half span seven inches. In this condition the other end and the centre were now aligned and could be joined. The raised end was next lowered back forcing the remainder of the two half spans into alignment except for gaps which could be closed using hydraulic jacks. But having dealt with the overall camber some local buckles remained, and these were squeezed out by placing stout beams above and below, passing long bolts through the sandwich and tightening up hard.

But at one section this would not suffice, so the transverse splice between two half boxes was undone. This splice ran not along the bridge from pier to pier but *across* the road deck. If the procedure (akin to sawing the tree branch you are sitting on) were taken too far the span would lose all strength and fall. But the operation was successful, the loosened seams allowed the buckle to be eased out; the bolts could be replaced with little enlargement of the holes.

Figure 12 Buckle on inner upper panel 14–15 north

Of course, the bending and straining of the plates would change the shape of the structure slightly, and alter the properties of the steel, but none of these effects were amenable to calculation, even if the engineers had wished to try. A consequence of the success of the operation was that it engendered a certain lack of concern when a somewhat similar buckle occurred on the similar span 10–11, which would later fall to the ground during the process of correction.

STRENGTH CALCULATIONS

Appointed as joint consultants, FF & P did little work on the preparation of details for tenders until the three months before August 1967 (see Figure 4), when a set of drawings detailed down to the location of every hole appeared. Later, in front of the Inquiry Commission, the firm was to be unable to produce more than the first stages of the calculations necessary to justify the disposition and sizes of steel used. Roberts stated in evidence that he knew the computer program used was not satisfactory. That the sizes of steel used were still being changed up to the time of collapse shows the need for detailed post-tender design calculations. Meanwhile, WSC had taken on the contract expecting the design to be satisfactory.

The Commission found more grounds for criticism of FF & P than of any of the Australian based firms. The Commission could not decide just who, if anyone, was the actual designer of the bridge. Roberts claimed the position, but added that he entrusted the actual design to Brown, who in turn had other engineers to undertake calculations. Brown said it was not his policy to give specific instructions to his team, nor to check their individual work. The Commission found him unfamiliar with details of much of the work on the bridge, making decisions largely on an intuitive basis, isolated from rational analysis.

We have already noted that the contractors were free to propose an erection method. WSC (Hardenberg and Van Veldhuizen) met with FF & P (Roberts and Brown) in March 1968 and it was agreed that: 'FF & P will supply to Werkspoor in the course of this or next week, three sets of full-scale contract drawings and the necessary data for establishing the camber in the end spans. To ensure that erection calculations will be in accordance with the engineers' design criteria – notably the end condition under full load – FF & P will supply to Werkspoor a set of the bridge design calculations.' The reference to Werkspoor rather than WSC is because the WSC calculations were to be made at the parent firm in the Netherlands.

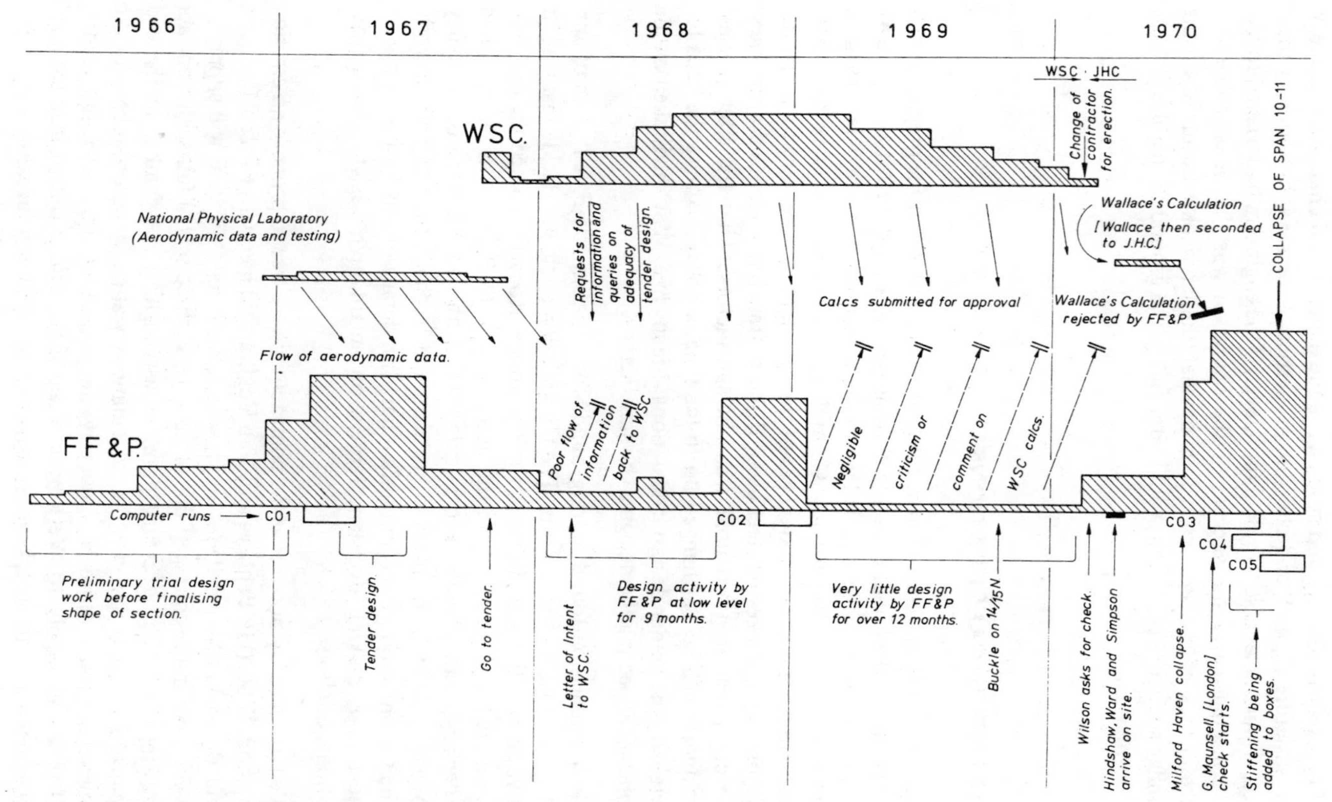

Figure 13 Design calculation activity on actual bridge structure

The contractual position was that in their Contract S with WSC the Authority used the above quotation referring to FF & P handing over calculations. But FF & P were not parties signatory to the contract, and so were not bound by it.

WSC would seek the proper data without success, for it was never supplied. Communication with FF & P was in any case very much a one-way process. Letters and telex messages to FF & P remained unanswered or the answer omitted the information sought. Roberts was to say later that the request could not be complied with as the calculations were not in a form suitable for handing over. The effect was that Hardenberg of WSC, who being qualified might well have been able to discuss the calculations and their basic premises intelligently with FF & P, was kept in ignorance (and therefore subservient). The Commission was to point out after the accident that an outsider could indeed have detected flaws in the calculations of FF & P. So WSC had to go ahead and perform the calculations alone. As a result of their Netherlands connection they were familiar with the Dutch and German codes, and it became obvious to them that by these codes the bridge would be overstressed in the incomplete state, as well as when finished. They assumed that FF & P had better knowledge, and pressed harder for data, persisting until as late as August 1969. Brown would later say that he did not take the requests seriously, because he thought Hardenberg of WSC wanted the information for his own private purposes.

WSC were unhappy about the inadequate thickness of some of the steel plates. They suggested for instance that the lower flange of box 8, shown on tender drawings as $\frac{1}{2}$ in. thick steel, should be $\frac{3}{4}$ in. thick. FF & P concurred, as they did after a further suggestion for $\frac{7}{8}$ in. thickness. FF & P's calculations for this last change were produced at the Inquiry. They contained arithmetical errors, and therefore could not have formed the basis of sound judgement.

Hardenberg telexed Brown that according to WSC's calculations the stress in service would still be too high. It finally needed the Milford Haven collapse to galvanize FF & P into action on this panel stress. Massive stiffening was added. Despite this a report by Maunsell of London (received after the collapse of the West Gate span and referred to later in this account) concluded that the panel would still be overstressed during erection and in service despite the post-Milford Haven stiffening.

As late as January 1970 WSC were still submitting erection stress calculations to FF & P, although by this time span 14–15 was being erected. FF & P acknowledged receipt and said they were in reasonable agreement with the stress values, but no evidence of an FF & P computer run on this check remained for the Commission to see.

TRANSFER OF CONTRACTS

Together with labour troubles the lack of proper communication was one factor leading to a dispute which came to a head in 1970 and culminated in WSC leaving. After long discussions designed to avoid it, the Authority finally had to accuse WSC of inordinate delay in executing Contract S for the steelwork on the bridge. Indeed, the failure to settle the labour troubles can be put down in part to the fact that the order of works was not laid down owing to communication difficulties. Changes in materials and design persisted, causing confusion bordering on chaos. The origin of this goes back to FF & P, for how could the schedule be laid down until the erection calculations were complete?

WSC's contract was terminated by the Authority and JHC were appointed instead. JHC began their new job in the spring of 1970. Choice of the new contractor was influenced (rightly) by the presence of JHC men and equipment on the site already, their familiarity with the project, their preparedness to take over immediately and their success on the contracts they already held. Further, JHC had put in a bid for the original Contract S, although in combination with two other firms. In contrast to WSC, JHC had shown an ability to achieve labour co-operation and fulfil contracts. On the other hand, however, their work at this bridge and elsewhere had not included more than a limited experience of the assembly and erection of steelwork. JHC themselves realized and admitted this when they took on the job as a 'labour management contract'. Under these terms JHC would physically erect the steelwork, but would have no responsibility for engineering design relating to erection stresses or final stresses.

The Inquiry Commission report sets out three requirements which if fulfilled would have gone a long way towards coping with the new situation:

1 Strengthening of JHC's engineering staff.

2 Greater assistance to contractors from the joint consultants.

3 Recognition (in a contract) of the extent of JHC's responsibility.

With the intention of meeting the first requirement WSC seconded to JHC Mr Spee, Mr Schot and Mr Hart (a jacking technician) and three others, while Hardenberg and Van Veldhuizen of WSC were retained by the Authority in an advisory capacity. By the terms of Contract E JHC were required to seek advice from these last, and Wilson of the Authority had received assurances from the joint consultants that they would help in the new situation, yet the contractual arrangements with the joint consultants did not change. No new document was drawn up. Neither the FF & P staff nor the JHC engineers there knew where they stood; the confusion was disastrous. The FF & P organization held the view that virtually all responsibility during erection lay with the contractors and the split situation disturbed them. On site the attitude of Hindshaw (sent out by FF & P as resident engineer to replace McIntosh in April 1970) reflected the confusion. He appeared to reject responsibility in some instances, and adopt dictatorial attitudes in others. Similarly, JHC would sometimes thrust responsibility on to FF & P, and yet at other times resent their interference.

The Inquiry Commission report suggests that the differences of attitude, approach and performance may be crystallized by noting the way different parties interpreted the word 'responsibility'. Did it mean 'job', legal liability, or moral duty? To FF & P principals in London the new arrangement was a new job for the firm. But Hindshaw on site in Australia, with the burden of engineering decision laid on him, had no new mandate to wield, no new contractual definitions to use as a weapon of attack or defence. The Authority merely added to the confusion when, during correspondence with Maunsell of Melbourne, it wrote that it expected from consultants the skill, care and diligence contemplated by common law and expressed in the 1967 contract, and that as far as the consultants were concerned the arrangements the Authority made with its contractors were immaterial. When questioning the parties after the incident the Commission found the differing views irreconcilable.

Seeking a solution to the communication difficulties with the FF & P London office the Authority demanded that a senior partner of FF & P, familiar with the design calculations and able to advise on the implications of the inevitable changes, be present on site. Wilson even threatened to terminate FF & P's appointment if this was not done. At the time that JHC took over from WCS, FF & P had responded by sending out three new men to replace McIntosh and join Crossley on erection work. Hindshaw was the most senior of the four, but he had worked mainly on concrete bridges and maintenance (rather than erection) of major steel bridges. Crossley had worked in the design office and on sites; since 1968 he had been deputy resident engineer for the West Gate Bridge. Simpson was well qualified, he had worked in the design office on four bridges and had studied the West Gate type of bridge in Europe. These three men were based on the east bank. Ward, the youngest and with no significant experience on site erection of steel bridges, was left on the west bank. He kept in daily touch with his colleagues, but Hindshaw in particular rarely visited the west bank. Span 10–11 was on the west bank.

ASSEMBLY OF HALF BOXES INTO HALF SPANS

The Inquiry Commission thought that the discrepancy between half spans could have been kept within one inch, by careful assembly on the ground. The blame that this figure had been exceeded lay partly with WSC and the way they joined the half boxes. WSC had expected that the Australian sunshine falling on to the half span would cause sufficient heat to bend the span, and could make nonsense of attempts at alignment. So a system was organized in which each half box was supported by its own hydraulic jack, fed with oil under pressure from a common line.

According to Hardenberg of WSC the boxes were in correct juxtaposition when the jacks were at their lowest or grounded position, the fluid pressure supporting only part of the weight. Rugless of JHC said he understood the jacks were to be kept fully floating at all times. Just what was happening to the alignment is difficult to say, as the half boxes did not each weigh the same, and the friction would vary from jack to jack.

The alignment of the half boxes was surveyed by instruments, but the work was not done with the half boxes at a uniform temperature; these uncertain effects of temperature changes coupled with the fact that one half span had a crane on it, rendered the surveys inconsistent and unreliable. As it was, greater reliance than was justified had to be placed on the accuracy of the holes drilled in the plates making up the half boxes. Each plate had been carefully drilled in a different pattern to achieve the complex camber and super-elevation of the bridge deck, but the accumulation of errors would necessarily entail some correction during the joining of half boxes into half spans. The errors should really have been measured, and then rectified by re-assembly of the half boxes while still at ground level. McIntosh of FF & P (Resident Engineer before Hindshaw) wrote to JHC in April 1970 pointing out that the experience of erecting the previous span should serve as a warning that care be taken to avoid alignment errors. But he was not precise enough in specifying the accuracy to be achieved and his warning was therefore ineffective.

McIntosh was concerned in another matter of standards. A plate which is in compression will fail by buckling – lurching sideways in a bowed shape. Obviously, a panel having an initial bow before loading will be weak. Preliminary trial panels made in 1969 showed considerable departure from flatness. McIntosh asked FF & P in London what limit of flatness was tolerable. FF & P merely replied with descriptions of how to make flat panels. Roberts inspected some panels in Melbourne with McIntosh, showing him, by way of example, some *acceptable* limits of flatness, but the records show no encounter at that time with *unacceptable* bowing. McIntosh was still left with no figures to work to.

Brown, in his calculations, assumed the top panels were all bowed in the downwards sense. There is no record that he checked this. The Commission found that at mid-span of the still standing span 14–15 some panels were bowed in the *upwards* direction, weakening them still further.

THE PROCEDURE MANUAL

On taking over Contract E JHC were virtually committed to erecting the bridge in the way WSC had proposed. Too much had been prepared already and further delay was to be avoided. It was intended to be of advantage to all that JHC should draw up a procedure manual, helped by WSC and FF & P. The manual grew as 1970 wore on; at the time of the collapse only the jointing of the span between piers 12 and 13 remained to be specified. However, the manual had little to say on the bolting up of half boxes 1–8 or raising them as half spans, for the work had virtually been done. As for instructions on getting the camber of a half span correct while still at ground level on the hydraulic jack supports, even WSC themselves had not been able to sort out that problem.

FF & P interfered with the sanctity of the manual by authorizing departures from it, such as the use of kentledge (described in the next section) and unbolting the critical transverse seams, successful once, but not a second time.

SPAN 10–11

It was in the nature of the task and the solution chosen that when the two half spans 10–11 were brought into proximity they met only at the ends. Elsewhere a vertical and horizontal discrepancy existed. In an attempt to avoid the previous difficulties and damage incurred on span 14–15 the Procedure Manual detailed a technique for rectifying the discrepancy. At each diaphragm a hydraulic jack was to be fitted. When activated, the jacks would apply a spread-out load to deal with the *vertical* discrepancy. Then special screwed connections would bring the half span edges together *horizontally*.

JHC, having taken over erection from WSC, proposed a different method to save time. Some blocks of concrete, each weighing eight tons, happened to be on hand. A group of ten of these would be placed at the middle of the higher half span to bring it into line. JHC were putting forward the kentledge idea without calculating the stresses which would arise in the steelwork. WSC could have given advice, and they had the only relevant calculations in Melbourne. As Hardenberg was away on leave JHC discussed the matter with Van Veldhuizen who was not as familiar with the stress problem as Hardenberg. Hindshaw for FF & P on site could not make calculations on the safety of the kentledge idea because he lacked the relevant data on the properties of the steelwork. The London office might have helped, but they were not informed. Hindshaw was unenthusiastic about the kentledge solution it was said, but being unable to advance any rational objection he reluctantly approved. From the tone of an entry in his diary he was not surprised when just seven blocks of kentledge on the offending half span caused a buckle near mid-span (Figure 14).

It may seem strange that a load of a mere 56 tons buckled the plates when the bridge was to be able to carry vehicles totalling up to 240 tons, until it is realized that the vehicle load would be well spread out, not concentrated. Secondly, the bridge deck lacked its concrete road surface (vital for the

Figure 14 Buckle on inner upper panel 10–11 north

design strength of the deck). Thirdly, the kentledge was supported by only a half width of the span, as the lateral connections between half spans were still to be made. Finally, for several reasons connected with the mechanics of open-section beams, each half-width span had far less than half the strength of a completed full-width span. Even supposing the concentrated kentledge had brought the half spans level, it would have stressed the bridge in a general sense to some $2\frac{1}{2}$ times the effect of the distributed loads exerted by the Procedure Manual's jacks. Locally the accentuation of stress was even greater, but all this is wisdom after the event, for we have seen that no calculation accompanied the proposal and execution of the kentledge scheme.

After the buckle formed, the general discrepancy of level was taken out with the jacks and the half spans were bolted together as far as the buckle would permit.

DEALING WITH THE BUCKLE

Actually the best way to deal with the buckle would have been to go on with the bridge, for the boxes of span 11–12 were to be added on next as cantilevers, beginning with boxes 9 and 10. This would have reduced the stress at the buckled deck plates allowing for safe removal of the bolts between boxes 4 and 5. The buckle could then have been squeezed out and the bolts re-inserted. To an extent, this is how the buckle in span 14–15 had been dealt with.

But the Procedure Manual required that span 10–11 be completed *before* cantilevering began. Hindshaw was already insisting that JHC adhere to the Manual, so he was not prepared to flout it himself. To complicate his difficulties still further, FF & P were in conflict with the Authority over the extra stiffening required as a result of the collapse of the box-girder bridge at Milford Haven, so Hindshaw did not want Wilson to see the buckle and have cause for complaint.

REMOVAL OF BOLTS

To allow the buckle to be removed, bolts in the transverse splice in the top deck plating near mid-span were removed as had been done before across the river. The work was done cautiously and with attention to the effect on the structure. The buckle reduced in height, but it extended in length, and the span was felt to settle. What had happened was that so much continuity had been removed that the half span could not hold itself up, and began to lean on the other half.

THE COLLAPSE

When loaded steadily, at the midday temperatures of an Australian October, structural steel does not snap suddenly: it gives warning by yielding slowly. The fifty-minute period between the gentle settlement just described and the catastrophic final collapse was one of increasingly frenzied activity on the part of the men on the span, as senior engineers were called in and bolts restored to their places.

Part of the original intention of the operation was achieved, for internal members which previously could not be joined could now be bolted up. These were, however, only temporary gains, for the span was folding where bolts had been removed between boxes 4 and 5. The folding increased, suddenly becoming more rapid until the end of the span came off pier 10 entirely and fell on to the huts below. The other end whip-lashed up and actually rose off pier 11, then in falling back knocked over that pier (Figure 15). Among the falling men and debris were a crane, compressors, tanks of fuel oil and of inflammable spirit, and so fire broke out in the fallen wreckage. Thirty-five men on the span or beneath it were killed outright or died of injuries.

ROYAL COMMISSION OF INQUIRY

The Inquiry after the collapse was particularly searching, as indeed was that into the failure of Kings Bridge in the centre of Melbourne itself in 1962. As mentioned earlier, the Royal Commission of 1970 extended its terms of reference to include 'whether any aspect of the design of the steel span between piers 10 and 11 is inadequate or undesirable'. One might say that the Commission exceeded even this brief, as we shall see.

The Inquiry and report were lengthy, involving not only witnesses and written evidence from before the collapse, but also specially arranged tests and reports. Much of the background work served to investigate and lead to the rejection of the claim by FF & P that they were not culpable. Thus, as late as 15 January 1971 a partner in that firm wrote 'We have carefully checked the design of the span for the erection conditions to which it was subjected and can find no fault or omission that would in any way have caused or been indirectly responsible for the collapse.' The Commission thought otherwise, going so far as to say that despite the strengthening applied after the collapse of the Milford Haven bridge the Commission was still not satisfied as to the adequate safety of the West Gate Bridge.

It is convenient, however, at this point to consider some of the other parties. The question of the role of FF & P will nevertheless inevitably arise.

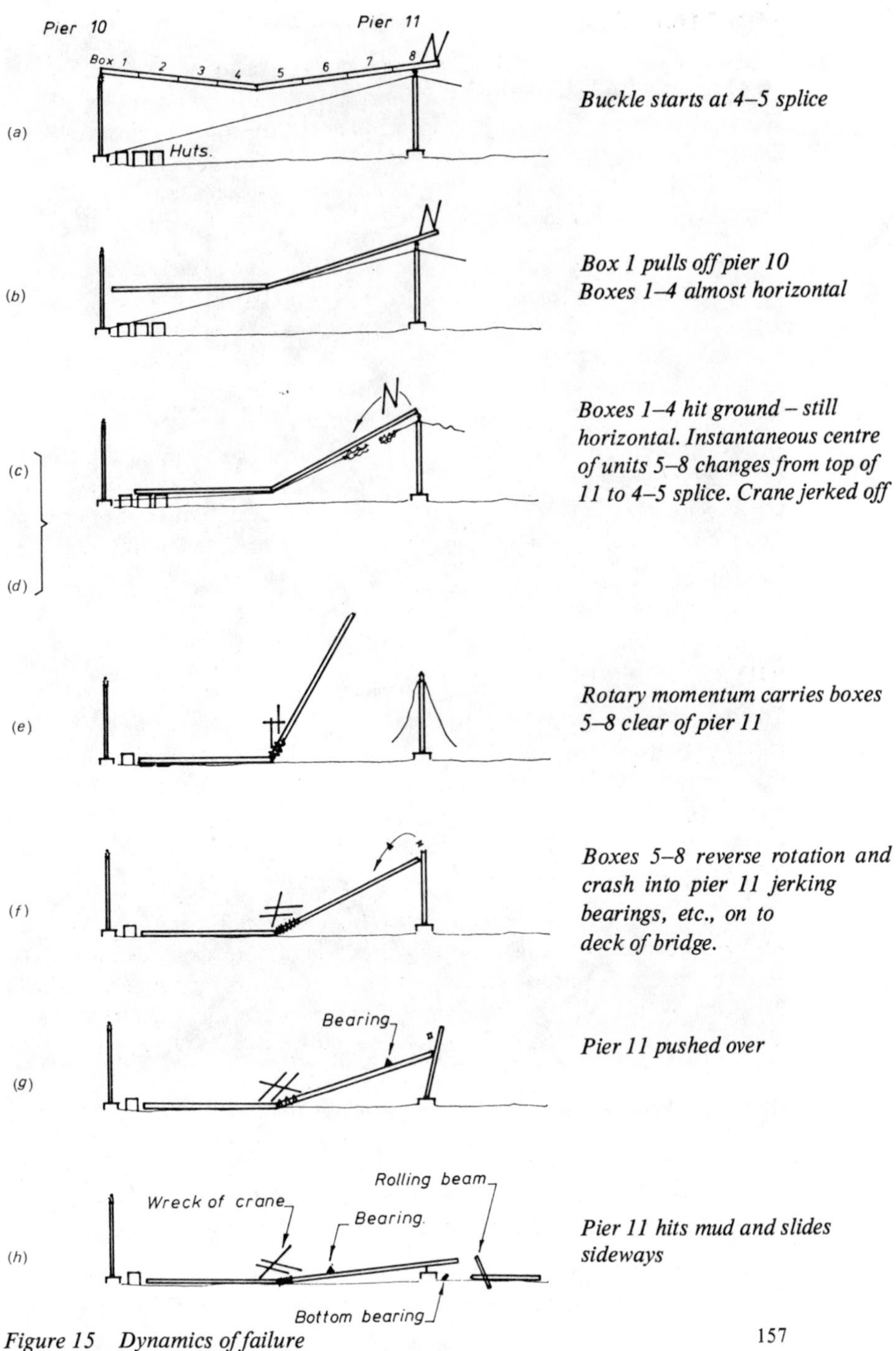

Figure 15 Dynamics of failure

Figure 16 View of collapsed span from top of pier 10

Figure 17 Transverse splice 4–5, inner upper panel, after collapse

Figure 18 Detail of 4–5 splice cut out from wreck

JOHN HOLLAND (CONSTRUCTIONS) LTD

JHC entered into Contract E knowing that they lacked experience of steel erection, but they believed they could cope by limiting their contractual responsibility to a 'labour and management' basis with no responsibility for making sophisticated calculations or highly technical decisions. After all, they had on site and in London the revered firm of Freeman Fox and Partners to guide them and fill gaps in their knowledge. There was also the arrangement of access to Hardenberg and Van Veldhuizen of WSC.

As the work went on and JHC managed to deal with new problems in new ways, perhaps they became over-confident. Certainly, JHC dispensed with the services of Spee and Schot, and ceased to follow (or indeed seek) advice from Hardenberg. JHC had a Project Manager on the contract but he was required to attend meetings elsewhere, and anyway labour troubles frequently occupied him when he was on site. Technical problems were mostly left to the inexperienced Burbury and Tracy for their respective sides of the river. That JHC realized they had allowed a gap in management to occur is suggested by the appointment of an Assistant Project Manager just before the collapse. He was not in office long enough to be effective.

It was JHC who decided to use kentledge rather than jacks to deal with the camber discrepancy. Nixon and Tracy had no calculations available to gauge the effect of using kentledge, but managed to persuade Hindshaw of FF & P to agree to it.

In the matter of removing the bolts joining boxes 4 and 5 in span 10–11 the Commission decided the blame lay with FF & P site staff rather than JHC staff. The Commission felt satisfied from the evidence put to them that Hindshaw intended to eliminate the buckle by removing and re-fitting bolts at some stage, and that before 15 October he had given Ward detailed instructions as to the method of removing the bolts. The Commission further decided that when Ward removed the bolts he honestly believed he was acting under Hindshaw's instructions. However, it could not be established what Hindshaw's instructions to Ward actually were. Was Ward to undo bolts when the span was made safe by further cantilevering out of boxes 9 and beyond? Or did Hindshaw tell Ward to remove the bolts and buckle as soon as possible? (Remember here that span 14–15 had been dealt with in a similar way, and that Hindshaw feared Wilson might get to know of the buckle.) As a final possibility, did Ward genuinely misunderstand Hindshaw's instructions?

Unusually, Ward wrote an authorization for Tracy at the latter's insistence, making it clear that he (Ward) would be personally responsible. Indeed, in place of the usual practice (whereby even if the orders for work emanated from FF & P staff, these orders were passed to JHC staff, who in turn instructed the men via the JHC foreman), Ward in this instance took direct charge and gave the orders directly. Tracy even moved away from the scene of the unbolting, leaving Ward solely in charge. When both Ward and Tracy were absent, Enness, an FF & P steel inspector, assumed control. It was a morning of unusual behaviour, and ended with span 10–11 collapsing.

Of JHC staff only Tracy knew of that day's decision to unbolt. Perhaps he should have reported to Nixon rather than confining himself to obtaining the note from Ward to proceed. But to have expected further resistance from Tracy would have been, the Commission felt, a counsel of perfection.

MAUNSELL AND PARTNERS OF MELBOURNE

Together with FF & P this firm made up the pair of joint consultants. Although no formal contract had been executed between them, Maunsell of Melbourne took on the responsibility for all contracts except those for the steel spans. FF & P were to be responsible for the design of the steelwork and would supply necessary staff to supervise and control construction, but Maunsell (being based in Australia) were to act as local spokesmen for the pair, and control all administrative matters. Thus, the resident engineer for steelwork was an FF & P man, responsible to London for technical matters but under the authority of Birkett, the senior Maunsell partner, for administrative purposes. Misunderstanding and friction was likely, as when Birkett on two occasions forbade Hindshaw to speak with FF & P London office about matters concerning responsibility, Maunsell of Melbourne's pigeon. Birkett was brought in when the Authority requested a senior partner of FF & P be on site. This was an administrative matter and he agreed with the Authority's request. But to FF & P he said the proposal was unnecessary and that he had advised the Authority against it. There is a hint of professional rivalry here, for a senior partner of FF & P on site might wish to adopt an administrative stance.

THE AUTHORITY

The Authority was not building the bridge, only holding the purse strings and looking forward to completion and ownership. Having selected consulting engineers and contractors, the Authority could have evaded a technical engineering role in the construction. But among the Authority and its staff were some experienced engineers, and it was right that they should speak out if they saw the need. Wilson had been connected with the planning of the ill-fated Kings Bridge in Melbourne. The lesson of failure there led him to insist on particular precautions against brittle fracture of the steel. The Commission report criticizes Wilson not for interfering, but for not interfering enough when keeping an eye on the project. Wilson could have acted through the Authority to see that FF & P gave more help to contractors, particularly to JHC on Contract E.

In March 1970 Wilson's growing fears of the sufficiency of strength in the bridge as designed led him to request FF & P to carry out a check on their design calculations. In June 1970, when little if any progress had been made on checking their West Gate Bridge, FF & P's Milford Haven Bridge collapsed during construction. After this event Wilson demanded that high priority be given to the check, and an independent check be made by G. Maunsell and Partners of London. These actions are commendable but while this was going on the arrangements were in progress for JHC to take over erection of steelwork. In allowing JHC to take over, the Authority failed to disclose their fears of inadequate safety margins on the bridge; safety margins which JHC could calculate even less well than the departing WSC; calculations which JHC were not required by contract to make anyway.

Further, the check demanded by Wilson was made by Maunsell of London; in theory independent of Maunsell of Melbourne, but Birkett was a partner in both. The background was that the joint consultants had been unhappy about submitting their designs to an outside organization, and had made the suggestion (with which Wilson concurred) that Maunsell of London do the job. To make matters worse Wilson commissioned the *joint consultants* to be the people dealing with Maunsell of London; in this way Wilson had no direct contract with or access to those checking the bridge design for him.

LABOUR

As if WSC and JHC did not have enough difficulties with professional colleagues, the job of steel erection was plagued by labour troubles. But labour unrest was just one result of loss of morale among the site workers, itself bred by absence of a tight work schedule, and in turn traceable to management indecision brought on by delay on the part of professional engineers.

WSC employed men of the metal trades unions for making the half boxes for the bridge. Little trouble occurred. But when men from the same unions were set on to assembling half boxes into half spans and raising them, WSC ran into severe trouble, of a kind they had not experienced in twenty years of Australian experience. The work rate slowed, demarcation disputes broke out, spreading back to the box makers where peace had reigned before. It would appear that the cause was that another union felt its members had the sole right to steel-erection work. Certainly, when WSC handed erection over to JHC and went back to mere half-box making their troubles disappeared and the work output doubled.

Some thirty-four men in WSC lost their jobs in the contract handover, and their unions put pressure on JHC to augment its labour force for the new task, with twenty-two of the thirty-four. Now JHC had always tried to keep to a minimum the number of unions on a job, and had been in the practice of employing members of the building labourers' union. It was with a lack of willingness and under threat that JHC agreed to take on the twenty-two men. On the one hand, JHC had the prospect of a work ban from the unions if they refused to accept the WSC men. On the other hand, they would face demarcation and other disputes if the unions were mixed. JHC got the trouble they expected, and not until just before the collapse did JHC feel they had made headway with their employees. That it then became possible to work three days without a stoppage was taken as a sign of success. Kerensky recorded notes of a telephone conversation with Hindshaw on 19 September 1970 in which he records Hindshaw as saying '. . . labour is out of control and takes every opportunity to strike. Any suggestions of lack of safety of the structure and the continuous revisions to permanent sections give additional grounds for the men's behaviour.' This was the atmosphere in which the engineers had to make decisions. It would appear that a frequent decision they were called on to make was to choose between attending to labour problems, or dealing with technical points such as the very safety of the bridge they were trying to build. The Commission goes further than this, involving labour in the responsibility for the accident in the following way.

The men refused to use two gantries below span 10–11 until ladder access to them could be improved. Thus, at the time of the collapse it had not been possible to join the lower plates of the north and south half spans 10–11. If this splice had been completed it would have increased the strength of the span. The Commission considered that failure of labour and management to co-operate contributed to the weakness of the span at the relevant time, and therefore to the ultimate collapse.

MAUNSELL AND PARTNERS OF LONDON

Having no hand in building the bridge this firm only comes into the story a few months before the collapse. The firm's performance is indicative of the way outsiders would approach a check of FF & P, i.e. expecting little to be amiss.

We have already seen how the firm came to be appointed as checkers. Their first interim report (prepared after discussion with Maunsell of Melbourne) noted some regions of local high stress, but they were reasonably confident the stresses would turn out to be acceptable. Nearly a month after the collapse Maunsell of London still claimed that the design was satisfactory, but two weeks later they said that certain details would need modification, and around December 1970 they wrote 'There are a number of areas which appear to us to be highly stressed and we consider that some modifications to the structure are required.'

In their final report of January 1971 only the design of the crash barriers escaped critical comment.

THE CONCEPT

Now to follow the Commission through an explanation of their view of the way the bridge was designed is an exercise every engineer should undertake. Not until a bridge falls is so much information released from files which are otherwise subject to company secrecy. Here we look only at the basis of the technical decisions made and their effects; the numerical analysis laid out in the Commission's report is not repeated.

The recent popularity of the box-girder bridge is not a designer's whim. The choice is the outcome of consideration of aims, objectives, alternatives, conflicts and compromises; all evaluated using economic criteria. Traffic loadings, availability of materials and jointing techniques change with the years; the costs of different items change at different rates. At any moment there is likely to be a convergence of opinion among designers across the world that a particular type of bridge is best for a given situation. Added to this effect is the extra expense of complete originality or even reversion to a bridge type long out of use by designers and contractors. In the late 1960s the box-girder bridge occupied a place on the frontiers of technology; some aspects lay beyond the frontiers and were the subject of hypothesis, research and occasional mistakes.

Every feature of the West Gate Bridge in its completed form had been used before, but not necessarily in combination or on such a large scale. While the use of simple design calculations on tried arrangements will give an adequate solution for design purposes, the effect of imponderables requires the use of high factors of safety. Willingness to cope with imponderables is one thing that separates engineers from scientists, but it is imponderables that can provoke failures.

IN CONCLUSION

The West Gate Bridge was developed to satisfy a tiny part of the world-wide demand for road space. With its box-girder construction, its layout was typical of a large number of road bridges under construction at about the same time, the major ones in the charge of a mere handful of firms. In these circumstances it is possible that some aspects of building these bridges tended to become matters of routine, despite the fact that the experiences which allow formulation of a successful routine had not yet been accumulated in sufficient numbers to allow useful feedback from experience into innovation.

The box-girder of this type of bridge had come to resemble a piece of aircraft structure. Indeed, the British Aircraft Corporation carried out some check calculations on panel strength. Yet the bridge-building fraternity was not able to go to the same lengths as aircraft firms in testing trial structures before embarking on designing and building the real thing. As an extreme example, only a full-size span 10–11, plus a good deal of the adjacent structure, built complete with the defects inherent in a real structure, could give a true picture of the behaviour of the fatal panels and their joints. The economic objections to such an experiment led to an alternative of testing small panels (which might be unrepresentative). Even the Commission itself, in considering the results of panel tests commissioned and conducted specially for the Inquiry on this bridge found the need for a good deal of interpretative skill in applying the results and estimating the strength of the West Gate Bridge as it was built or intended.

Technical imponderables have been mentioned before in this account. The bridge builders were required to weigh these against economic cut-off levels, and compound the equation with a dose of political influences large and small. In the design office, and on the partially completed bridge in October 1970 the remarkable thing is not that the decision making was poor, rather that men found it in themselves to make decisions at all.

Case Study 6

The Foundering of the Motor Vessel *Burtonia*

by Christopher Pym

CONTENTS

Page

On 30 November 1972 the British Motor Vessel *Burtonia* of Goole, carrying a cargo of concentrated lead ore and bound for Ghent, sank in coastal waters some seven miles east of Benacre Ness with the loss of four lives.

This case study is based on *MV Burtonia (O.N. 300222) Report of Court No. 8062 – Formal Investigation,* published by Her Majesty's Stationery Office (London) in 1974. Any mistakes or misplaced emphases are solely the responsibility of the author.

INTRODUCTORY NOTE

This is really a case study in two parts – why did the *Burtonia* sink, and why were lives lost? The first part is described in the Annex to the Report as 'The Cause of Foundering'. The second part, described in the Annex to the Report as 'Search and Rescue' has been dramatically reconstructed in a Granada television documentary part of which is viewed by students of the Open University Course *Systems Performance: Human Factors and Systems Failures* (TD342).

NARRATIVE

The vessel itself

The motor vessel *Burtonia* was built in Holland in 1959 and registered in Goole. She was a dry-cargo ship of 498 tons gross, and could do a speed of 8 or 9 knots. Her single hold was divided by a temporary wooden bulkhead into two holds (No. 1 and No. 2). Each hold had one hatchway and two ventilators. Underneath the holds there was a double bottom subdivided into a well and ten tanks (five starboard, five port) all with main deck air vents.

The *Burtonia* had two inflatable life rafts, one stowed vertically against the funnel casing and the other in a cradle. There was also a wooden lifeboat and a workboat. The equipment included MF RT, VHF, radar, Decca navigator, echo sounder and a magnetic compass. The wheelhouse, which did not extend to the ship's sides, was at the forward end of the boat deck.

The crew

The *Burtonia* had a crew of eight: the Master (Captain William Ash) who was not the regular master, the Mate (Walter Hudson Pheasant), the Chief Engineer, the Second Engineer (Edwardo Nunez), the Cook/Steward, and three deckhands (Leston, Torea and Priegue). The crew's accommodation was on the main deck. Above this was the poop deck with the Master's quarters, messrooms and galley.

The departure from Keadby

On 27 and 28 November 1972 the *Burtonia* loaded a cargo of wet lead concentrate at Railway Wharf, Keadby, on the river Trent. Most of this concentrate was produced from locally mined fluospar ore in the Cavendish Mill (Laporte Industries Limited) at Eyam in Derbyshire. In the early hours of 29 November the *Burtonia* sailed for Ghent. The Trent River Pilot noticed nothing unusual. This was the eighteenth time that the *Burtonia* had set out for Ghent with this type of cargo. Concentrate simply means concentrated ore.

The *Burtonia* begins to list

During the early evening of the *Burtonia's* first day at sea (29 November) she began to encounter a rough sea and swell. The wind was South West Force 7, backing later to South South West and increasing to Force 7 to 8, gusting to 9. Between rain showers visibility was good. Just before 8 pm, when Deckhand Torea was at the wheel, the *Burtonia* rolled to starboard and shipped a lot of water on to the main deck. Pheasant, the Mate, switched on the floodlights and saw the water clear quickly from the deck. At about 8.15 pm, when Pheasant was at the wheel, there was a crash. It appeared as if the sea had come over the starboard bulwark rail on the main deck and hit some part of the vessel quite hard. The *Burtonia* heeled to starboard and never regained her upright position. The list was sufficient to awaken Deckhand Leston who told the crew to get on deck with their lifejackets.

Attempts to deal with the danger

Captain Ash came on to the bridge and took the wheel while Pheasant looked for damage on the deck. All seemed to be well. Pheasant then ascertained that the crew had lifejackets and also checked all main deck accommodation portholes and skylights. Meanwhile, the *Burtonia* was continuing to ship water on the starboard side, and the list to starboard was increasing. At this point some ballast may have been pumped into the port side tanks within the double bottom below the hold.

The MAYDAY signal

At about 8.40 pm the *Burtonia* transmitted a MAYDAY distress signal which was picked up by the Post Office's North Foreland Coast Radio Station and heard as a series of separate signals from 8.42 until 8.48. Two minutes later the North Foreland Coast Radio Station relayed the MAYDAY signal on distress frequency. At the same time, two lifeboats were placed on readiness to launch by the Coastguard. At 9 pm a 1308-ton tanker called the *John M* reported that she was going to the assistance of the *Burtonia*, and at 9.07 a tugboat offered to come out from the Hook of Holland. It would take the *John M* about an hour and a quarter to reach the *Burtonia*, whereas the tugboat faced a voyage of five hours. At 9.13 the *Burtonia* was offered a lifeboat, and at 9.35 a Royal National Lifeboat Institution lifeboat was launched from the beach at Aldeburgh on Coastguard advice.

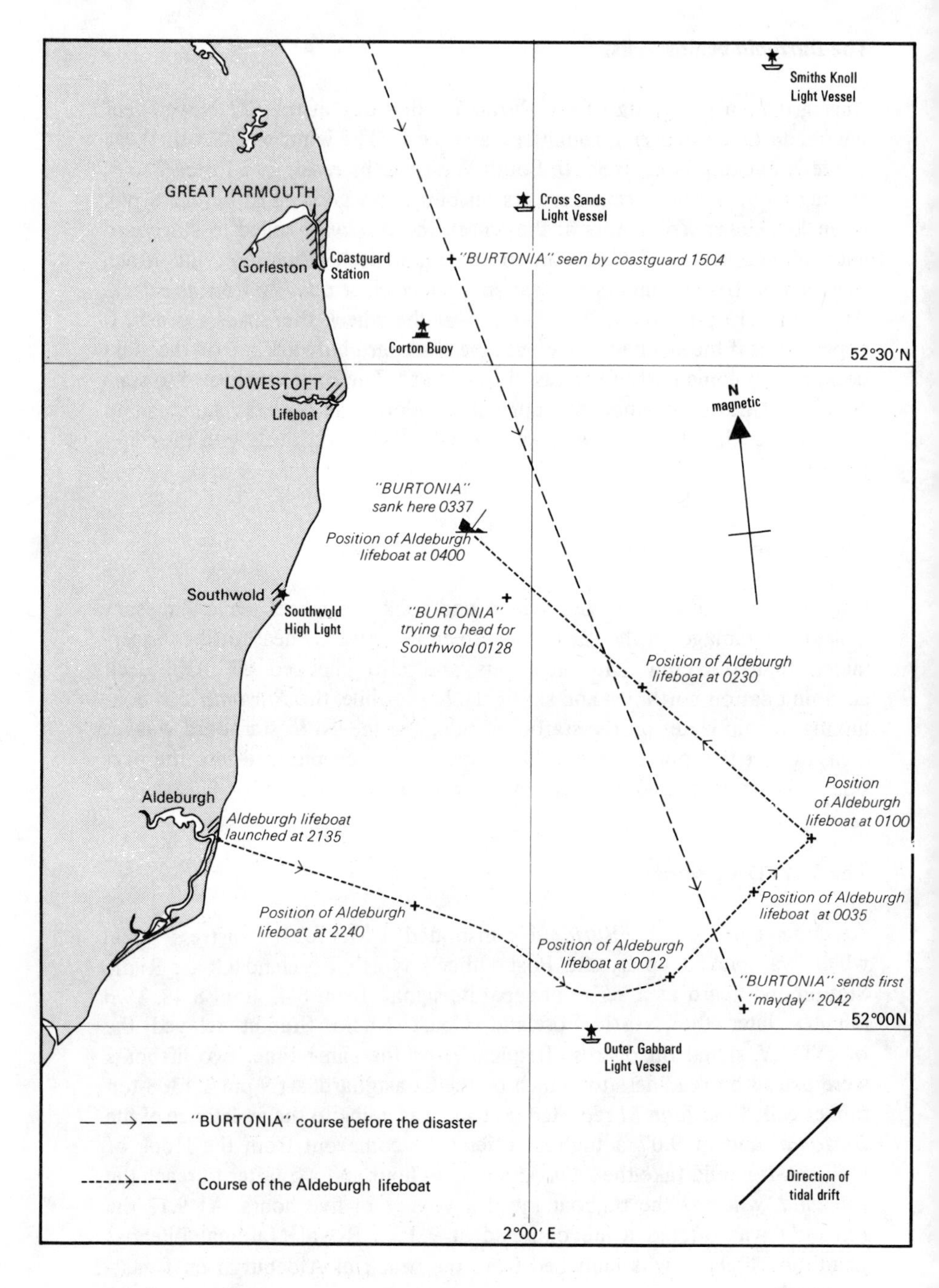

Figure 1 The last voyage of the Burtonia

The *Burtonia* changes course

The MAYDAY signals, the relay and the subsequent contacts, carried details of the *Burtonia's* position. Captain Ash now turned his ship west towards land, hoping no doubt to get into more sheltered water. Various offers of help from other vessels were refused. At 9.48 Captain Ash spoke by telephone for six minutes with Stanley Smith, a director and secretary of Trent Lighterage Limited (the owners). Mr Smith felt that if help was needed the *John M* was the best bet. But because the *Burtonia* was making practically no headway towards land, Captain Ash next turned north. Now the elements (wind and tide) helped him make a speed of 5–6 knots as he headed in the general direction of Lowestoft or Great Yarmouth. Captain Jones of the *John M* contacted the *Burtonia* by radio on the distress frequency and also identified her lights two miles away. The conversation was picked up by the North Foreland Coast Radio Station, but was not passed on to the coastguards.

Reduction of the MAYDAY signal

At 10.39 pm the North Foreland Coast Radio Station asked the *John M* to inquire from the *Burtonia* whether the MAYDAY signal should be cancelled, because the *Burtonia's* situation seemed to have improved. Captain Ash agreed to a reduction of the distress signal from MAYDAY to PAN and started to make for Great Yarmouth Roads.* The practice existed both in the UK and other countries of reducing MAYDAY to PAN when immediate assistance was no longer required. Captain Ash also refused assistance from the other vessels which were standing by. For the next two hours the *Burtonia* continued to list, but the sea was not washing over its hatch covers. Thirty-eight minutes after midnight the *John M* reported that the *Burtonia's* list had got noticeably worse and that the seas were coming on to the hatch covers for the first time.

At about 1 am Captain Ash turned the *Burtonia* yet again, this time west towards Southwold and by 2.28 he was about eight miles from the shore.

**MAYDAY and PAN are international radiotelephonic signal words. The essential difference between them is this: MAYDAY (derived from the French* m'aider*) signals the beginning of a* distress *message, whereas PAN signals the beginning of an* urgent *message. MAYDAY messages (but not PAN messages) are transmitted on a distress frequency. There may be a signal on the distress frequency indicating that a PAN message is being transmitted on a working frequency.*

Figure 2 The Aldeburgh lifeboat

The vessel abandoned

But as the *Burtonia* drifted slowly north of Southwold the list got worse. Captain Ash is thought to have given the order to abandon ship at 2.40, but was knocked unconscious or killed before he could leave the wheelhouse. The two life rafts broke free and became inaccessible to the crew. Edwardo Nunez jumped off the stern in his lifejacket and was picked up dead from a lifebuoy three hours later. At 2.52 the *Burtonia* lay right over on her side. Deckhands Leston, Torea and Priegue jumped off the stern in their life-jackets and were picked up by the *John M.* Meanwhile the Cook/Steward had disappeared from the boat deck with his lifejacket on, but was never seen again. Pheasant and the Chief Engineer took to the sea from the boat deck and tried to swim clear. This proved impossible so they reboarded the *Burtonia* and clung to the wreckage until it sank at 3.37. The Chief Engineer disappeared, but Pheasant was picked up by the Aldeburgh life-boat which arrived just before 4 am.

The search for survivors

Unfortunately, the Aldeburgh lifeboat had arrived at the scene too late to help the crew of the *Burtonia*, and only picked up Walter Pheasant because he attracted attention by waving a lighted lifebuoy. More than six hours had passed since the lifeboat was launched from the beach at Aldeburgh. It had

Figure 3 The minesweeper HMS Bildeston

been present neither when the *Burtonia* sank, nor during the previous two hours at which time its presence would have been an additional factor taken into account by Captain Ash when deciding whether to abandon ship.

The search for survivors continued until 10 am. Many resources, including ships, lifeboats and helicopters were deployed in an all-out attempt to comb the area.

The *John M*, the Aldeburgh and Lowestoft lifeboats, the colliers *Duncansby Head* and *Troup Head,* the minesweeper *HMS Bildeston,* a USAF Hercules, the Dutch *Vlidek,* the tug *Wrestler,* the motor vessel *Alexis* and USAF helicopters were all in the area and joined in the search. But no more survivors were picked up. Four men had been saved and four lost.

Note: Figure 1 tries to give a reasonably accurate impression of the *Burtonia's* position and of the Aldeburgh lifeboat's different positions at different times; no positions for the *Burtonia* are shown between 8.42 pm (2042) and 1.29 am (0129).

To gain an impression of how erratically the *Burtonia* moved from the MAYDAY position (2042) to a point off Southwold, one must look at the different courses which Captain Ash tried to steer and the difficulty he encountered.

(i) *Towards the Outer Gabbard Light Vessel* – hopeless.

Figure 4 The Lowestoft lifeboat returning to port

(ii) *Towards the north* – there was a tendency to drift north-east with the tide and be taken out to sea.
(iii) *Towards the west* – very difficult to make any progress.

Eventually the *Burtonia* ended up being pushed north north-west, in the general direction of Lowestoft and Great Yarmouth.

THE FORMAL INVESTIGATION

The Court

The inquiry into the loss of the *Burtonia*, referred to as a 'Formal Investigation', was set up under the Merchant Shipping Act 1894 and conducted in Court. A Queen's Counsel acted as judge and was assisted by four assessors, two of whom were master mariners in the Merchant Navy and one of whom was a naval captain. The fourth assessor, an expert in the field of radio communications, attended the hearings when evidence concerning communications was being given.

Organizations and people involved

The following official or voluntary bodies, private organizations and individuals were either served with notice of the investigation or applied to become parties to it. They were represented by eleven advocates briefed by six solicitors (including the Treasury Solicitor and the Solicitor to the Post Office).

Official bodies

The Department of Trade responsible for sea safety and HM coastguards at Gorleston, but *not* obliged by statute to set up a Court. Their authority to set up a Court is a discretionary power, to be used in the public interest.
The Post Office (responsible for North Foreland Coast Radio Station).

Voluntary bodies

The Royal National Lifeboat Institution (responsible for the Aldeburgh and Lowestoft lifeboats).

Private organizations

Trent Lighterage Limited (Owners of the *Burtonia*),
Laporte Industries Limited (Owners of the Cavendish Mill where the lead concentrate was prepared),
Cargo Superintendents (London) Limited (Forwarding Agents at Keadby).

Individuals

Walter Hudson Pheasant (Mate of the *Burtonia*),
Officer-in-charge, North Foreland Coast Radio Station,
Deckhand Leston,
Deckhand Torea,
Deckhand Priegue,
The personal representatives of Edwardo Nunez (Second Engineer of the *Burtonia*).

The widow of the *Burtonia's* Master was served with a notice, but she did not appear and was not represented. Under the Rules governing the proceedings at Formal Investigations, the Master of the ship concerned must always be made a party. Mrs Ash was, therefore, as Captain Ash's next of kin, served with a Notice of Investigation but was advised that, as it was not intended to criticize her late husband, it appeared to be unnecessary for her to incur the cost of legal representation. If it had been intended to criticize

Captain Ash, Mrs Ash would have been warned and would undoubtedly have wished to be legally represented to defend her husband.

The USAF Helicopter Rescue Service was not served with a notice and did not apply to become a party.

In addition, the following organizations were referred to by the Court:

J. Wharton (Shipping) Limited (the Management company within the same group as Trent Lighterage Limited),
Minmet Financing Company (the Swiss purchasers of the cargo),
Glebe Mines Limited (a subsidiary of Laporte Industries),
J. H. Wharton (Stevedoring) Limited (the stevedoring company which worked for Cargo Superintendents (London) Limited),
Trentside Boating & Engineering Company (sub-agents for Cargo Superintendents (London) Limited at wharves on the River Trent).

The Court's operations

The investigation started on 6th February 1974 and finished on 3rd May 1974. The Court actually sat on forty-three days. Two quite distinct inquiries were conducted during this period. First, why did the *Burtonia* sink? Second, why was there loss of life? The findings of the investigation were published on 31st July 1974 in two parts – a report and an annex. The report is only a few sentences long, whereas the Annex runs to about eighteen thousand words. The Annex is presented in three chapters – a narrative of the disaster (on which Sections 2.1–2.10 of this study are based), a chapter on why the *Burtonia* sank, a third chapter on search-and-rescue operations, then a summary. The narrative chapter also contains some comments on the evidence. The second chapter singles out certain statements as being specially important (e.g. the evidence of the physicist, Dr Suddaby). The criticisms of one party against another (e.g. the criticism of the *Burtonia's* owners by the Department of Trade) are recorded in a section called 'Criticisms'. The second chapter also contains recommendations which the Department of Trade was advised to adopt. The third chapter describes what faults were alleged in the search-and-rescue operations, makes a lot of comments, states eleven general observations, and concludes with recommendations for consideration by the Committee to Co-ordinate Marine SAR (Search and Rescue). At the end of the Annex comes a four-page summary of the Court's findings in the form of questions and answers.

REPORT OF THE COURT AND ANNEX

The substance of the report (No. 8062) is very short and is contained in the few phrases which follow: 'The Court having carefully inquired into the circumstances attending the above-mentioned shipping casualty, finds for the reasons stated in the Annex hereto, that the said foundering and loss of life were caused by the shifting of the *Burtonia's* cargo of lead concentrate and that the said shifting, foundering and loss of life were contributed to by the wrongful act or default of Trent Lighterage Limited, the owners of the *Burtonia.*'

THE CAUSE OF FOUNDERING

Chapter 2 of the Annex to the Court's Report deals with the cause of foundering, i.e. it presents the Court's analysis, conclusions, apportioning of blame and recommendations.

Theories about why the cargo moved

The Court disposed of the suggestion that a leak had liquefied the lead concentrate so that it moved. Evidence indicated that the *Burtonia* had been properly repaired, surveyed and maintained. So a leak was ruled out, and two other theories advanced as to why the cargo shifted.

The theory of Mr Tope, a naval architect, who was at that time employed as a senior ship surveyor in the Department of Trade was that the cargo had not been properly trimmed (i.e. made level before leaving port). *A heavy sea would cause it to move.* If one imagines the lead concentrate being tipped into a hold, there might be voids on either side of a mound. In other words, the *Burtonia* had been carrying wet lead tips the composition of which reminds us superficially of the wet coal tips of Aberfan. If the standards for levelling such a cargo (i.e. filling up the voids before leaving port) had been observed there would have been less chance of the cargo moving. Mr Tope held that vibration and ship motion during the voyage had caused moisture migration from certain parts of the cargo to other parts, thereby creating internal surfaces with low resistance to shear. When the sea crashed on deck parts of the cargo started to slide along these planes of weakness. The more liquid the cargo became, the more it moved in the direction of the list. Water too probably entered the holds through hatch covers, and later through ventilators. The more liquid the cargo became, the more it slid. Thus, the list to starboard gradually became worse until the *Burtonia* at last turned over on her side.

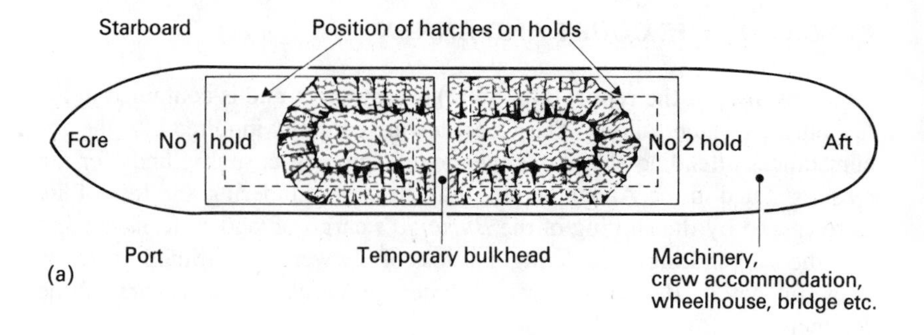

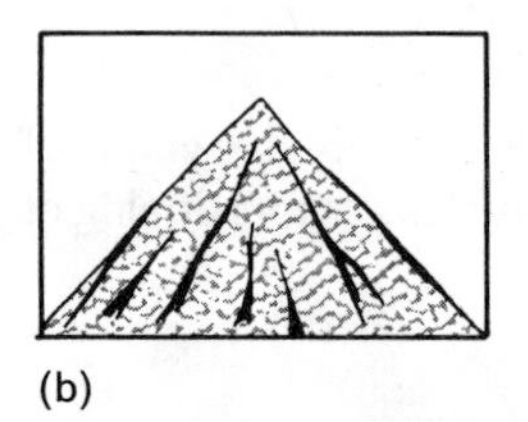

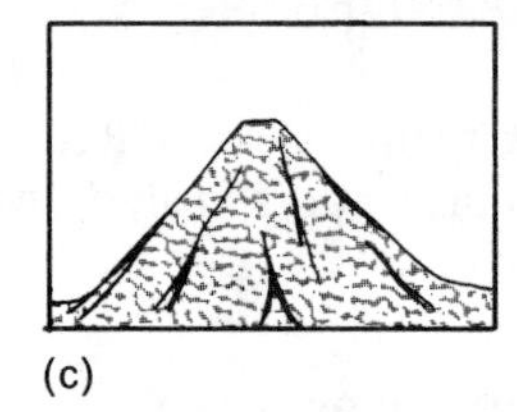

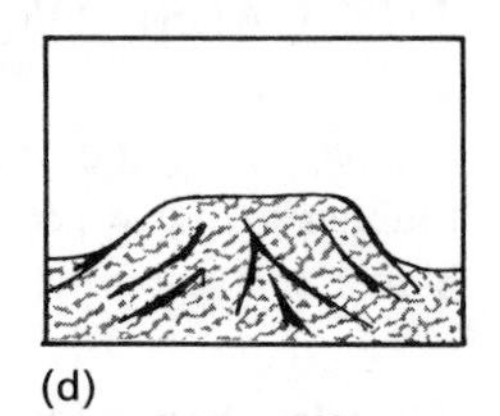

Figure 5 An artist's impression of the Burtonia's *hold*
(a) The general layout
(b) The cargo before trimming
(c) No. 1 hold
(d) No. 2 hold

The theory of Dr Suddaby, a physicist called by the owners of the *Burtonia*, conflicted with that of Mr Tope in one important respect. Dr Suddaby said that *whether or not the cargo was trimmed properly* its free moisture content was such that parts of it would fluidize, and a heavy sea would cause a list due to cargo shift. He also made the point that vibration during the voyage would tend to level the cargo in the first instance, i.e. make it more safe against the effects of cargo slides as opposed to cargo fluidizing. In 1957 Dr Suddaby had contributed expert evidence during an investigation into the shift of coal slurry which sank the *Traquair* (Court No. 7999).

Tests for determining whether the moisture content of lead concentrate is within safety limits

Laporte Industries Limited were in the habit of filtering their lead concentrate so that the main stockpile at Cavendish Mill did not receive any discharge with a moisture content of more than 10 per cent by weight. Moist concentration was removed to an interim stockpile which in time was cleared back to the main stockpile, the hard-core base of which was usually waterlogged in winter. The testing of concentrate for moisture content was carried out at Eyam by Laporte Industries Limited before export, and after a normal voyage would have been carried out again at Ghent, for commercial reasons. Table 1 shows the results of tests made in connection with earlier voyages, plus the result of the Cavendish Mill test made before the last voyage. There was a South Easterly Force 7 wind on voyage A.

Table 1 Moisture content of lead concentrate shipped on the *MV Burtonia* in 1972

	Tests at Cavendish Mill	Tests at Ghent	Variation
Voyage A	9.80	10.08	+0.28
Voyage B	9.20	8.87	–0.33
Voyage C	9.20	8.54	–0.66
Voyage D (27th Nov.)	8.80	—	—

At that time the Inter-Governmental Maritime Consultative Organization (IMCO) recommended that a safe transportable moisture limit was one where the moisture content was not above 90 per cent of the flow point. We can explain this further by saying that a cargo will flow at a certain point, for example, if its moisture content is 20.0. In this imaginary example the safe transportable moisture limit would then be 20.0×90 per cent=18.0. However, there are different methods of ascertaining the flow point and these methods produce conflicting results. Differences in flow points can arise too in time if there is a difference in the particle size distribution of the concentrate, or these differences may arise because of the way the concentrate is tipped. A considerable number of tests were carried out by different methods after the disaster, and some of these are detailed in Table 2. If a flow point is likely to be miscalculated, the adequacy of the IMCO 10 per cent safety margin becomes questionable.

Moisture can be present inside a concentrate (inherent moisture) and also in the voids between the particles (free moisture). It is generally held that it is the amount of free moisture present which decides whether or not a cargo will reach a flow state although for laboratory convenience it is the total, i.e. free plus inherent moisture, which is measured using standard drying oven techniques. For metallic concentrates such as lead it is expected that the inherent moisture would be low, of the order of 1–2 per cent.

Trimming the cargo

The lead concentrate shipped in the *Burtonia* had an angle of repose of about 45 degrees. In the middle of No. 1 hold it was piled about three-quarters up the temporary wooden bulkhead, and at the sides it varied from a few inches to eighteen inches in depth. There were, therefore, sizeable void spaces on either side of the pile. In No. 2 hold, the pile was trimmed so that the depth of concentrate at the sides of that hold was probably about three to four feet.

The Court analysed reasons why the cargo had not been trimmed properly and came up with many relevant facts. The loading of No. 1 hold was supervised by Captain Ash while the Mate was on leave (27th November 1972), whereas the loading of No. 2 hold was supervised by the Mate (28th November 1972). It seemed, however, that the cargo had not been trimmed in either hold, as recommended in the IMCO *Code of Safe Practice for Bulk Cargoes*. The fact that Captain Ash was not the regular master of the *Burtonia* was not thought significant. In April 1971 M Notice No. 613 was issued to masters. The Court's Annex quoted two paragraphs from this notice which read as follows:

> Heavy density cargoes leave considerable void space in the holds of smaller cargo vessels and, unless the surfaces of the cargo are trimmed level, the ship's motion is likely to cause the cargo to take a sudden shift into the void on one side and thus produce a list. There is every probability, especially in severe weather, that such a list will progressively increase until the vessel capsizes.
>
> In all cases where such cargoes are carried in small single deck vessels the Master should pay close attention to official weather forecasts and if necessary follow a course which will allow shelter to be taken in an emergency.

Despite this notice the practice when loading the *Burtonia* was to pile the lead concentrate up to the temporary wooden bulkhead, then only to knock the top of the pile off. It was said that the practice avoided undue stiffness in

Table 2 The flow point of lead concentrate at Cavendish Mill as estimated by various sampling methods immediately after the disaster and at later dates. The disagreement between Tope and Suddaby is indicated in the last column.

Date	Source of sample	Method used	Flow point	Safe transportable moisture content (Tope) flow state during voyage (Suddaby)
6th Dec. 1972	Interim stockpile at Cavendish Mill	NCB viscometer	9.6	$\simeq$ 8.8
6th Dec. 1972	as above	As above using same sample	9.95	= 8.9
Feb. 1973	Production sample at Cavendish Mill	Endecott's sieve shaker	7.9	
Feb. 1974	as above	Endecott's sieve shaker	9.25	
Feb./March 1974	as above	Suddaby's flow table	9.2–9.25	
Feb./March 1974	as above	Suddaby's simulated IMCO test	9.2–9.25	
Feb./March 1974	as above	NCB viscometer	10.5	

Note: Two main points came out of these and other tests. Dr Suddaby succeeded in convincing the Court that the NCB viscometer test produced a higher flow point than other tests, but he failed to prove that the NCB test was unrealistic. The reluctance of the cargo to shift initially (and its continued reluctance for quite some time after the first shift) did not seem compatible with a moisture content equal to the flow point when the *Burtonia* sailed.

the ship, i.e. in the way the ship rolled. It saved time trimming and doubtless made the cargo easier to discharge at Ghent. Captain Ash had been relief master of the *Burtonia* on three occasions, but had never before carried a cargo of lead concentrate.

Migration of moisture after loading

The Court also analysed the possibility that moisture had migrated through the cargo after loading, in such a way as to cause internal shear weaknesses allowing slides to take place. This was Mr Tope's theory. It was agreed that if the concentrate was already near flow point then moisture was more likely to migrate. Moreover, a deceptive aspect of this likely migration was that the cargo would appear to be progressively *more coherent* until the flow point was actually reached. Whenever he looked at the cargo, Captain Ash might have been deceived into thinking that such an apparently heavy and solid mass could not shift.

The likely moisture content of the two holds was also considered. It was confusing that No. 2 hold (which had at least been trimmed in part) was probably more moist than No. 1.

Eighteen tons of a drier 'jigged' concentrate had been mixed into No. 1 hold, whereas two lorry loads of very wet lead concentrate had gone into No. 2 hold. These two loads, the last to be shipped, had to be jerked out of the vehicles. This was how the stevedores and the Mate remembered them as being very wet. Other recollections by the stevedores confused the issue. They said that on this occasion the *Burtonia's* cargo (except for the last two lorry loads) was 'generally drier than usual'. The Court preferred to rely on Laporte's test (see Table 1) as a more reliable index of the moisture content. But account had to be taken of more tests by various persons which indicated that moisture in certain metal concentrates tends to travel from the centre to the edges, and that moisture levels will vary.

Summary of the Court's analysis

Before announcing its conclusion the Court tried to summarize the results of its analysis. There were, it felt, sufficient margins of error and possible variations in the figures of moisture and flow point to make either Mr Tope's or Dr Suddaby's theory possible (see Section 4.1). Previous experience in the shifting of cargoes of moist concentrates all indicated that the cargoes had liquefied in part or in whole. The small progressive increases in the list of the *Burtonia* were more consistent with some part or parts of the cargo reluctantly flowing in a thixotropic* manner than in slides or movements of the cargo. The big increases in list (at about 8.15 pm and again some four hours later) were consistent with slides in the top or sides of the cargo. The moisture content (slightly higher in No. 2 hold than in No. 1) was on average at about the safe transportable limit. But there were slight variations in flow point,† and the moisture content could well have migrated so as to reach flow point in certain parts. Engine vibration might well have caused some levelling of the cargo in No. 2 hold before the initial slide which caused the list. One more point, the NCB viscometer test had not been proved inadequate.

Conclusion of the Court

The Court's conclusion was that: 'the *Burtonia's* cargo was sufficiently moist to liquefy and flow in some places and in others to slide on internal planes of shear weakness or on the hold ceiling. Slides were most likely in No. 1 hold where the cargo had had little trimming, while the marginally higher moisture in No. 2 hold enabled some parts of the cargo in that hold to liquefy and flow. The original list and subsequent noticeable increases were consistent with parts of the cargo sliding, while the periods of gradual increase in list were probably due to a sluggish flow of cargo. Both slides and flows contributed to the loss of the *Burtonia*. The former could have been avoided by trimming. The latter was evidence that the cargo was unsafe to ship.'

Apportioning the blame

It was within the Court's terms of reference to assign blame. The Court held that the owners of the *Burtonia* were to blame for going to sea with an insufficiently trimmed cargo of lead concentrate. The more difficult question remained as to who (if anyone) was to blame for the fact that the cargo was also near flow point when the *Burtonia* sailed. Figure 6 shows the flow of criticism levelled by one party against another.

The Court inquired into the history of the quayside issue of certificates or guarantees for shipments of lead concentrate from the river Trent to Ghent. Table 3 shows the main events.

**Exhibiting a dough-like or mayonnaise-like property.*

†*Possible reasons for these variants were explained in Section 4.2.*

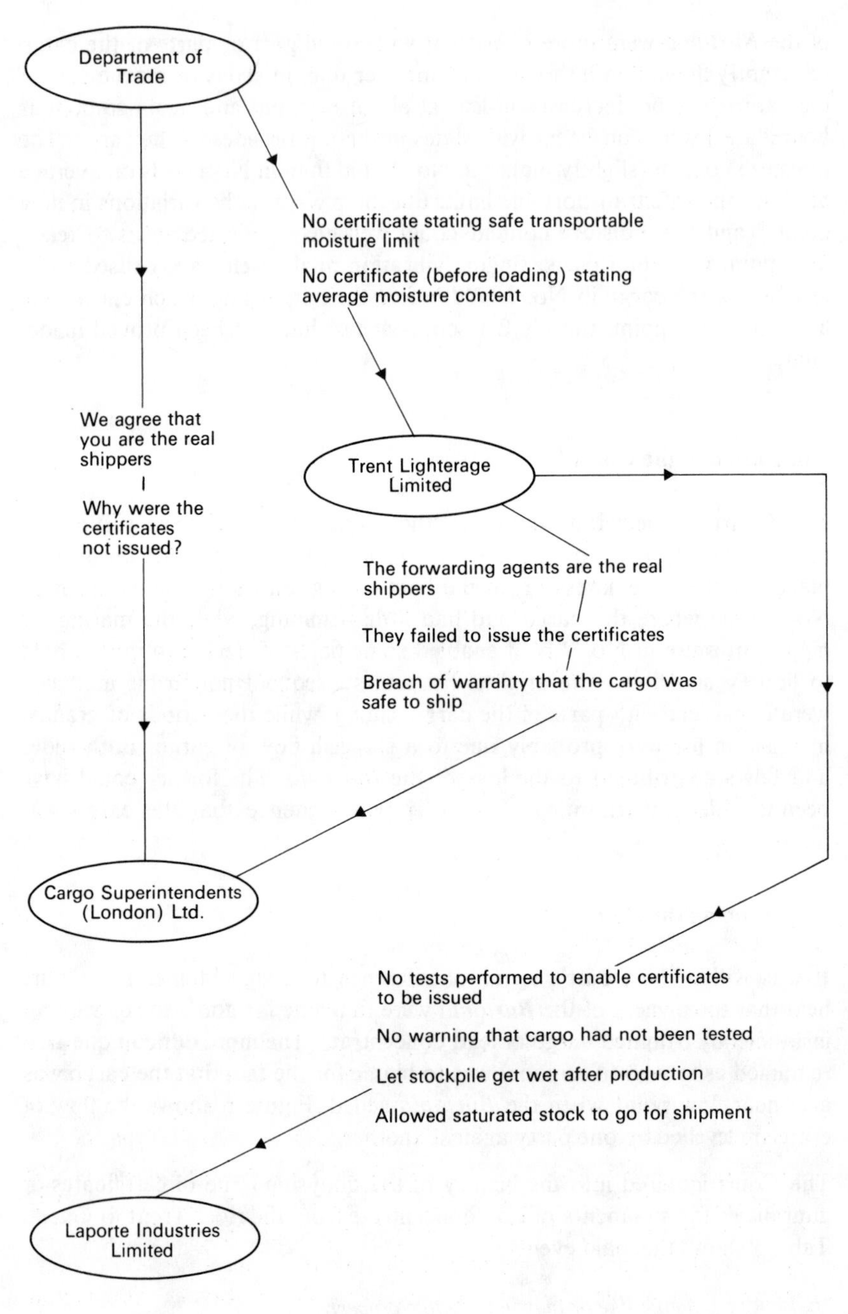

Figure 6 The main criticisms levelled by the parties against each other (The Cause of Foundering)

Table 3 Events relating to the issue of guarantees on moisture content in cargoes of lead concentrate

Date	Event
1964	Glebe Mines Ltd start selling lead concentrate to Minmet Financing Company.
	Minmet Financing Company instruct their agents (Cargo Superintendents (London) Ltd) *not* to weigh or sample the product before shipment.
	Shipowners demand and get guarantees on moisture content.
1964–66	Part of one shipment rejected because of excess moisture.
1966	Guarantees on moisture content begin to lapse.
1969	Last guarantee on moisture content issued.
1969 (late)	Agreement between Cargo Superintendents (London) Ltd (as agents of Minmet Financing Company) and Trent Lighterage Ltd to charter the *Burtonia* for future shipments.
1971	Trentside Boating & Engineering Company appointed as sub-agents of Cargo Superintendents (London) Ltd.
	Procedure established for protecting cargo on quay from rain and reporting contamination.

The Court's analysis of who was to blame

Laporte Industries Limited knew that lead concentrate could be unsafe to ship if the moisture content was too high, and its employees were well aware of the IMCO *Code of Safe Practice for Bulk Cargoes*. They did let the stockpile get wet after production, and they did have a duty to carry out tests. But Laporte Industries Limited were also entitled to believe that proper checks would be carried out at Keadby by those responsible for inspecting the cargo on the quayside and by Captain Ash himself. The IMCO Code actually recommended that samples for ascertaining the moisture content should be taken at the time of loading. If the moisture content had varied in the stockpile and this variation was carried forward into one or other of the *Burtonia's* holds, this was not something that Laporte Industries Limited could reasonably foresee.

In the 1969 agreement Trent Lighterage Limited had been given an inadequately defined warranty that the *Burtonia* would load 'lead concentrates in bulk, harmless, non-dangerous' and Minmet (acting through Cargo Superintendents (London) Limited) further provided that the cargo had to be 'loaded, stowed and discharged by charterer's stevedores free of all risk and expense to the vessel'. It appeared that Cargo Superintendents (London) Limited were employed to load the *Burtonia,* not to test the cargo. Instructions to load a cargo did not infer a duty to ascertain whether that cargo was safe.

Captain Ash should have asked for a certificate to assure himself that the cargo was safe. But just supposing tests had been carried out after the cargo was loaded in order for a certificate to be prepared, the chances were that if the test was performed in No. 1 hold, then the cargo would have been declared safe to transport. But a test in No. 2 hold might well have shown the cargo to be at flow point. Moreover, a tester might have regarded No. 1 and No. 2 holds as *one* compartment – separated as they were by only a *temporary* wooden bulkhead. There would then have been a fifty-fifty chance that the dangerous No. 2 hold would not have been tested.

The Court's conclusion on who was to blame

Having already apportioned blame to Trent Lighterage Limited for not trimming the cargo properly the Court then declared that 'none of the parties to the Inquiry contributed by their wrongful act or default to the loss of the *Burtonia* by reason of the fact that the cargo she loaded was unsafe', i.e. that the cargo was at or near flow point.

The Court's recommendations as they relate to the foundering of the *Burtonia*

There were four recommendations – first, that the Department of Trade should look into the tests which might be applied to various metallic concentrates before shipment; secondly, that it should consider possible amendments to the IMCO *Code of Safe Practice for the Carriage of Bulk Cargoes* concerning the meaning of the word 'compartment' and the length of time for testing the flow pattern of metallic concentrates. The third recommendation was to 'establish by discussion within the shipping industry a voluntary procedure in respect of sampling, certification and reporting prior to sailing (including a feedback of voyage experiences) to operate in those loading ports where concentrates are regularly loaded'. The fourth point concerned the publicizing both of procedures and of the IMCO Code recommendations.

These recommendations concluded the chapter in the Annex devoted to 'The Cause of Foundering'.

REPORT OF THE COURT AND ANNEX

SEARCH AND RESCUE

Introduction

The third chapter of the Annex dealt with search and rescue. It differs greatly from the chapter on 'The Cause of Foundering' because the Department had a dual role to play in that it had a responsibility to direct the attention of the Court to all relevant facts and possible matters for investigation, while it was itself responsible for HM Coastguard, who were involved in the incident. Thus, Counsel for the Department alleged that the loss of life was contributed to by faults in the Search and Rescue organization (of which HM Coastguard are an integral part), but concluded his case by inviting the Court to find that there was no default by the Coastguard within the meaning of the relevant Act under which the Court was convened. The Court was also invited to find in similar terms for the Post Office. So far as Counsel satisfied the Court that there was no wrongful act or default within the small print of the 1894 Merchant Shipping Act, the Court was bound to clear the Post Office and HM Coastguard.

Figure 7 shows the flow of criticisms between the parties. The absence of a connecting line with arrows emphasizes that *no Court criticisms were made of the Royal National Lifeboat Institution.* To make the Open University context of this case study more comprehensible a hypothetical fourth party has been added to the diagram representing the Granada television documentary about the loss of life following the foundering of the *Burtonia*. We might extend the diagram by including the Independent Broadcasting Authority (which upheld the Post Office's complaint against Granada) and the Open University (which by its use of the Granada film provoked another complaint from the Post Office).

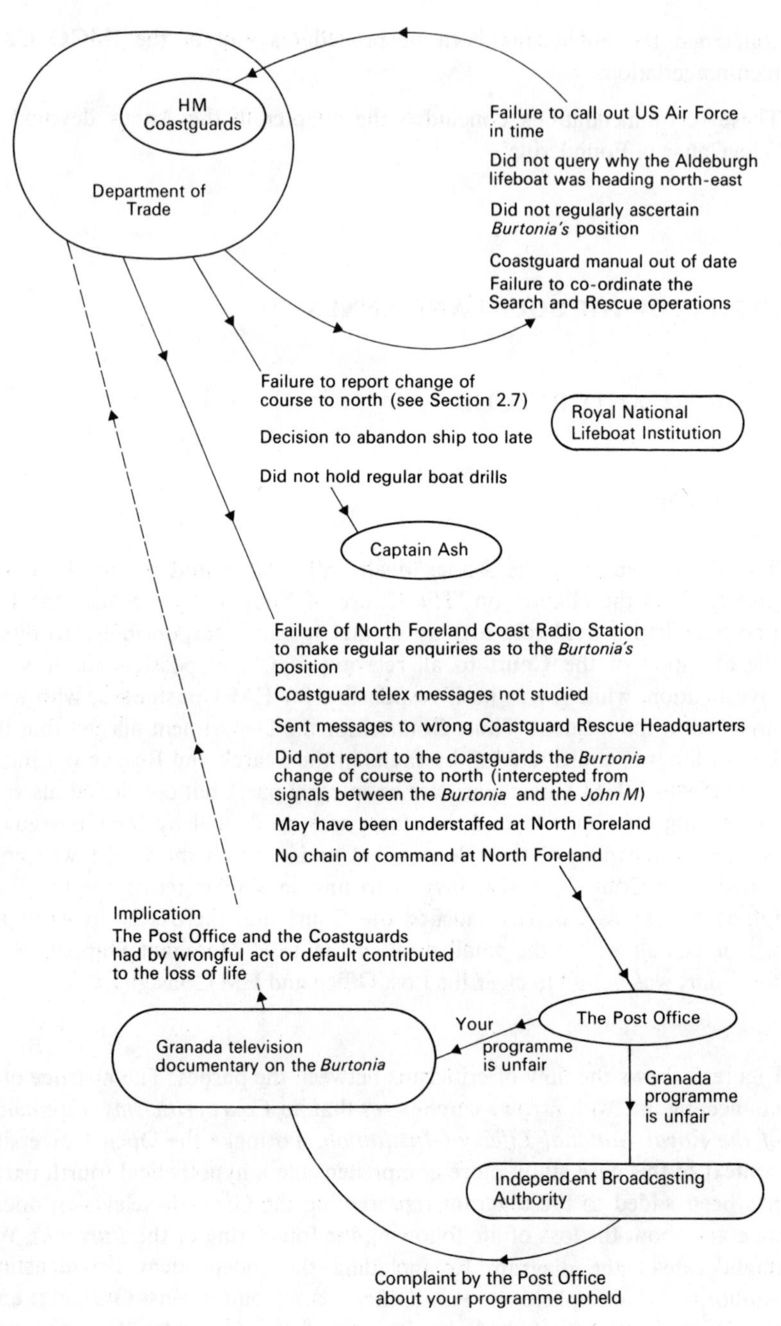

Figure 7 The main criticisms levelled by the parties against each other (Search and Rescue)

Figure 7 shows the kinds of matters which occupied the Court's attention during the investigation into Search and Rescue. One of the cumulative effects of these failures was to delay the arrival of the Aldeburgh lifeboat until after the *Burtonia* had sunk.

The lifeboat's course

At 9.35 it will be recalled (see page 171) an RNLI lifeboat was launched from the beach at Aldeburgh. The lifeboat steered a course west towards where the *Burtonia* would have been if her engines had not been working. Subsequently, she was redirected by the Coastguard towards the Outer Gabbard Light Vessel, where the Master had stated she was making for. When she got near the Outer Gabbard, the lifeboat reported she could not see the *Burtonia*, nor could she make contact with the *Burtonia* by radio, the *Burtonia* having turned north (down sea) and not reported this change of course. Four minutes before midnight the lifeboat misheard a message from the *Burtonia* to the North Foreland Coast Radio Station. According to the correct version of this message the *Burtonia* was seventeen miles away *north by east*. Bad reception in the lifeboat caused this bearing to be heard as *north east*. The lifeboat then set a course of *north east,* but this was not reported to the shore nor did anyone ask for it. At about a quarter past midnight the coastguards at Goreleston did plot the correct relative positions of the lifeboat and the *Burtonia*, which were now found to be 13.5 miles apart. At 12.45 the lifeboat reported that she was six or seven miles from the *Burtonia.* This underestimate was made because of a misapprehension as to the *Burtonia's* true position. What is more, since the MAYDAY signal had been reduced to PAN, the lifeboat could not receive correct news of the *Burtonia's* position because it did not tune its radio to the PAN frequency. The lifeboat was still heading in the wrong direction (north east), and this was not yet queried by the coastguards at Gorleston. However, the lifeboat did fire a flare at 1 am which was seen by the *John M*. Only then were the lifeboat crew advised to change course. At 1.07 the lifeboat was 12 miles from the *Burtonia* and heading now in the right direction. The Aldeburgh lifeboat finally arrived after a voyage of six and a half hours – some twenty minutes after the *Burtonia* sank.

The Court's comments on the lifeboat's course

The first comment by the Court concerned the course which the lifeboat steered on being launched. Although this initial bearing did not adversely affect the operation, the investigation revealed disparity of wording between the coastguard's instructions and the lifeboat regulations. HM coastguards and the Royal National Lifeboat Institution held copies of each other's regulations. The intention was that a course would be given by the coastguards to the lifeboat if requested. The RNLI regulations made no provision for any subsequent reporting of the lifeboat's course and speed. The coastguards' manual made no mention of obtaining information from a lifeboat after launch. Article 82(h) stated in part: 'If during a lifeboat service the coastguard receives information of immediate importance to the coxwain it should be passed on at once to the lifeboat, e.g. any change in the position of the casualty.' The Court felt that this sentence reflected too passive a role for the coastguards at Gorleston. It did not imply that, when necessary, action would be taken by the coastguards to obtain that information.

The second comment read as follows: 'A co-ordinating station' i.e. of coastguards 'should be informed of the course of the lifeboat launched to a casualty, and if not should make inquiries. The co-ordinating station should plot the lifeboat's positions at reasonably frequent intervals and advise the lifeboat if the plot indicates that the course does not seem to be appropriate.'

The third comment noted that there was no communications procedure for repeating or repeating back important portions of a message, such as the casualty's position. Inclusion of such a procedure in the Post Office *Handbook for Radio Operators* and the manuals of the coastguards and RNLI needed to be considered. (*Note:* The coastguards at Gorleston did not communicate directly with the radio operators at North Foreland, but through the coastguards at Dover.)

The fourth comment concerned the fact that the PAN signal was not transmitted on the frequency to which the lifeboat was normally tuned. So the lifeboat did not hear the *Burtonia's* correct position broadcast with the PAN signal. To change frequency on the Aldeburgh lifeboat was not easy. It would have required the opening in a heavy sea of the forward hatch. The Court commented that if a distress signal is reduced to PAN the coastguards must ensure that the lifeboat receives all the information contained in any PAN signal.

The fifth comment centred on the mishearing of bearings (e.g. *north east* instead of *north by east*). The Court felt that there would be less chance of mistakes being made if three figure notations (e.g. 110°, 120°, etc.) were used by mariners, instead of compass points (e.g. north east).

The last comment concerned the failure of the coastguards to call out the Lowestoft lifeboat. The Court noted that this failure was a reflection of the immediate lifeboat assistance at that moment. Twenty-eight minutes after midnight the coastguards decided against calling out the Lowestoft lifeboat. The Court considered that the Lowestoft lifeboat would still have got to the *Burtonia* first even at this stage of the night – *whether or not* the Aldeburgh lifeboat had been steering the correct course. Since MAYDAY had been reduced to PAN and the *Burtonia* was proceeding with the *John M*, the situation (as reported to the coastguards) was stabilized.

Figure 1 shows how near Lowestoft the *Burtonia* was when it finally sank.

The Court's further analysis and comment

The following is a list of paragraph headings with comment summaries in the 'Search and Rescue' chapter of the Court's Annex which have *not* been touched on so far in this study.

Steps to initiate search and rescue
The station to co-ordinate

(Comments on these paragraphs concentrated on the coastguards' failure to make sufficiently clear which station was co-ordinating the search-and-rescue operation, and on the cumbersome delay (up to nine minutes) in transmitting messages from North Foreland to Gorleston *via* Dover and vice versa.)

Pass all information

(Comment on this paragraph referred to Part 4 of the *Annual Summary of Admiralty Notices to Mariners 1972,* paragraph 25, which lists the components of a distress message. There was no reference to a case like the *Burtonia* in which a vessel in distress retains use or partial use of her engines and steering. Such information, plus course and speed, was needed, as well as a follow-up procedure. Clear and unambiguous language was also desirable in all signals.)

Reduction to PAN

(Comments highlighted the disjunction of understanding between various publications as to the meaning and method of a reduction from MAYDAY to PAN. The main danger had arisen because after the reduction to PAN neither the *John M*, nor the *Burtonia*, nor the Aldeburgh lifeboat ever listened to a PAN broadcast.)

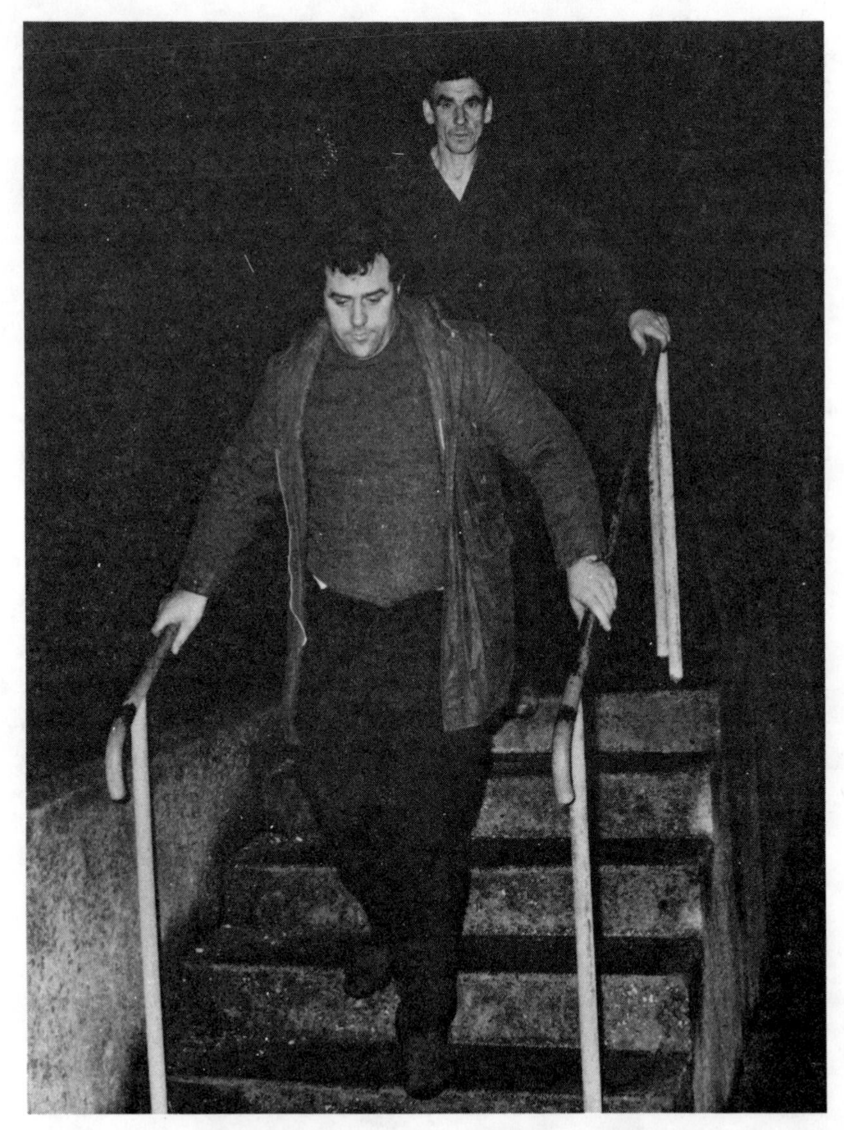

Figure 8 Survivors from the Burtonia *come ashore at Gorleston*

The co-ordinating role

(Comments on this paragraph were directed towards deficiencies in the coastguard manual and the lack of a clear task description for a coastguard station appointed to co-ordinate a search-and-rescue operation.)

Figure 9 The body of a victim is brought ashore at Lowestoft

Manning of Co-ordinating Stations and Coastal Radio Stations

(Comments here were directed at the need to have senior staff more readily available at the coastguard stations, e.g. Gorleston, and towards the better use of resources, both human and machine, at the Post Office's coastal radio stations, e.g. North Foreland.)

Some of this material is enlarged upon and certain points generalized in the Granada television documentary on the *Burtonia*, and in the television programme produced in connection with the Open University Course *Systems Performance: Human Factors and Systems Failures* (TD342). A complaint by the Post Office to the Independent Broadcasting Authority about the Granada film was successful.

General observations of the Court

The Court made eleven general observations which had the same status as its comments (see Sections 5.3 and 5.4) because both are bracketed together in the final recommendations (see Section 5.6). The general observations are reproduced *verbatim* in Section 5.5. Explanatory footnotes have only been added to amplify statements which may not be explicit to readers whose sole source of information is this case study.

(a) The desired objective in the *Burtonia* search-and-rescue (SAR) operation was to get an RNLI lifeboat to the casualty in the shortest possible time. Had the lifeboat's course been co-ordinated with the casualty's movements the lifeboat would have reached the *Burtonia* at about midnight. Such a degree of co-ordination was impossible because of the inadequate or inaccurate exchange of information between all the ships and shore authorities concerned.

(b) The most striking deficiency in the passing of information was the lack of any message to North Foreland reporting the *Burtonia's* change of course to the north shortly after 10 pm.

(c) This lack of information tested the procedures of the shore authorities. North Foreland, assuming the casualty to be more or less stationary, did not make regular inquiries as to the casualty's position. There was no procedure requiring a station operator to do so. No inquiry was made by the co-ordinating station as to the intervals at which North Foreland was obtaining the casualty's position and no inquiry as to the casualty's course and speed was made. The responsibility of co-ordination properly understood should have made these matters instinctive. As stated these are the sort of matters which the Coastguard Instructions could, with advantage, specify.

(d) The advent of better means of communication available to all in SAR has extended the responsibility of HM Coastguards for co-ordination. As a body, its personnel are more aware of that responsibility than a reading of their instructions would lead one to suppose. The active role which the coastguards should play in co-ordinating an SAR operation is not simply a matter of outlining such actions in their Instructions. The bigger problem which must be resolved by all interested parties is whether the role of co-ordination is purely advisory or whether it ought in certain respects to be supervisory. Once such a role has been defined it must be understood by HM Coastguards and, equally important, recognized by the other authorities concerned in SAR.

(e) In the United Kingdom, the SAR organization is made up of different authorities each with its own expertise. This places a premium on the fullest co-operation between all those authorities. We consider that the true role of the coastguard is that of giving the best informed advice available. Such advice should be respected and acted upon when received by a ship or another authority unless any unforeseen circumstance precludes such action. The key to the situation is that the co-ordinator must be the person best informed of the overall picture. Ship masters and authorities alike must recognize the paramount importance of keeping the co-ordinator fully informed. To this end it may well be desirable that a co-ordinator with the approval of the CRS* should be able to speak on 2182 kHz† to the casualty's master or to the master of any ship in close company at sea.

(f) It is not necessary for the coastguard to instruct a particular lifeboat to launch. It would seem far more desirable to continue the practice that the coastguard should request a lifeboat authority to launch. At the same time he should be able to provide a full picture of the circumstances prevailing and the needs of the casualty concerned.

(g) The need for close co-operation between the authorities has been appreciated. Exchange visits have been arranged between personnel at CRSs and CRHQs‡ and between coastguards and lifeboat stations. If time and manpower were to allow, joint training and joint exercises would clearly be desirable. In serious casualties or cases where the SAR operation has been prolonged or complicated or where there has been a loss of life, it might prove valuable if the coastguards and the Coast Radio Stations were to exchange copies of their casualty reports and log books. At present, each authority studies the facts of a certain operation from the contents of their own documents only. A very incomplete appreciation of the *Burtonia* SAR operation would be gained from the study of the documents of only one of

**CRS=Coastal Radio Station.*

†2182 kHz was one of the distress frequencies. The Burtonia's *MAYDAY signal utilized 2182 kHz. PAN signals go out on working frequencies, but there may be a signal on the distress frequency to warn listeners of a PAN signal on another frequency.*

‡CRHQ=Coastguard Rescue Headquarters.

the authorities concerned. It is for the authorities to consider whether such exchanges would better take place at Headquarters or District level.

(h) It was apparent that the Coastguard Manual is badly out of date and that procedures for amending this and other coastguard documents are imprecise. We recommend priority be given to re-writing the Coastguard Manual which should state the policy on which the Coastguard Service should base its expanding training effort. A proper system for issuing and recording the insertion of amendments to coastguard documents is needed.

(i) Consideration should be given by the authorities concerned to the redrafting of certain of their instructions so that where possible any instruction dealing with the same matter is expressed in the same words. Furthermore, thought should be given to the feasibility of a standard SAR manual for the coastguards, Coast Radio Stations and the RNLI. One standard manual would be more easily understood and, when necessary, amended than the present system where each authority's stations have copies of the other authority's instructions.

(j) Mr Pheasant was able to attract the attention of the lifeboat by waving a light attached to a lifebuoy. In that way his life was saved. At present there is only a requirement for half the lifebuoys supplied to a merchant ship to be fitted with lights. It seems desirable for all lifebuoys to be equipped with lights.

(k) The importance of boat drills has frequently been emphasized. Mr Pheasant stated that he had not attended a boat drill during nearly two months of service in the *Burtonia*. That was in breach of the regulation as to the frequency of such drills. Where life rafts are fitted as part of the life saving appliances such drill must include instruction in the proper releasing of life rafts.

The Court's recommendations as they relate to the search-and-rescue operations

The following recommendations are reproduced *in toto* from the Annex to the Report of Court No. 8062:

We would recommend that our 'Comments' and 'General Observations' be placed before the Committee to Co-ordinate Marine SAR with a view to the Committee taking such action as they deem appropriate. In our opinion the principal points requiring attention are:

(a) The better defining and understanding of the coastguard's co-ordinating role.

(b) The organization and manning of CRHQs co-ordinating off-shore SAR operations.

(c) Standardizing so far as possible the SAR instructions of each of the authorities, and giving consideration to the desirability of a single SAR manual for all authorities.

(d) Pursuing steps to further the co-operation between the various authorities concerned in SAR.

(e) Evaluating the usefulness of the practice of reducing MAYDAY to PAN and considering the desirability of giving publicity to the practice if it is to continue.

SUMMING-UP

The findings of the Formal Investigation into the loss of the *Burtonia* were anticipated by the Department of Trade. At the beginning of 1974 a full review of the search-and-rescue organization was set in motion such that when the *Burtonia* findings were published on 31st July 1974 questions about the coastguard's co-ordinating role were already being considered. At that time the search-and-rescue services of the United Kingdom were being called on to deal with nearly five thousand incidents a year, and it was estimated that about the same number of lives were being saved yearly.

Case Study 7

The Crash of Trident Papa-India

by Geoff Peters

CONTENTS

Page

On the 18 June 1972, British European Airways (BEA) Trident 1 G–ARPI crashed in a field near Staines. All the 118 people on board were killed. Up to the time of writing, this has been the worst crash in British aviation history. The following case study is based almost entirely on the official report:

> 'Report of the Public Inquiry into the causes and circumstances of the accident near Staines on 18th June 1972' Civil Aircraft Accident Report 4/73, Trident 1 G–ARPI. Published by Her Majesty's Stationery Office in 1973.

The author wishes to thank the Accident Investigation Branch of the Department of Trade for their assistance in the preparation of this case study.

Trident 1 flight-deck 1 Droop lever 2 Flap lever 3 Thrust levers 4 Stick-push 'dump' (stall recovery override) 5 Droop position indicator 6 'Stall recovery low pressure' and 'droop out of position' warning lights

THE LAST FLIGHT

The details of what happened on this last flight of the Trident Papa-India are almost entirely derived from the flight data recorders that were carried on the plane. These, together with tape recordings of conversations between air traffic control and the crew, make it possible to give a second-by-second account of the flight. Information abstracted from the flight data recorders is presented in an appendix. In the words of the official report of the Inquiry 'all four parties (Hawker Siddeley Aviation, British European Airways, the Civil Aviation Authority, and the Accident Investigation Branch of the Department of Trade and Industry) agree that the results represent the most accurate interpretation possible of the raw data, and there has been no valid suggestion that the figures so deduced are other than substantially accurate'. On the 18th June 1972, Papa-India was to be the aircraft on Flight BE548 from London, Heathrow, to Brussels. It was due to depart at 1545.* However, because of load readjustment, the crew did not request permission to leave their parked position until 1600 hours. Clearance to taxi was given three minutes later, and after that clearance for a standard instrument departure was granted. At 1606 hours 53 seconds the crew reported that they were ready for take-off from runway 28 right, and were cleared to do so. There was a short delay and the plane was finally cleared for take-off at 1608 hours 24 seconds.

Aircraft like the Trident have devices called flaps and droops which allow the shape of the aircraft's wings to be changed. Put simply, the wing shape is extended by these devices so that during take-off and landing at low speeds the aircraft remains aerodynamically stable. Once the aircraft is flying fast enough they are retracted. In this case, the aircraft started down the runway at 1608 hours 30 seconds with the droops and flaps in the correct position. Forty-four seconds later the aircraft had reached a speed of 145 knots and started to climb off the runway. The autopilot was later engaged and 30 seconds after take-off the aircraft started a left turn towards Epsom. Twenty seconds after that the flaps were selected up and the power reduced in a standard noise-abatement procedure. There were various exchanges between the crew and air traffic control. Then 70 seconds after take-off at an airspeed of 162 knots and an altitude of 1 772 feet the droop levers were selected up. Normally this would not have happened until the airspeed was 225 knots and the altitude was 3 000 feet. As the droops moved the aircraft immediately went into a stall and an automatic stall recovery device was operated. This device disengaged the autopilot and pushed the nose of the

**All times are in GMT.*

Figure 1 A British Airways Trident 1 similar to the one which crashed at Staines. This particular aircraft is shown using both droops and flaps to maintain aerodynamic stability as it comes in to land.

aircraft forward so that the aircraft would pitch downwards. Had this continued the aircraft would have picked up speed and been at a less dangerous attitude. The position improved slightly, but as the droops were fully retracted a second 'stick-push' occurred eight seconds after the first and then a third three seconds later. One second after that the stall recovery system was manually inhibited by the pulling of an override lever. The aircraft then pitched up and lost speed and height, it entered a true aerodynamic stall. One hundred and six seconds after take-off the aircraft crashed, in a field near the Staines by-pass.

The crash at 1611 was witnessed by a thirteen-year-old boy who ran to the house of an ex-nursing sister a quarter of a mile away who was familiar with accident procedure. In the words of the Inquiry report 'she was one of the first on the scene and she made heroic efforts amidst the wreckage to help any of the victims who were still alive. Her actions cannot be praised too highly. However, the decelerative forces of the impact were too great for the human frame to survive.' Emergency services were quick to get to the scene of the crash and by 1627 police, fire and ambulance services had arrived from several different areas. Again in the words of the Inquiry report 'The field was sufficiently inaccessible to prevent all but the most persistent sightseers from reaching it. The police were successful in controlling spectators, and contemporary reports that members of the public had impeded rescue services by their presence near the scene are not borne out by the facts. All the services involved acted with commendable dispatch.'

Figure 2 The scene of the disaster shortly after the crash.

MECHANICAL ASPECTS

There is no question that the reasons for the crash were, first, the premature retraction of the forward droops and, secondly, the subsequent failure to retrieve the situation. Why then did the droops retract?

High-lift Devices

The Trident prototype first flew in 1962. In February 1964 when the first aircraft was certified and registered it met all the airworthiness requirements and did not have to seek any variation from standard requirements or the provision of 'equivalent levels of safety' as most aircraft in the past had done.

As already stated, aircraft that fly at high speeds in normal flight need the ability to vary the shape of their wings to achieve the low speeds necessary for take-off and landing. In the past this was achieved by the familiar trailing edge flaps, but in the case of the Trident additional leading edge high-lift devices were also necessary. The Trident was the first British civil aircraft to incorporate such retractable 'droops' (as for convenience they are referred to here). In short, these devices alter the speed at which the aircraft will stall. If the droops and flaps are both out then the aircraft is aerodynamically stable at much lower speeds. For example, in level flight with a weight of 50 000 kg the retraction of the droop in Papa-India raised the stalling speed by about 30 knots. Could the retraction of the droops have been due to a mechanical failure?

Two suggestions were made at the Inquiry about possible mechanical reasons for retraction of the droops. The first involved an incident to a Trident 2 known as Foxtrot Hotel. In May 1970 the crew experienced the same stall warnings as Papa-India, but they noticed in time that the slats (a leading edge high-lift device serving the same purpose as the droops on a Trident 1) had been retracted. The incident was reported as a mechanical

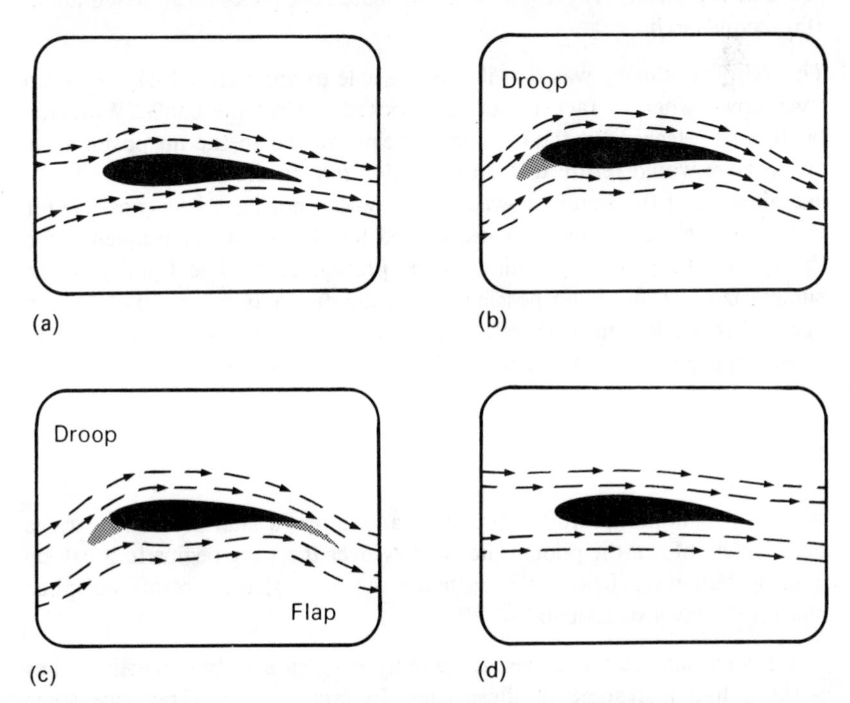

Figure 3 The effect of droop and flap extension on the air-flow around a wing cross-section

(a) At high speeds the wing gains lift without having to use either flaps or droops.

(b) Extension of the leading edge droop guarantees lift at low speeds.

(c) A combination of leading edge droops and trailing edge flaps maximizes lift.

(d) With droops and flaps retracted at low speed the wing experiences no lift and the plane stalls.

failure, but nothing was discovered in a subsequent examination. This incident is dealt with more fully later, but the Inquiry report stated '. . . we are satisfied that this was not a case of mechanical malfunction at all'.

The second set of ideas about mechanical failure was contained in a report by First Officer Schofield in 1970 subsequent to the Foxtrot Hotel incident.

Because of the possibility of inadvertently operating the droop lever instead of the flap lever or vice versa, a baulk between the two was fitted which prevented such movement in most circumstances. The design of this baulk was such that in situations where one might have to be moved the other could not be. It should be noted that once the flaps were selected up on take-off the baulk did not offer any protection against subsequent retraction of the droops. In a normal climb out this time when the droop lever was unguarded was short. At Heathrow noise-abatement procedures added about 100 seconds to it.

The Schofield theory was that it was possible to apparently lock the droop lever down when in fact it was only locked against the baulk. When the baulk was released by the flaps lever being moved to the up position the droop lever would return to the up position too. In the case of Papa-India, examination of the baulk showed that 'it would not have been possible for the lever to have remained lodged behind the baulk, and consequently the theory can have no application to the present case'. The Inquiry report summarized: 'There is no possibility that the droop lever moved of its own accord.' It would appear therefore that the droops were retracted manually at an inappropriate time. What warnings did the crew then receive?

Stall Warnings

As a conventional aircraft approaches and enters a stall there are various cues which inform the pilots. The air-flow over the wing begins to break-up causing buffeting, if no action is taken the nose of the aircraft will pitch sharply downwards as it stalls.

The Trident had been designed to be more efficient aerodynamically and as a result had lost some of these cues. In fact, it does experience some buffeting on approach to a stall but as it enters a stall the slight nose down pitching is quickly followed by a nose up position.

To compensate for the lack of 'natural' information about the state of the aircraft, the designers Hawker Siddeley Aviation, with assistance from BEA, BALPA, and the Applied Psychology Research Unit at Cambridge, devised two complementary stall safety systems. Both the stall warning and

Figure 4 The reconstruction at Farnborough of wreckage from Papa-India.

the stall recovery systems rely on information about the angle of incidence provided by probes on either side of the fuselage together with data about the position of the aircraft's flaps and droops, and its upward pitch rate.

As the angle of incidence approaches a potential stall, the *stall warning system* comes into operation. It activates an electric motor which causes both control columns to vibrate. If no action is taken then just before the true aerodynamic stall, the *stall recovery system* operates. A pneumatic ram physically pushes the control columns forward with considerable force. In doing this the 'stick-push' both simulates the sharp nose down pitch of a stall, and takes the first action necessary to retrieve the situation. If the pilots do not take follow up action the stick-push will operate again as a stall is approached again and this cycle will continue until the aircraft is out of the stall condition, the air in the system is exhausted or the pneumatic ram is evacuated by means of the override lever.

Both systems can be manually inhibited by circuit-breakers in the event of any malfunction. For the stick-push there is a 'stall recovery override lever' on the central control pedestal to evacuate the pneumatic ram if the system fails to disengage.

Because the reliability of the stall recovery system is all important, it only operates if both the probes on the fuselage indicate a stall.

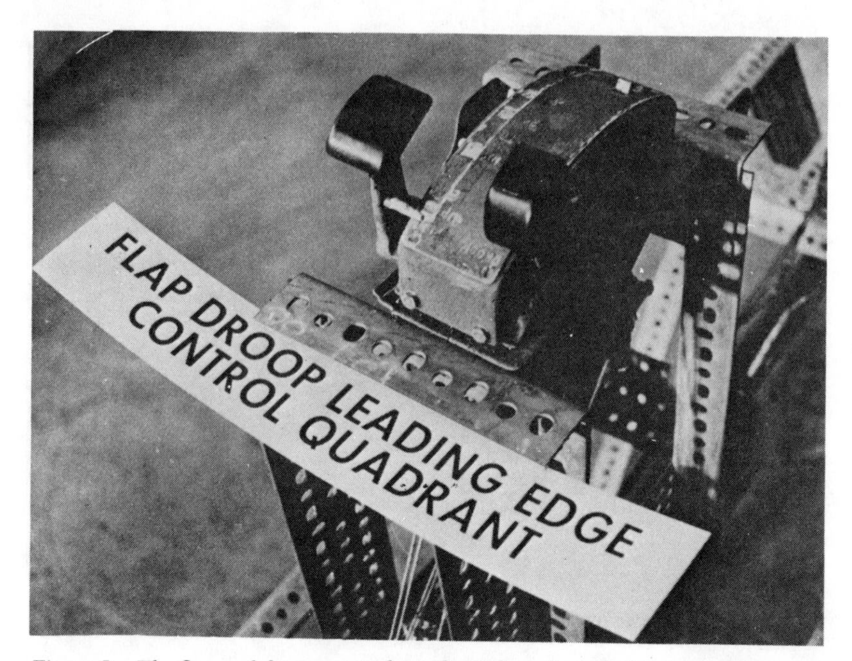

Figure 5 The flap and droop control quadrant from Papa-India.

In addition to the stick-shaker and stick-push mechanisms, other warnings would have been apparent in Papa-India. Any significant movement of the joystick automatically disengages the autopilot, so once the first stick-push had happened the autopilot disconnect warnings would operate. These consist of a flashing red alert lamp, a red illuminated 'autopilot' window in the central warning system, and an audio warning to each pilot. Though these can be cancelled, the evidence is that they were not cancelled in the case of Papa-India.

The movement of the droop lever at an inappropriate speed would result in the illumination of an amber droop-out-of-position warning light near the lever, a flashing amber caution lamp and an amber controls lamp. The last two are also associated with other conditions.

Finally, when the stick-push operated an amber stall recovery operating light would come on. This lamp is next to the airspeed indicator in front of each pilot. It is paired with a red light that shows when half of the stall warning system has failed. It is thought possible that this light might briefly have lit if there was a delay between the operation of the droop surface microswitches on the aircraft's wings. So within three seconds of the droop lever being moved to the up position, the following warnings would have occurred.

Figure 6 The leading edge droops from one of the Trident's wings.

Amber droop-out-of-position warning light,
Flashing amber caution lamps,
Amber controls lamp,
Stick-shaker,
Stick-push,
Amber stall recovery operate light (possibly red fail light briefly),
Red autopilot light,
Red alert lamp,
Autopilot audio warning.

Despite all these warnings the crew would still need to diagnose that the droops had been moved. The Inquiry report said that as far as the captain and second pilot were concerned this mass of warnings would not enable them to pick up the fault. Their attention would be exclusively concentrated on the airspeed and altitude indicators in an endeavour to fly what they considered to be a safe speed. 'These considerations would not necessarily apply to the third pilot.'

Reliability

One experienced Trident captain gave evidence about pilot's views of the stall warning and recovery systems. Even before the Papa-India crash, Captain Childs had questioned pilots with him about their reaction should the stall warning system operate. He found that more than half of them suggested pulling the stall recovery override when the stick-shaker operated, and less than a quarter suggested stall recovery action. Captain Childs was so concerned that he went to see four different flight managers in BEA and the Department of Trade and Industry Operations Inspector in order to suggest that training might be at fault.

The history of the stall warning systems reliability was examined by the Inquiry. It was found that between 1965 and 1973 there were ten recorded or known stick-pushes in BEA including Papa-India. One was on the ground in 1966, one at 60 knots on take-off in 1965, four were certainly genuine and one which occurred during training may well have been. So three probably false warnings occurred in the air. One of these was after the Papa-India crash and the remaining two were to the same aircraft in February 1966. So in the $6\frac{1}{2}$ years before the crash there had been no false stick-pushes in flight.

The stick-shaker mechanism is, by design, not as reliable because it is triggered by either of the two probes rather than both as is the case for the stick-push. The likelihood of a stick-shaker operating is far higher than a stick-push because it is the lower level warning. The Inquiry found that incidences of stick-shake operation had dropped from 1.7 per thousand hours in 1966 to 0.65 per thousand hours in 1972. On average each pilot would experience the stick-shake about once every three years. Whether these warnings are false or not is difficult to judge because it relies on the pilot's interpretation.

Speed

The speed of the aircraft during its last flight was always low. At the point the flaps were selected up it was 7 knots below the normal climb speed of 177 knots and 105 seconds into the flight it was 20 knots below this figure. These speeds were compared statistically with flights of previous Tridents in similar conditions. One hundred flights were taken from 1968 and 34 from January to March 1972. In the first case it was found that a speed loss of 20 knots could be expected only once in 400 flights using autopilot (1 in 3000 manual flights). In the case of the 1972 flights the expectation was one in 10 000 flights, but it was impossible to distinguish between manual and autopilot flights.

Further comparisons were then made between Papa-India in the sixteen days immediately before the accident and other flights, and the captain and other captains. In both cases no substantial differences were apparent.

The Inquiry report summarized:

(1) The low speed after flap retraction resulted from a combination of lower than normal speed throughout the initial climb and a greater than normal error after flap retraction and power reduction. A discrepancy of anything like this amount is a very rare occurrence indeed.

(2) The average speed loss after noise abatement for flights by Papa-India in the sixteen days leading up to the accident is similar to that on other Trident 1 aircraft. Three of the longest speed losses occurred during the 24 hours preceding the accident. This, we believe, was due to prevailing turbulent conditions.

(3) Captain Key's speed control on other flights was at least as good as that of other pilots.

INDUSTRIAL SCENE

At the time of the accident there had been a dispute between BEA and the British Airline Pilots Association (BALPA) about pay and conditions of work. The dispute was not only between these two parties but also between pilots themselves as to whether there should be strike action or not. The possible effect of industrial action manifests itself in several ways.

The Crew Room Incident

An hour and a half before the departure of Papa-India there was what one eye witness described as 'the most violent argument he had ever heard', between Captain Key, who was the Captain of the Trident and a First Officer who asked him how successful he had been in enlisting the support of other senior captains in his opposition to strike action. Captain Key replied that the matter was as confidential as the BALPA ballot. The incident was witnessed by Second Officer Keighley who was to fly with Key and it is not known whether the third pilot (Ticehurst) was also present.

Graffiti

The third-pilot's table of Papa-India was marked with 'offensive scribbles' directed at Captain Key and at members of the BEA management staff. A handwriting expert came to a conclusion that in all probability neither co-pilots were the author but it was just possible that the Second Officer, Ticehurst, was responsible for one of them. However, what is known of his views of strike action indicates that in the words of the official reports 'it seems to us as certain as anything can be that the graffiti were not the product of anyone aboard Papa-India on the 18th June'. This is strengthened by the fact that another flying officer flew with Captain Key on Papa-India on 6th June and many of the items of graffiti were then already present. An inspection of other Trident aircraft revealed similar writings on the third-pilot's table. In the words of the official Inquiry 'Thus, what at first sight appeared to be a sinister fact, namely, that on P3's table in an aircraft with Captain Key in command were found offensive remarks directed at Captain Key, turns out to be no more than an exercise in puerility which could have been found repeated in a number of other places and aircraft. The graffiti are no basis for even suspecting that there was any dissention on the flight deck of Papa-India on this occasion'.

Supervisory First Officers

Part of the training of young pilots takes place actually in service. In normal circumstances, a trainee would complete his training in service with a training captain in command, an experienced co-pilot, the trainee as the third pilot, and a supervisory first officer (FSO) as the fourth pilot. However, at the time of the incident, twenty-two of the FSOs had 'declined to render these particular services' as part of the industrial dispute. There were therefore thirty-six pilots, although fully qualified as second pilots, who had not been able to qualify as third pilots. Second Officer Keighley was one of the thirty-six.

Normally, the second and third pilots would change places for the return journey of the flight, although the Captain might well exercise his overriding right to place his crew as he thought best. However, because of the industrial situation, BEA had directed that these thirty-six young pilots should only fly as second pilots (P2). The third pilot would automatically be more experienced and might be somewhat annoyed at not having his turn as second pilot. Additionally, the Captain no longer had any flexibility in crew placement.

The Dublin Incident

On 15th June 1972 a flight from Heathrow to Dublin, and back, and then to Nicosia, was manned as for the Papa-India with the Captain, a second pilot who could only be the second pilot, and a third pilot who was more experienced and could be either second or third. Although the meteorological reports were favourable, the Captain was 'sensitive to the ever present possibility of rapid deterioration of conditions at Nicosia, and the fact that landing facilities there, although adequate, are not as good as at some airfields'. As a result, he decided that he would prefer a more experienced pilot as his second pilot. He therefore approached first the crew controller for a replacement. This was not allowed. He then approached the assistant flight manager who gave the same view, and told the Captain that it was his duty to fly as rostered and if he did not do so he would be in breach of his contract. The Captain returned to the crew room and spoke to the inexperienced co-pilot in harsh terms implying that he would be little help in an emergency. The P2 was upset and his confidence was damaged.

When it came to the noise-abatement procedure on the trip to Dublin the P2 selected the flaps fully down instead of up. The third pilot noticed immediately and reversed the action. There were no further incidents during the flight.

The P2 concerned shared a house with Second Officer Keighley and told him what had happened.

PREVIOUS INCIDENTS

On at least two occasions incidents had occurred to Trident aircraft belonging to BEA which with hindsight can be seen as forewarnings of such a disaster.

(i) The Orly Incident

In December 1968 a BEA Trident bound for Heathrow took off from Orly. Soon after the undercarriage was retracted the Captain without telling anybody else moved the flaps to the fully up position to get a better rate of climb. When it came to the time for the noise-abatement procedure, when the Captain would normally have pulled up the flaps, he retracted the droops and reduced the power. The aircraft began to sink rapidly but the second pilot who later claimed he knew the reputation of the Captain involved, pushed the stick forward to increase speed, and the Captain then selected the droop lever down again. The autopilot was not at any time engaged and the stall warning or recovery systems did not have time to come into action. The incident was not reported until 1970 when BEA introduced a confidential reporting scheme. The second pilot made a report and consequently the following paragraph was published in the Trident Flight Safety Group file:

> **9. Non-standard after take-off drill**
>
> First Officer's report. First Officer handling. On take-off for Orly after the undercarriage was locked up the Captain raised the flap fully up to achieve a better climb-out. At 75 seconds the Captain again reached across and moved the only lever there forwards reducing power to normal climb. As the *droop* had been selected up the aircraft 'dropped like a brick' and speed was increased and droop re-selected down.
>
> *Comment* – this highlights the necessity of following standard procedures.

(ii) The Foxtrot Hotel Incident

A second incident, the details of which were in fact published earlier than the Orly incident, occurred on the 8th May 1970. The aircraft this time was a Trident 2, the forward wing devices of which are called slats rather than droops. On this occasion the aircraft took off for Naples from Heathrow. After take-off the autopilot was engaged and the aircraft started to climb away. When it came to the noise-abatement procedure they got the stick-shaker and the stick-push followed by another stick-shake and stick-push in the same way as the Papa-India aircraft was to do. The Captain checked the airspeed and altitude and came to the conclusion that it must be a false warning. He told the first pilot to check the stick-shaker circuit breakers, and the second pilot was about to pull the stall recovery override lever assuming that it must be a false warning when he noticed that the slat gauge registered 'up'. He then selected the slats down again. The Captain did not realize what had happened until later in the flight when after some discussion between the three pilots it was concluded that there must have been some mechanical failure. The incident was reported and BEA and Hawker Siddeley Aviation carried out tests to discover what if anything could have gone wrong with the system. The incident was reported in the *BEA Air Safety Review* in May 1970 as follows:

> **Trident 2 G–AVFH Heathrow/Naples 8.5.70 BE 326**
>
> At a height of 1000 feet when flap was selected up after take-off there was a stall warning followed by operation of the stall recovery system. IAS was 175 knots. The autopilot was then disconnected and the speed increased to 200 knots. A check on the controls showed that the droop had retracted and the droop lever was in the forward (retracted) position. It was lowered again and the flight continued without further trouble. At no time was there a droop out of position light, a controls warning or a take-off configuration warning.
>
> Following this incident the controls, including the controls warning system, were comprehensively checked but no faults could be found. The aircraft has since flown over 140 hours with no recurrence of defect. CLOSED.

In the words of the official report 'many details of the incident emerged at the inquiry for the first time. No one, for instance, previously knew that the crew was on the point of operating the stall recovery override lever. No one knew that the Captain occasionally (as he admitted) operated non-standard procedures when flying out of Rome by raising his flaps very soon after take-off to obtain a better rate of climb. No one knew, as now appears probable, that this Captain was the man in command at the aircraft involved in the Orly incident'. Although these incidents were both reported in 1970 the discussion of them in BEA continued for some time afterwards. Each one was investigated by a number of people in BEA, including the Air Safety Branch. Before he wrote the report on Foxtrot Hotel detailed above on the 20th May 1970 their Mr Brinjes had asked for a read out of the flight data recorder. However, it had already been erased. (Although it's unlikely to have been helpful because it only recorded attitude, heading, speed and altitude, and not events for slats or slat retraction). The incident was discussed at the meeting of the BEA air safety committee on the 25th June 1970, and again at the July meeting when it was decided not to pursue the matter. On the 19th August the General Manager, Flight Operations, of BEA issued the following memorandum:

> I believe we should not be satisfied to leave this incident as closed. We must see what further training or procedure aspects could be revised to avoid a similar dangerous situation.
>
> I hope that when you've looked at all these possibilities you'll be able to make firm recommendations. It may be that the whole investigation will have to be reopened.

A copy went to the head of the Air Safety Branch, Mr Gordon Burge, and to Captain Dell, who was the person charged with the technical matters on the operations side of Trident aircraft. However no action was taken. There then followed the report of the Orly incident, about which the official report said 'one would have expected the incident to be picked up by the Air Safety Branch, and collated with the Foxtrot Hotel incident. If for no other reason than because of the short time elapsing between the reports of the two incidents.' However, Mr Brinjes did not see the file at all and Mr Gordon Burge was away from the office for a long period and did not see it until late 1970 or early 1971. He did not connect it with Foxtrot Hotel. The Air Safety Branch did have a cross-indexing system which could have linked up two such incidents, however, incidents such as Orly, which were reported only in confidence, were not inserted in the cross-index. Finally, Captain Dell who did read the report of the Orly incident thought that it might be 'a highly camouflaged version of the Foxtrot Hotel incident'. In the Autumn of 1971 a new General Manager of Flight Operations (GMFO) was appointed who followed up the memo sent by his predecessor a year earlier, by asking Captain Dell what had been done. Captain Dell replied in November 1971:

> So far as normal operating procedures were concerned, it was felt that a hazardous situation might arise as soon after take-off flaps were retracted to give a better climb performance which would then leave but one lever – the droop lever – which could be moved inadvertently at the moment of power cut-back.
>
> This then reinforced the view that strict adherence to our normal procedure provided the chief safeguard rather than introducing a further change. The main gist of the foregoing was made known to the then GMFO at the time.

On 29 November the new General Manager of Flight Operations closed the matter.

Figure 7 An aerial photograph of the crash scene showing the spread of wreckage and the position of impact between the busy by-pass and Staines itself.

MEDICAL ASPECTS

Autopsies on all the crew showed that Second Officers Keighley and Ticehurst were apparently well. However, investigation of the heart of Captain Key showed that over a period of 30 years the three coronary arteries had suffered severe atherosclerosis. Atherosclerosis is the narrowing of the arteries by the deposit of fatty or fibrous tissue, and in Captain Key's case the effective diameters in places had been reduced by between 50 and 70 per cent. Although there was no recorded evidence of previous incidents involving the heart muscle in the left coronary artery there were two points of damage. The first indicates a previous cardiac incident possibly without symptoms that had been dealt with naturally. The second area of damage consisted of a torn piece of partially detached arterial wall that was lying across the already narrowed artery. The timing of this partial blockage was thought by medical experts to be between two hours and one minute before death. The effect on Captain Key can never be known for certain, but eminent medical evidence to the Inquiry suggested it would be anything from a slight pain to probable collapse. The initial cause of the partial detachment of this piece of arterial wall was thought likely to be a sharp rise in blood pressure, which might in turn have been caused by many things. Some of the possible causes have been mentioned here already. The graffiti, the delay in starting the flight due to the need for load readjustment and of course the crew-room incident which had happened just over an hour and a half before the crash. To these the Inquiry report sought to add the apparent store Captain Key set on spending Sundays at home.

CONCLUSIONS AND RECOMMENDATIONS OF THE INQUIRY

The following extracts are taken directly from the Inquiry report.

Answers to Questions

Civil Aviation (Investigation of Accidents) Regulations 1969. Regulation 16 (13)

Accident involving Trident G–ARPI

Notice of Inquiry

Final Questions

1. *Was the aircraft fit to perform the intended flight? If not, in what respects was it unfit?*

   Yes.

2. (a) *How many passengers and crew were carried in the aircraft on its last flight?*

   There were 3 flight crew, 3 cabin crew and 112 passengers being carried.

   (b) Was the aircraft properly loaded and trimmed before take-off?

   The aircraft was some 24 kilograms overweight on take-off and the centre of gravity was marginally forward of BEA limits though within the specified range of the *Flight Manual*. These matters had no effect on subsequent events.

3. (a) *How many pilots were carried on the flight-deck for its last flight?*

   There were four pilots carried on the flight-deck for the last flight. Three of these were flight crew, one was a passenger.

   (b) *Had they been properly trained and were they adequately experienced to perform their duties?*

So far as the three flight crew were concerned, Captain Key and S/O Ticehurst were properly trained and adequately experienced to perform their duties. S/O Keighley was properly trained but we doubt whether he was adequately experienced.

(c) *Were they physically and mentally fit for their duties?*

S/O Ticehurst and S/O Keighley were physically and mentally fit for their duties. Captain Key was not physically fit to perform his duties by reason of the chronic abnormal condition of his coronary arteries and an acute condition in one of them. He was mentally fit except insofar as his acute abnormal physical condition may have affected him mentally.

(d) *Were they duly licensed to perform their duties?*

Yes.

4. *Did the Air Traffic Control service function efficiently during the flight?*

Yes.

5. *Was there any defect, malfunction or failure of the aircraft's air frame, powerplants, instruments or equipment before impact?*

(a) The three-way cock in the pneumatic stick-pusher system had not been wire-locked in its operating position as it should have been. The cock was one-sixth of a turn out of its proper position on impact.

(b) A pressure-reducing valve in the same system was unserviceable.

6. (a) *Were the flight procedures laid down for take-off and climb (including those relating to noise-abatement) safe and practicable?*

Yes.

(b) *Were these procedures followed?*

No.

(c) *If not, in what respects and why were they departed from?*

The procedures were departed from in that the proper speed levels were not maintained; the droops were retracted some two minutes too soon, 1300 feet too low, at about 60 knots under the placarded retraction speed and in a banked turn.

They were departed from, so far as we can determine, probably because of the medical condition of Captain Key, the inexperience of S/O Keighley, and the inattention of S/O Ticehurst.

(d) *What action was thereafter taken by the pilots or any of them?*

So far as can be ascertained, there was some small attempt to reduce the incidence of the aircraft after the stick-pusher mechanism had operated and the port bank-angle was taken off. After the third stick-push the stall recovery override lever was operated. It is not possible to say what other action if any was taken by any of the pilots.

(e) *What action could have been taken by the pilots or any of them to prevent this accident after the flight procedures had been departed from?*

The actions which could have been taken by the flight-crew to prevent the accident after the said departures from the flight procedures are as follows:

(i) Re-selection of the droops to the extended position.

(ii) Reduction of incidence by holding the control-column forward of the trim position after the stick-push had operated.

(iii) Allowing the stick-push to continue to operate until a speed of about 200 knots was achieved.

(iv) Increase of thrust.

7. *What was or were the cause or causes of this accident?*

The immediate causes of the accident were as follows:

(a) A failure by the handling pilot to achieve and maintain adequate speed after noise-abatement procedures.

(b) Retraction of the droops at some 60 knots below the proper speed causing the aircraft to enter the stall regime.

(c) Failure by the crew to monitor the speed error and to observe the movement of the droop lever.

(d) Failure by the crew to diagnose the reason for the stick-pusher operation and the concomitant warnings.

(e) Operation of the stall recovery override lever.

The underlying causes were these:

(a) The abnormal heart condition of Captain Key leading to lack of concentration and impaired judgement sufficient to account for his toleration of the speed error and (possibly) his retraction of or order to retract the droops in mistake for the flaps.

(b) Some distraction, possibly to be found in the presence of Captain Collins, which caused S/O Ticehurst's attention to wander from his monitoring duties.

(c) Lack of training in the dangers of subtle pilot incapacitation.

(d) Lack of experience in S/O Keighley.

(e) Lack of knowledge in the crew of the possibility or implications of a change of configuration stall.

(f) Lack of knowledge on the part of the crew that a stick-shake and push might be experienced almost simultaneously and of the probable cause of such an event.

(g) Lack of any mechanism to prevent retraction of the droops at too low a speed after flap retraction.

8. *What steps ought to be taken to prevent a recurrence?*

The following steps ought to be taken to prevent a recurrence:

(a) A speed-operated baulk should be provided to prevent premature droop/slat retraction.

(b) Specific instruction and training should in future be given to Trident pilots on the following subjects:

   (i) The causes and results of a change of configuration stall.

   (ii) Circumstances in which the stick-shaker may operate almost simultaneously with the stick-pusher.

   (iii) The difference in design concept between the stick-shaker and stick-pusher mechanisms.

(c) The attention of pilots should be drawn to the possibility and dangers of subtle as well as obvious pilot incapacitation.

(d) Young trainee pilots should be given more experience than at present on the flight deck of the aircraft before being permitted to operate as P2 on passenger-carrying flights.

(e) The possibility of using 'stress test' electrocardiograms should be kept under review.

(f) Consideration should be given to the question whether it is desirable to allow the P4 seat to be occupied during critical stages of flight by anyone except a person having a flight function to perform or under training.

(g) Pilot's folding arm-rests on the Trident should be kept in the stowed position during take-off, initial climb, approach and landing.

(h) BEA's Air Safety Branch should be revitalized and given more authority.

(i) Although strictly speaking it is not designed 'to prevent a recurrence', we recommend the provision of cockpit voice recorders on all civil passenger-carrying aircraft of more than 27 000 kg auw.

9. *Were all proper steps taken by the rescue services after impact to save life?*

Yes.

Summary of Conclusions

The immediate causes of the accident were these:

(1) A failure by Captain Key to achieve and maintain adequate speed after noise-abatement procedures.

(2) Retraction of the droops at some 60 knots below the proper speed causing the aircraft to enter the stall regime and the stick-shaker and pusher to operate.

(3) Failure by the crew to monitor the speed errors and to observe the movement of the droop lever.

(4) Failure by the crew to diagnose the reason for the stick-pusher operation and the concomitant warnings.

(5) The dumping by the crew of the stall recovery system.

The underlying causes were these:

(1) The abnormal heart condition of Captain Key leading to lack of concentration and impaired judgement sufficient to account for his

toleration of the speed errors and to his retraction of, or order to retract, the droops in mistake for the flaps.

(2) Some distraction, the nature of which is uncertain, possibly due to the presence of Captain Collins as a passenger on the flight deck, which caused S/O Ticehurst's attention to wander from his monitoring duties.

(3) Lack of training directed at the possibility of 'subtle' pilot incapacitation.

(4) Lack of experience in S/O Keighley.

(5) Lack of knowledge in the crew of the possibility or implications of a change of configuration stall.

(6) Lack of knowledge on the part of the crew that a stick-shake and push might be experienced almost simultaneously and of the probable cause of such an event.

(7) Lack of any mechanism to prevent retraction of the droops at too low a speed after flap-retraction.

Recommendations and Observations

We recognize and applaud the fact that the parties, and particularly BEA, have already taken steps to implement in advance much of what follows:

1. The dangers inherent in premature retraction of the leading-edge droops or slats are demonstrably so great that a speed-operated baulk to prevent such retraction is required and we so recommend.
2. We recommend that specific instruction and training should in future be given to pilots on the following subjects:
   (a) The causes and results of a 'change of configuration' stall.
   (b) Circumstances in which the stick-pusher may operate almost simultaneously with the stick-shaker.
   (c) The difference in design concept between the stick-shaker and the stick-pusher mechanisms.
3. We recommend that the carrying of cockpit voice recorders should as soon as is practicable be made a mandatory requirement on all civil passenger-carrying aircraft of more than 27 000 kg auw.

4. We suggest that the attention of pilots should be drawn to the possibility and dangers of subtle as well as obvious pilot incapacitation.

5. We recommend that young trainee pilots should be given more experience than at present on the flight deck of the aircraft before being permitted to operate as P2 on passenger-carrying flights. The extent of that extra experience should be the subject of discussion between airline and CAA. It should be enough to give the trainee the opportunity of seeing a variety of crews flying operational sectors before he himself acts as P2.

6. We recommend that should the 'stress-test' electrocardiogram in future become significantly more reliable it should be substituted for the present 'resting' ECG. This matter should be kept under review.

7. We question the desirability of allowing the P4 seat to be occupied during critical stages of flight by anyone except a person having a flight function to perform or under training.

8. We suggest that pilots' folding arm-rests on the Trident should always be kept in the stowed position during take-off, initial climb, approach and landing.

9. We suggest that BEA should consider whether their Air Safety Branch could not be made more effective by giving the Air Safety Officer greater authority to direct investigation of potentially dangerous incidents. There are at present, it seems to us, too many different organizations concerned in this vital matter, with the result that responsibility and enthusiasm may be diluted.

10. We suggest that CAA should encourage closer co-operation between their operational and airworthiness branches.

TABULATED CHRONOLOGY OF THE L

Seconds from start of take-off	*Events*
0	Brakes off[1]
42	Rotation
44	Unstick
54	
63	Autopilot engagement
74	Start of left turn
83	*Bealine 548 is climbing as cleared
85	*548 airborne at 09 contact 128.4 Goodday
90	*Roger
93	Flap selected up (start of noise-abatement)
100	*Bealine 548 is climbing as cleared passing 1500
103	*548 climb to FL 60 squawk 6615 (flap fully retracted)
108	*Up to 60
114	Droop selected up
116	Autopilot disengagement – stick-shake and first stick-push
122	Droop retracted[1]
124	Second stick-push[1]
127	Third stick-push[1]
128	Stick-push 'dump' operated[1]
130	Last reliable IAS and altitude
134	IAS on lower stop
150	Impact

Notes:

1. These events deduced from flight recorder data.
2. Inaccurate due to aircraft altitude change.
3. Estimated altitude.

HT OF TRIDENT G-ARPI 18 JUNE 1972

	Time						
conds n start ake-off	*dT*	*GMT*	***Pilot's indicated alt QFE***	***Indicated airspeed knots***	***Hdg °M***	***Pitch att***	***Bank angle*** [5]
0	0	1608:30	0	54[4]	277	0.4	–0.7
42	42	1609:12	2[2]	144	277	4.6	–0.7
44	2	1609:14	79[2]	145	276	11.6	–0.4
54	10	1609:24	99	163	275	14.4	+2.8
63	9	1609:33	355	170	272	14.4	–0.7
74	11	1609:44	690	170	272	14.4	–10.5
83	9	1609:53	989	172	256	15.5	–20.0
85	2	1609:55	1064	171	252	15.5	–20.7
90	5	1609:60	1239	169	241	14.8	–21.8
93	3	1610:03	1339	168	236	15.5	–22.5
100	7	1610:10	1566	165	221	16.2	–22.1
103	3	1610:13	1637	160	215	15.8	–23.2
108	5	1610:18	1708	158	203	14.1	–20.7
114	6	1610:24	1772	162	191	14.4	–21.4
116	2	1610:26	1788	162	188	13.4	–24.3
122	6	1610:32	1637	170	179	0.7	–4.6
124	2	1610:33	1562	177	180	5.6	+3.5
127	3	1610:36	1403	182	182	–2.5	+4.6
128	1	1610:37	1360	187	184	1.8	9.5
130	2	1610:39	1276	193	186	3.5	+16.2
134	4	1610:43	1200[3]	54[4]	185	31.3	+6.7
150	16	1611:00	—	54[4]	217	–6.0	+14.1

4. Lowest figure that can be recorded.
5. Minus indicates left bank. Plus indicates right bank.
6. Underlined words indicate timing points.

* Radio calls.

BIBLIOGRAPHIES

Case Study 1

Annual survey — *Railway accidents: report to the Secretary of State for the Environment on the safety record of the railways in Great Britain during the year*, Annual, HMSO (Until 1970, the report was made to the Minister of Transport; until 1968, it was . . . 'on the accidents which occurred on the railways . . .' Railway Inspectors' reports on individual accidents are issued by the Department of the Environment formerly Ministry of Transport – and published by HMSO).

1957 Level crossing protection report — Ministry of Transport and Civil Aviation, and British Transport Commission. *Report on level crossing protection based on a visit to the Netherlands, Belgian and French railways by officers of the Ministry . . .*, HMSO, 14 p.

1958 — 'Level crossings in Great Britain: their history, the law today and future practice', *Engineering*, June 27, pp. 811–813.

1959 — Ministry of Transport and Civil Aviation, *The highway code, including motorway rules,* HMSO, Nov., 34 p.

1961 — 'First BR automatic level crossing barriers', *Railw. Mag.,* Vol. 107, April, pp. 235–236.

Langley, P. A. *Level crossing protection,* Institution of Railway Signal Engineers, 98 p.

1965 — Stevenson, I. D. 'Railway level crossing protection', *NZ Eng.*, Vol. 20, no. 11, Nov., pp. 452–460 (means of warning, superiority of half arm barrier).

1966 — McClelland, E. 'Level crossings', *Perm. Way Inst. J.,* Vol. 84, part 3, pp. 188–197.

Requirements of the Minister of Transport in regard to automatically operated half-barriers at public level crossings (July 1966), MoT, July (Reproduced in 'Hixon report', pp. 129–136).

Explanatory note on the requirements (July 1966) for automatic half-barrier protection at level crossings, MoT, July (Reproduced in 'Hixon report', pp. 128–129).

1967 — British Rail. *Automatic level crossing half-barriers will operate at Hixon, near Colwich, Staffs. on Sunday 2 April 1967* (Leaflet bound into 'Hixon report' between pages 142 and 143).

Railways, level crossings (automatic half-barriers), *Hansard,*

Vol. 742, HC Debate, March 6, col. *228* (Question on number of accidents and warning policy).

Richards, H. A. *Rail-highway grade crossing safety evaluation,* Texas Transp. Inst., 73 p. (PB–180 703).

1968
Hixon accident
January 6

Half-barrier level crossings (accidents), *Hansard*, Vol. 759, HC Debate, Feb. 29, col. *413* (10 year figures).

'Automatic half barrier crossings', *Mod. Railw.,* Vol. 24, no. 234, March, pp. 117–119.

Hixon
Inquiry report

Report of the public inquiry into the accident at Hixon level crossing on January 6th 1968, HMSO, 154 p.

'Collision at Hixon level crossing', *Railw. Gaz.,* Vol. 124, August, pp. 631–632.

'Rockets all round in Hixon report', *Commer. Mot.,* Vol. 127, August 2, p. 15+.

'Hindsight after Hixon, *Railw. Mag.,* Vol. 114, Sept., p. 521.

'Hixon verdict', *Mod. Railw.,* Vol. 24, no. 240, Sept., pp. 449–450.

'Accident report – Hixon level crossing, London Midland Region', *Mod. Railw.,* Vol. 24, no. 240, Sept., pp. 453–454.

Schoppert, D. W. *et al. Factors influencing safety at highway-rail grade crossings* . . . Nat. Res. Council, Nat. Coop. Highw. Res. Program report 50. 113 p., 248 refs. (Review of human factors considerations in improved protection devices, new signs, etc.).

1969

Richards, R. A. *et al.* 'The diagnostic team approach to rail-highway grade crossing safety evaluation', *Highw. Res. Rec.,* no. 272, pp. 1–13.

Schultz, T. G. *et al.* 'Evaluation of rail-highway grade crossing protection in rural areas', *op. cit.,* no. 272, pp. 14–23.

'Level crossings on high speed railways', *Railw. Gaz.,* Vol. 125, May 2, pp. 342–343.

'Aftermath of Hixon', *op. cit.,* Vol. 125, Oct. 3, p. 746+.

'Half-barrier level crossings', *Hansard,* Vol. 792, HC Debate, Dec. 2, col. *241* (cost: pre-Hixon £8 600, post-Hixon £13 000).

Ministry of Transport. *The highway code,* HMSO, 50 p.

1970

Baluch, H. 'Method of the optimum design of the crossing arrangement', *Rail. Int.,* Vol. 1, no. 9, Sept., pp. 601–612.

'Additional safeguards for level crossings', *Railw. Mag.*, Vol. 116, Oct., pp. 551–552.

'Modified auto half-barriers are commissioned', *Railw. World*, Oct., pp. 437–438.

Eicher, J. P. *The railway-highway interaction: a model for evaluating safety for presentation at Operations Research Society, Detroit, 1970,* US Federal Highway Administration, 16 p.

Schneider, A. and Mase, A. *Railway accidents of Great Britain and Europe: their causes and consequences,* David and Charles, 334 p.

1971

Hopkins, J. B. and Hazel, M. E. *Technological innovation in grade crossing protective systems,* US Dept. of Transportation, Cambridge, Mass., 89 p. (PB–201 624).

US Federal Railroad Administration. *Railroad-highway safety, pt. 1: A comprehensive statement of the problem: report to Congress . . .,* Nov., 95 p. (PB–206 792).

1972

Sanders, J. H. *Speed profiles and time delay at rail-highway grade crossings, Final report,* BioTechnology Inc., May, 152 p.

US Federal Railroad Administration. *Railroad-highway safety, pt. 2: Recommendations for resolving the problem: report to Congress . . .,* Aug., 108 p. (PB–213 115/0).

1973

Halagera, R. T. 'The initial evaluation and priority setting analysis of rail-highway crossing improvements', *Chicago Area Transp. Study Res. News,* July, pp. 4–13.

Halagera, R. T. and Miller, N. S. *Economic analysis of grade crossing improvements,* Chicago Area Transportation Study, Dec., 55 p. (CATS 313–05).

Sanders, J. H. *et al. Human factors countermeasures to improve highway-railway intersection safety: final report . . .,* BioTechnology Inc. (PB–223 416/9).

1974

ANSI Standard D8.1. *Railroad-highway grade crossing warning systems,* Am. Nat. Stand. Inst., 32 p. (components, layout, general evaluations).

Department of the Environment. *Proposed new highway code,* Green paper, HMSO, 72 p. (Supplement, Feb. 1975, 4 p.).

Proceedings of 1974 National Conference on Railroad-Highway crossing Safety held at USAF Academy, Colo., Aug. 1974, US Dept. of Transportation, Washington DC, 101 p.

1975 Vassel, R. 'Automatic detection of obstacles at level crossings' (French), *Rev. Gen. Chemins Fer,* Jan., pp. 26–40.

'What progress for federal grade-crossing safety program?' *Railw. Track Struct.,* Vol. 71, no. 5, May, pp. 27–31.

Sanford, J. L. 'Reducing grade crossing hazards', *Am. Road Build.,* August, pp. 16–18.

Hopkins, J. B. *et al. A communication-link approach to actuation of grade-crossing motorist-warning systems,* Transp. Syst. Cent., Cambridge, Mass., 110 p. (PB–244 584/9ST).

Case Study 2

1927 Knox, G. 'Landslides in the South Wales valleys', *Proc. South Wales Inst. Eng.,* Vol. 43, no. 2, April 21, pp. 161–233.

Discussion (of Prof. Knox's paper), *op. cit.,* Vol. 43, no. 2, April 21, pp. 234–291.

1945 Technical Advisory Committee. *Coal mining: report of the Technical Advisory Committee . . .* Cmnd 6610, HMSO.

1955 National Coal Board, Advisory Committee on Reorganisation. *Report of the Advisory Committee . . .* NCB, 105 p.

1959 Watkins, G. L. 'The stability of colliery spoilbanks', *Colliery Eng.,* Vol. 36, no. 429, Nov., pp. 493–497 (reprinted in Vol. 43, 1966, pp. 459–463).

1964 Browne, H. 'Future of the South Wales coalfield', *Colliery Guardian,* Vol. 208, April 24, pp. 542–545.

Sanders, G. W. 'Management in a specialist's world', *op. cit.,* Vol. 209, Sept. 11, pp. 347–352.

Barker, R. 'Management of the future at colliery level', *op. cit.,* Vol. 209, Oct. 23, pp. 557–559.

Wilkie, J. F. 'Management practices', *op. cit.,* Vol. 209, Nov. 13, pp. 649–654.

1965

Nelson, J. R. 'The Fleck report and the area organisation of the National Coal Board'. *Public Adm.* Vol. 43, Spring, pp. 41–57.

'Refuse disposal', *Colliery Eng.,* Vol. 42, Oct., pp. 444–445.

1966

Tucker, R. H. 'Changing pattern of mine management', *Min. Eng.,* Vol. 125, May, pp. 527–532.

Disaster
Oct. 21

'We told them the lot would fall', *Sunday Times,* Oct. 23, pp. 4–5.

Aberfan disaster, *Hansard,* Vol. 734, HC Debate, Oct. 24, col. 643–649.

Aberfan disaster (Tribunal), *op. cit.,* Vol. 734, HC Debate, Oct. 27, col. 1315–1320.

Potter, D. 'Aberfan', *New Society,* Oct. 27, pp. 638–639.

Aberfan disaster (Tribunal), *Hansard,* Vol. 735, HC Debate, Nov. 1, col. 254–264.

Morton, J. 'Television and Aberfan', *New Society,* Nov. 10, pp. 726–727.

Lowe, H. J. 'Colliery waste: a national or local problem?', *Town Ctry. Plann.,* Vol. 34, Dec., pp. 511–512.

Inquiry
1966–67

(Aberfan inquiry – coverage of sittings) *Colliery Guardian,* Vol. 213, Dec. 2 1966, pp. 707–709/Dec. 9 1966, pp. 739–740/Vol. 214, Jan. 20 1967, p. 70/Jan. 27 1967, pp. 94–95/Feb. 3 1967, p. 124+/Feb. 10 1967, p. 152/Feb. 24 1967, pp. 208–209/March 3 1967, p. 236+/March 10 1967, p. 264+/April 21 1967, p. 430+.

(Aberfan inquiry – coverage of sittings) *Engineering,* Vol. 202, Dec. 9 1966, pp. 1004–1005/Vol. 203, Feb. 17 1967, p. 247/Feb. 3 1967, p. 161/March 10 1967, pp. 374–375/April 28 1967, p. 667.

1967

Simpson, D. N. 'Winds of change: Presidential address to the South Wales Institute of Engineers', *Min. Eng.,* Vol. 126, April, pp. 469–482 (history of mining in South Wales).

'What kind of heritage for Aberfan?', *Economist,* Vol. 224, July 15, pp. 196–197.

Inquiry
report

Tribunal Appointed to Inquire into the Disaster at Aberfan on October 21st 1966. *Report of the Tribunal . . .,* HL 316, HC 553, HMSO, 151 p. (*see also below,* 1969, Welsh Office . . .).

'Aberfan: no policy', *Economist,* Vol. 224, Aug. 5, p. 475.

'Aberfan: technical report', *Engineering,* Vol. 204, August 11, pp. 208–209.

'Report of the Aberfan Tribunal, pt. 6: Lessons and recommendations', *Colliery Guardian,* Vol. 215, August 11, pp. 144–148.

'Problems of scale', *Nature,* Vol. 215, Aug. 12, pp. 683–684.

Parsons, O. H. 'Aberfan report', *Labour Res.,* Vol. 56, Sept., pp. 149–151.

Aberfan disaster, *Hansard,* Vol. 751, HC Debate, Oct. 26, col. 1909–2014.

Barker, J. C. 'Premonitions of the Aberfan disaster', *Soc. Psych. Res. J.,* Vol. 44, Dec., pp. 169–181.

Austin, A. *Aberfan: the story of a disaster,* Hutchinson, 230 p.

England, E. O. *The mountain that moved,* Hodder & Stoughton, 93 p.

1968
Ruhr

Corner, J. T. 'Waste tip stabilisation in the Ruhr', *Colliery Guardian,* Vol. 216, March 1, pp. 250–253.

USA

Davies, W. E. 'Coal waste bank stability', *Min. Congr. J.,* Vol. 54, no. 7, July, pp. 19–24 (US Geol. Surv. survey of 60 banks – 38 showed signs of instability).

Howe, R. E. G. 'The Aberfan disaster', *Medico-Legal J.,* Vol. 36, pp. 107–121.

Smith, G. N. 'Coal spoil heaps: site investigation and stability analysis', *Colliery Guardian,* Vol. 216, August, pp. 585–586.

Smith, G. N. 'Soil mechanics and coal spoil heaps, pt. 1', *Min. Electr. Mech. Eng.,* Vol. 49, Sept., pp. 190–194.

Smith, G. N. 'Soil mechanics and coal spoil heaps, pt. 2: shear strength of soils', *op. cit.,* Vol. 49, Oct., pp. 212–216.

Smith, G. N. 'Soil mechanics and coal spoil heaps, pt. 3: stability of slopes', *op. cit.,* Vol. 49, Nov., pp. 231–234.

Woodland, A. W. 'Field geology and the civil engineer', *Proc. Yorks, Geol. Soc.,* Vol. 36, p. 531 (background to Aberfan discussed, pp. 564–574).

Coal tips, Glamorgan, *Hansard,* Vol. 775 HC Debate, Dec. 19, col. *470* (Question about six dangerous complexes).

Aberfan Disaster Fund. *The first report of the Aberfan Disaster Fund, covering the period 21st Oct. 1966 to Aug. 1968,* Aberfan.

Press Council. *The Aberfan inquiry and contempt of court: a statement by the Press Council,* Press Council, 20 p.

1969

Bishop, A. W. and Penman, A. D. M. 'Aberfan: technical aspects', *Proc. Inst. Civ. Eng.,* Vol. 42, Feb., pp. 317–318.

Bishop, A. W. 'Geotechnical aspects of the Aberfan disaster', *Civ. Eng. Public Works Rev.,* Vol. 64, August, pp. 764–765.

Alexander, D. W. 'For safety's sake – communicate', *Min. Eng.* Vol. 129, Dec., pp. 183–186.

Advisory Committee on Tip Safety. *Guidance notes for the initial inspection of disused tips,* HMSO, 20 p.

Mines and Quarries (Tips) Act, 1969, HMSO, 48 p.

Summers, J. *The disaster,* New English Library (Novel).

Reports submitted to Tribunal

Welsh Office. *A selection of technical reports submitted to the Aberfan Tribunal*, 2 volumes, HMSO, 218 p. (Text plus portfolio).

1971

'Spoil heaps', *Colliery Guardian,* Vol. 219, July, p. 326+ (stability).

Berry, J. P. 'Problems associated with the management of a large colliery', *Min. Eng.,* Vol. 131, Oct., pp. 1–10.

Draft Mines and Quarries (Tips) Regulations, 1971, Mines safety circular no. 271, HMSO, 12 p.

Mines and Quarries (Tips) Act, 1969, and Mines and Quarries (Tips) Regulations, 1971. Notification in respect of certain tipping operations, Mines and quarries form 319(T), HMSO, 2 p.

Mines and Quarries (Tips) Regulations, 1971. Book for record of defects, action taken, and operations affecting tip security, Mines and quarries form 320(T), HMSO, 52 p.

Mines and Quarries (Tips) Regulations, 1971. Book for record of refuse deposited on active classified tips, Mines and quarries form 321(T), HMSO, 52 p.

National Coal Board, Mining Department. *National Coal Board (production) codes and rules: tips: first draft,* NCB, 82 p.

1972

Smalley, I. J. 'Boundary conditions for flowslides in fine-particle mine waste tips', *Trans. Inst. Min. Metall.,* Vol. 81, Jan., pp. A31–A37.

Lawrence, J. A. 'Some properties of South Wales colliery

discards, parts 1–2', *Colliery Guardian,* Vol. 220, June 6, pp. 270–278/July, pp. 329–333.

Spears, D. A. and Taylor, R. K. 'The geotechnical characteristics of a spoil heap at Yorkshire Main Colliery', *Q. J. Eng. Geol.,* Vol. 5, pp. 243–263.

Thomson, G. M. *Colliery spoil tips – after Aberfan,* Institution of Civil Engineers, 60 p. (Inst. Civ. Eng. papers, no. 7522).

1973 Taylor, R. K. 'Compositional and geotechnical characteristics of a hundred year old colliery spoil heap', *Trans. Inst. Min. Metall.,* Vol. 82, Jan., pp. A1–A14.

Bishop, A. W. 'The stability of tips and spoil heaps', *Q. J. Eng. Geol.,* Vol. 6, pp. 335–376.

USA coal refuse dam failure Wahler, W. A. and Associates. *Analysis of coal refuse dam failure, Middle Fork Buffalo Creek, Saunders, West Virginia,* 2 volumes, Palo Alto, Wahler & Associates, 268 p and 198 p.

1974 Miller, J. B. *Aberfan: a disaster and its aftermath,* Constable, 207 p.

USA Wahler, W. A. and Associates. *Reconnaissance survey report of coal-mine refuse dumps and impoundments. Final report,* 6 volumes (PB–233 732–Set) (each volume deals with a State, e.g. Vol. 6: State of West Virginia; 312 p.).

1975 Joynes, F. J. 'Some thoughts on engineers, education and safety in the mining industry', *Min. Technol.,* Vol. 57, March, pp. 100–104.

Williams, R. M. and Parkes, C. M. 'Psychosocial effects of disaster – birth-rate in Aberfan', *Br. Med. J.,* Vol. 2, no. 5966, pp. 303–304.

Bell, F. G. (ed.) *Methods of treatment of unstable ground,* Newnes-Butterworth, 215 p.

1976 'Disaster at Buffalo Creek', *AM. J. Psychiatr.*, Vol. 133, March, pp. 295–316 (psychological and social effects of a disaster similar to that of Aberfan).

Cohen, D. 'Death of a township – the legal and psychiatric aftermath', *New Sci.,* Vol. 70, May 20, p. 397 (Buffalo Creek).

Case Study 3

1946 Ministry of Works. *Fire grading of buildings, part 1: General principles and structural precautions: report by a Joint Committee,* Post-war building studies no. 20, HMSO.

1948 British Standards Institution. *Code of basic data for the design of buildings: Chapter IV: Precautions against fire,* CP 3, Chapter IV, BSI. (Parts 1–3 issued in 1968 and 1971).

1949 Ministry of Works. *Fire grading of buildings . . . part 3: Personal safety,* in Post-war building studies no. 29, HMSO.

1950 *Local Government (Building Byelaws) Act,* HMSO.

1953 British Standards Institution. *Fire tests on building materials and structures: Part 1: Fire tests . . .,* BS476: Part 1: 1953, BSI (Definitions used in Manx bye-laws; superseded by Part 8: 1972).

1957 Cleveley, H. *It should never have happened: a book about notable fires,* Cassell, 177 p.

1958 British Standards Institution. *Fire tests on building materials and structures: Part 3: External fire exposure roof tests,* BS476: Part 3: 1958, BSI, 12 p.

1964 Ashton, L. A. 'Fire safety in buildings and the use of plastics', *Plast. Inst. Trans.,* Vol. 32, April, suppl., pp. J27–J32.

1965 Bindsley, B. 'Challenge of co-ordinated building communication', *RIBA J.,* Vol. 72, Feb., pp. 62–65.

Osborne, J. B. 'Communication between architect and contractor', *Builder,* Vol. 208, March 12, p. 583–585.

Ashton, L. A. 'Reinforced plastics and fire protection in buildings', *Reinf. Plast.,* Vol. 9, June, p. 298+.

Ashton, L. A. 'Fire regulations and plastics', in *Conf. on Plast. in Build. Struct.,* Plastics Institute, June, Paper 5.

Ackroyd, G. C. 'Plastics in building and fire insurance', in *Conf. on Plast. in Build. Struct.,* Plastics Institute, June, Paper 6.

Fire Protection Association. *Introduction to fire: nature, effects, and control,* Planning for fire safety in buildings ser. no. 1, FPA.

1966
Building Regulations, pt E Ministry of Public Building and Works. *Building regulations 1965,* HMSO, Jan. 1, 71 p. (Part E: Structural fire precautions).

Ward, E. J. 'Important new concepts in fire-precaution provisions', *Munic. Eng.,* Vol. 143, Jan. 21, pp. 119–120.

Ward, E. J. 'Building regulations analysed, part 3: New concepts shaping the fire precaution provisions', *op. cit.,* Vol. 143, Jan. 28, pp. 200–201.

'Interpretation of new building regulations', *Fire,* Vol. 58, March, p. 538+.

'Your guide to the building regulations: Part E (cont.): Structural fire precautions', *Master Build. J.,* Vol. 11, April, p. 35+.

'Solarium using plastics (Derby Castle)', *Arch. Build. News,* Vol. 229, May 11, p. 867.

Bullivant, D. (ed.) *Basic reference list on fire, for architects, surveyors and builders,* Planning for fire safety in building ser. no. 2, Fire Prot. Ass.

1967

Didsbury, F. 'Fire and the Building Regulations Part E and its relationship to means of escape', *Building,* Vol. 212, pp. 139–140 (need for uniformity in interpretation of various codes, e.g. Post-war building studies, BS CP3; Chapter IV, LCC, etc.).

Bliss, B. D. 'Why is it so difficult to relax the building regulations?', *Build. Tech. Manag.,* Vol. 5, April, pp. 16–17.

Langdon-Thomas, G. J. 'Fire regulations and the architect', *RIBA J.,* Vol. 74, July, pp. 286–290 (Sources of information for the architect).

Lawn, O. H. 'Administration of Building Regulations with special reference to relaxations', *Arch. Surv.,* Vol. 12, Sept./Oct., pp. 97–99.

Royal Institute of British Architects. *Handbook of architectural practice and management,* rev. edn., RIBA, 4 Vols.

1968

Barrett, G. H. 'Structural fire precautions and public safety', *Arch. Surv.,* Vol. 13, March/April, pp. 11–16.

Entwhistle, F. D. 'Relation of fire precautions to structural design and strength, parts 1–3', *Munic. Eng.,* Vol. 145, March 29, pp. 576–577/April 4, pp. 629–630/April 12, pp. 678–679.

'AJ Metric guide to the Building Regulations, 2: Part E: Structural fire precautions', *Arch. J.,* Vol. 148, July 10, suppl., pp. 37–76.

British Standards Institution. *Code of basic data for the design of buildings: Chapter IV: Precautions against fire: Part 2: Shops and department stores,* CP 3: Chapter IV: Part 2, BSI, 72 p.

British Standards Institution. *Code of basic data for the design of buildings: Chapter IV: Precautions against fire: Part 3: Office buildings,* CP 3: Chapter IV: Part 3: 1968, BSI, 60 p.

British Standards Institution. *Fire tests on building materials and structures: Part 5: Ignitability test for materials,* BS476: Part 5: 1968, BSI.

British Standards Institution. *Fire tests on building materials and structures: Part 6: Fire propagation test for materials,* BS476: Part 6: 1968, BSI, 17 p.

Greater London Council. *Places of public entertainment technical regulations,* new edn., GLC, 60 p.

1969

Kirby, D. 'Architects and fire protection', *RIBA J.,* Vol. 76, April, pp. 163–166.

'Designer's guide to information on fire protection', *op. cit.,* Vol. 76, April, p. 167.

'Perpetual sunshine for Manx holiday makers (Derby Castle)', *Surveyor,* Vol. 133, May 16, pp. 28–29.

Fire Protection Association. *Fire prevention design guide: a handbook for architects,* Planning for fire safety in buildings ser. no. 4, FPA, 80 p.

1970

Raynham, E. A. 'Flame propagation test and building regulations', *Build. Mat.,* Vol. 30, Jan., pp. 42–43.

'AJ Handbook, Building services and circulation, section 8: Circulation', *Arch. J.,* Vol. 151, March 18, pp. 689–703 (includes fire regulations).

Munro, J. H. 'History of fire prevention in buildings, parts 1–2', *Arch. Surv.,* Vol. 15, May–June, pp. 17–20/July–Aug., pp. 17–19.

'AJ Handbook, Building services and circulation, section 13: Security and fire', *Arch. J.,* Vol. 151, July 1, pp. 37–52/July 22, pp. 205–220/Aug. 5, pp. 323–334.

'Swimming baths at Derby Castle, Isle of Man', *Building,* Vol. 219, Aug. 14, pp. 49–52.

Jobling, P. 'Development of plastics in building and associated fire hazards', *Inst. Fire Quart.,* Vol. 30, Sept., p. 323–331.

Scott, K. A. 'Fire performance of plastics in buildings', *Brit. Polym. J.*, Vol. 2, Sept., pp. 244–248 (relevance of existing regulations and tests).

Symposium on thermoplastic glazing for space structures, London, Oct. 1970, (organized by) Williaam Cox and others.

British Standards Institution. *Fire tests on building materials and structures: Part 4: Non-combustibility test for materials,* BS476: Part 4: 1970, BSI, 12 p.

British Standards Institution. *Methods of testing plastics,* BS476 BS2782: 1970, BSI, 332 p. (Amendments to Flammability tests published July 17 1974, AMD 1524).

Rogowski, B. F. W. *The 'fire propagation' test: its development and application,* HMSO, 10 p.

Royal Institute of British Architects. *Management of building contracts,* RIBA.

1971

'Sunbathing in the rain (Summerland)', *Munic. J.,* Vol. 79, July 23, p. 1026.

Plans published

'Leisure centre at Douglas, Isle of Man', *Arch. J.,* Vol. 157, Sept. 22, pp. 633–648.

'Transparent plastic cladding: Summerland Solarium, Douglas', *op. cit.,* Vol. 157, Sept. 22, pp. 649–650 (working detail).

Malhotra, H. L. 'Fire behaviour of building materials', *Build. Int.,* Sept./Oct., pp. 275–279.

British Standards Institution. *Code of basic data for the design of buildings: Chapter IV: Precautions against fire: Part 1: Flats and maisonettes (in blocks over two storeys),* CP 3: Chapter IV: Part 1: 1971, BSI, 64 p.

British Standards Institution. *Fire tests on building materials and structures: Part 7: Surface spread of flame tests for materials,* BS476: Part 7: 1971, BSI, 20 p.

Fire Precautions Act, 1971, HMSO.

Ives, G. C. *et al. Handbook of plastics testing methods,* Iliffe.

Plastics Institute. *Conference on plastics in fire: building,* Plastics Institute and Agrement Board Conference.

Royal Institute of British Architects. *Working with your architect,* RIBA.

Williamson, J. J. *General fire hazards and fire prevention,* 6th edn., Pitman, 169 p.

1972

'Use of plastics in building – their performance in fires', *Dev. Mater. Bull.*, no. 56, June, pp. 1/1–1/8.

Parnell, A. C. *et al.* 'How the Fire Precautions Act affects the architect, parts 1–2', *Arch. J.*, Vol. 155, June 14, pp. 1339–1344/June 21, pp. 1393–1397.

Hodgkinson, A. 'Safety – fire protection', *op. cit.*, Vol. 155, June 21, pp. 1401–1404.

Wicker, G. L. 'Fire safety regulations for reinforced plastics', *Polym. Age,* Vol. 3, August, pp. 298–300 (British, American and German standard tests).

Hilado, C. J. 'Overview of the fire behavior of polymers', *Am. Chem. Soc., Div. Org. Coatings. Chem., Prepr.* Vol. 33, no. 1.

Hilado, C. J. 'Predicting limits for safe application of combustible materials', *ASTM Spec. Tech. Publ.,* no. 502, pp. 112–118.

Barley, S. *Fire: an international report*, Hamilton, 293 p.

British Standards Institution. *Fire tests on building materials and structures, Part 8: Test methods and criteria for the fire resistance of elements of building construction,* BS476: Part 8: 1972, BSI, 16 p. (Supersedes part 1).

Building Regulations 1972, SI 317, HMSO.

Lie, T. T. *Fire and buildings,* Applied Science Publishing, 276 p.

Langdon-Thomas, G. J. *Fire safety in buildings: principles and practice,* Black, 296 p.

Marchant, E. W. *A complete guide to fire and buildings,* Medical and Technical Publishing, 268 p.

Wood, P. G. *The behaviour of people in fires,* BRE Fire Research Note 953.

1973

Hanlon, J. 'Do routine tests guarantee fire safety?', *New Sci.,* Vol. 57, Jan. 25, pp. 176–178 (Dangers of plastics in building).

Kennington, J. A. 'Plastics and part E of the Building Regulations, 1972', *Plast. Polym.,* Vol. 41, Feb., pp. 34–38.

Malhotra, H. L. 'Significance of fire tests for plastics', *op. cit.,* Vol. 41, Feb., pp. 44–49.

Kelley, R. T. and Stevenson, W. W. 'Use of plastics in building, with particular reference to their performance in fires', *op. cit.*, Vol. 41, Feb., pp. 28–34.

Glover, J. G. 'Automatic sprinkler systems', *Build. Mater.*, March/April, pp. 26–31.

Read, T. and O'Brien, T. 'Glass fibre reinforced plastics for building claddings, Part 1: The material and its uses/Part 2: Translucent GRP/Part 3: Pigmented GRP', *Arch. J.*, Vol. 157, March 21, pp. 699–706/April 4, pp. 817–826/May 2, pp. 1035–1047.

Williams, M. 'Structural fire precautions, the changing scene', *Build. Technol. Manag.*, Vol. 11, April, p. 3+.

Fire precautions in buildings, *Elect. Rev.*, Vol. 192, no. 7, pp. 235–252 (Legislation, causes, alarms, escape, automatic systems).

Summerland fire, Aug. 2

Taylor, K. 'Isle of Man tragedy: Summerland's flaming tangle of advice and waivers', *New Civ. Eng.*, August 9, pp. 12–14.

'Summerland fire raises doubts over use of acrylics', *Building*, Vol. 225, Aug. 10, pp. 36–38, 55–56.

'Summerland', *Arch. J.*, Vol. 158, Aug. 15, pp. 345–347.

Scott, K. A. 'Plastics and society: fire', *Plast. Polym.*, Vol. 41, Oct., pp. 248–253.

Field, A. 'Fire defence systems, part 1: Selection criteria', *RIBA J.*, Vol. 80, Nov., pp. 567–573.

Holland, G. 'Fire defence systems, part 2: Specification in practice', *op. cit.*, Vol. 80, Nov., pp. 573–574.

Butcher, E. G. 'Fire hazards of plastics in building', *Arch. J.*, Vol. 158, Nov., pp. 1181–1184.

Fire risks (polymeric materials), *Hansard*, Vol. 866, HC Debate, Dec. 19, pp. *315–316*.

Designing to survive Disaster, Conference, Illinois Inst. of Technol. Res. Inst., Chicago, Nov. 1973, IITRI, 283 p. (Human responses in disasters; designing to minimize effects).

Fire-resistance requirements for buildings: a new approach: proceedings of the symposium held ... London, Sept. 1971, HMSO, 89 p.

National Joint Consultative Committee of Architects, Quantity

Surveyors and Builders. *Client's guide: the role of the client in the design of buildings,* RIBA, 23 p.

Royal Institute of British Architects. *Architect's job book,* 2nd edn., RIBA.

Royal Institute of British Architects. *Architectural practice and management handbook,* RIBA, 440 p.

1974

Harms, H. 'User involvement: towards a new professionalism', *RIBA J.,* Vol. 81, Feb., pp. 26–29.

Rubin, A. I. *Occupant behavior in building fires,* US National Bureau of Standards, Tech. note 818, Feb.

Harmathy, T. Z. 'Design approach to fire safety in buildings', *Progr. Arch.,* April, pp. 82–87.

Butcher, G. 'Smoke control and pressurisation of escape routes', *Arch. J.,* Vol. 159, May 22, pp. 1159–1164.

Inquiry report, May

Report of the Summerland Fire Commission, Government Office, Isle of Man, 85 p.

Kelly, R. 'Design control failure blamed: Summerland inquiry: architects are blasted', *Build. Des.,* no. 202, May 24, pp. 1, 40.

'Summerland: the lessons', *Arch. J.,* Vol. 159, May 29, pp. 1177–1178.

'Summerland: the analysis, the course of the disaster, the blame, the recommendations', *op. cit.,* Vol. 159, May 29, pp. 1183–1188.

Lenssen, S. 'Summerland disaster report', *New Civ. Eng.,* May 30, pp. 10–11.

Eastham, G. 'Summerland – the fatal errors', *Building,* Vol. 226, May 31, pp. 42–45.

'Why 50 people died', *Fire,* Vol. 67, June, suppl., pp. i–viii.

'Summerland – the anatomy of disaster', *RIBA J.,* Vol. 81, July, pp. 3–23.

Phoenix. 'Summerland – the aftermath', *Fire,* Vol. 67, July, p. 70+.

Emmons, H. 'Fire and fire protection', *Sci. Am.,* Vol. 231, July, pp. 21–27 (Need to evaluate the entire system potentially involved in a fire).

Summerland Fire, *Hansard,* Vol. 876, HC Debate, July 9, pp. *454–455* (Government involved in 'consultations and considerations').

British Standards Institution. *Amendment slip no. 3, published*

17 July 1974 to BS2782: 1970, Methods of testing plastics, part 5: Miscellaneous methods, methods 508A to 508E: Flammability, AMD 1524, BSI, 10 p.

Cooke, G. M. E. 'Structural fire precautions', *Consult. Eng.*, Vol. 38, Sept., p. 34+.

Sullivan, P. J. E. 'Structural design for fire', *op. cit.*, Vol. 38, Sept., p. 45–47.

Greater London Council, Department of Architecture and Civic Design, Building Regulations Division. *Code of practice, means of escape in case of fire,* GLC, 138 p.

Phoenix. 'New London code on means of escape', *Fire,* Vol. 67, Nov., p. 285+.

Jefferson, B. 'Should the Institute monitor competence?', *RIBA J.*, Vol. 81, Dec., pp. 10–12.

'Looking hard at the profession at work', *op. cit.*, Vol. 81, Dec., pp. 20–21.

British Standards Institution. *Plastic domelights,* BSI, 69 p. (Technical help to exporters, special investigation report).

Fire Protection Association. *Fire and the architect,* FPA.

MacEwen, M. *Crisis in architecture,* RIBA, 111 p.

Silcock, A. and Hinkley, P. *Report on the spread of fire at Summerland in Douglas on the Isle of Man, 2 August 1973,* BRE current paper, CP74/74.

1975

Harper, D. 'Implications of the Summerland report', *Build. Tech. Manage.*, Vol. 12, no. 12, Dec. 1974, and Vol. 13, no. 1, Jan. 1975, p. 29.

Hart, R. J. *et al.* 'Summerland disaster', *Br. Med. J.*, Vol. 1, no. 5952, p. 256+.

'Design for fire safety', *Building,* Vol. 228, Jan. 17, pp. 97–128 (articles include Developing the architect's work plan; The provision of information and advice; The future of building regulations; Fire protection and the fire authority; Availability of fire testing; Fire bibliography, etc.).

Pring, J. L. 'Sprinkler system engineering', *Build. Serv. Eng.*, Vol. 43, April, pp. 301–313.

MacEwen, M. 'What can be done about architectural incompetence?', *Arch. J.*, Vol. 162, Nov. 19, pp. 1063–1084.

Addeson, L. *Materials for building, vol. 4: Heat and fire and their effects,* Newnes-Butterworth, 181 p.

Department of the Environment. *Structural fire precautions: guidance note,* HMSO, 74 p.

Fire safety of combustible materials: international symposium, Oct. 1975 . . . Univ. Edinburgh Centre for Industrial Consultancy and Liaison, 401 p.

Results of fire resistance tests on elements of building construction, compiled by R. W. Fisher and P. M. T. Smart, rev. edn., HMSO, 165 p.

Case Study 4

1952 British Standards Institution. *Code of functional requirements of buildings: Chapter 5: Loading,* CP3: BSI, 3 p.

Ministry of Housing and Local Government. *Model byelaws, series IV, buildings,* HMSO.

1953 *Annotated model byelaws, Vol. 1: Buildings* . . . 10th edn., Knight, 194 p.

1958 Clark, C. 'The economics of high building', *Town & Ctry. Plann.,* Feb., pp. 73–75

Ministry of Housing and Local Government, *Flats and houses, 1958: Design and economy,* HMSO, 154 p.

1961 Ministry of Housing and Local Government. *Homes for today and tomorrow,* HMSO, 92 p.

1962 'Larsen and Nielsen system of building', *Arch.,* Vol. 222, no. 20, pp. 727–730.

Symposium on the design of high buildings: proceedings of a meeting held in September 1961 . . ., OUP, 517 p.

McKaig, T. H. *Building failures: case studies in construction and design,* McGraw-Hill, 261 p.

1963 Scruton, C. and Newberry, C. W. 'On the estimation of wind loads for building and structural design', *Proc. Inst. Civ. Eng.,* Vol. 25, June, pp. 97–126 (recommended in Ronan Point Inquiry report).

'System Building 14: The Larsen Nielsen system of load-bearing crosswall construction', *Builder,* Vol. 204, pp. 1155–1156.

Aldershot collapse

Building Research Station. *The collapse of a precast concrete building under construction for the Ministry of Public Building and Works: Technical statement . . .,* HC 1963–64, No. 36, HMSO, 20 p. (Aldershot Mess buildings).

Craig, C. N. *Multi-storey flats: design, building methods and costs,* National Building Studies, spec. reports, no. 34, HMSO.

Wind effects on buildings and structures: proceedings of the conference held at the National Physical Laboratory, Teddington, 1963, NPL, Symposia, no. 16, HMSO, 2 Vols.

1964

McMeekin, R. D. 'Review of industrialised building', *Struct. Eng.,* Vol. 42, no. 2, Feb., pp. 63–72.

Brock, G. 'Tall flats: factors affecting construction and design', *Struct. Concr.,* Vol. 2, March/April, pp. 65–71.

Humphreys, E. F. J. 'Tall Flats: history and development', *op. cit.,* Vol. 2, March/April, pp. 54–64.

Rupert, D. 'Meeting the challenge: industrialised building', *op. cit.,* Vol. 2, March/April, pp. 91–96.

'Industrialised homes to be built in London and Sunderland: Larsen and Nielsen system adopted by Taylor Woodrow-Anglia Ltd', *Surveyor,* Vol. 123, May 16, pp. 67–68.

Hefford, J. J. V. 'The collapse of a block of flats under construction in Paris', *Builder,* Vol. 206, no. 6298, p. 247.

White, T. T. 'Gas services in industrialised buildings', *Indust. Build.,* Vol. 1, Sept., pp. 28–31.

Yee, A. A. 'Domino system for high-rise buildings', *J. Prestressed Concr. Inst.,* Vol. 9, no. 6, Nov., pp. 60–74.

1965

Bendixson, T. 'Industrialised building: social and economic background', *Design,* April, pp. 35–38.

Honikman, B. 'Need for a critical appraisal of industrialised building', *Off. Arch. Plann.,* Vol. 28, August, p. 1123+.

Ministry of Housing and Local Government. *Industrialised housebuilding,* Circular 76/65, HMSO, Dec.

Bor, W. G. *High buildings policy,* Liverpool City Planning Dept., 71 p.

Shellard, H. C. *Extreme wind speeds over the United Kingdom during periods ending 1963,* Meteorological Office Climatological Memorandum no. 50, HMSO (recommended in Ronan Point Inquiry report).

White, R. B. *Prefabrication: a history of its development in Great Britain,* National Building Studies, Special reports, no. 36, HMSO, 354 p.

1966

Ministry of Public Building and Works. *Building regulations, 1965,* HMSO, Jan. 1, 71 p.

Honikman, B. 'Critical appraisal of industrialised building', *Off. Arch. Plann.,* Vol. 29, Jan., p. 123+.

Jones, A. 'Efficient teamwork essential to success in system building', *Munic. Eng.,* Vol. 143, May 20, p. 1045+.

'Industrialised – building systems with factory-made components: tall buildings, parts 1–2', *Concr. & Constr. Eng.,* Vol. 61, May, pp. 173–183/June, pp. 217–222.

Barr, A. W. C. 'Industrialised building', *J. R. Soc. Arts,* Vol. 114, June, pp. 554–572 (Author was Chief Architect, NBA. Origin of IB and effect on client organization, manufacture, construction and design).

Lewicki, B. *Building with large prefabricates,* Elsevier, 460 p.

1967
CEB report

Comité Européen du Béton. *International recommendations for the design and construction of large panel structures,* CEB, March (French – translated July 1968, Cement and Concrete Association. 'House of cards' warning.)

Skerrett, B. 'Gas and industrialised housing', *Inst. Gas Eng.,* Vol. 7, Sept., pp. 670–681.

Pike, A. 'Failure of industrialised building in housing programme', *Arch. Des.,* Vol. 37, Nov., pp. 507–509.

Akroyd, T. N. W. 'Building regulations, structural safety and codes of practice', *Arch. & Surveyor,* Vol. 12, Nov./Dec., pp. 122–124.

Wood, K. M. 'Technological development and its effect on designer/constructor relationships', *Build. Technol. & Manage.,* Vol. 5, Dec., p. 21 (summary).

Symposium on industrialised building and the structural engineer, London, May 1966, Institution of Structural Engineers, 332 p. (BRS warning on hazards of joints in system blocks).

Stevenson, A. *et al. High living: a study of family life in flats,* Melbourne UP, 172 p.

1968

Diamant, R. M. E. *Industrialised building,* Butterworth, 3 Vols.

Field, J. *Construction failure,* Wiley, 399 p.

Regional Advisory Council for Technological Education for London and Home Counties. *Safety in the design and construction of buildings: report of a sub-committee . . .,* 18 p.

Shinozuka, M. *et al.* 'Dynamic safety analysis of multi-storey buildings', *Proc. Am. Soc. Civ. Eng. (J.Struct. Div.)* Vol. 94, No. ST1, pp. 309–330.

Ronan Point collapse, May 16

'Point-block disaster', *Arch. J.,* Vol. 147, May 22, pp. 1125–1127.

Frischmann, W. W. and Copp, P. W. 'Stability of tower blocks', *New Sci.,* Vol. 38, May 23, p. 388.

'Collapse of flats: explosion in high-rise IB building, Newham', *Building,* Vol. 214, May 24, p. 134.

'Safety in high blocks', *Nature,* Vol. 218, May 25, p. 718.

Cowan, H. J. 'Bridging the inter-professional gap', *RIBA J.,* Vol. 75, June, pp. 272–273.

'Ronan Point inquiry', *Building,* Vol. 214, June 28, p. 87.

Clark report

Report of Structural Considerations on Partial Collapse of Ronan Point. Preliminary Report (issued 27 May), M. A. R. Louks (Solicitor) Bernard L. Clark & Partners (Consulting Engineers) published July 5, 26 p.

Report of Structural Considerations on Partial Collapse of Ronan Point. Preliminary Report (issued May 27) M. A. R. Louks (Solicitor) Bernard L. Clark & Partners (Consulting Engineers), published July 15, 10 p.

'Ronan Point – must gas be penalised?', *Gas J.,* Vol. 335, August 21, pp. 181–182.

'Ronan Point lack of continuity at joint', *Surveyor,* Vol. 132, August 23, pp. 17–19.

'After Ronan Point: nationwide precautionary measures', *Building,* Vol. 215, August 23, pp. 85–86.

'Decline and fall of Ronan Point', *Private Eye,* no. 175, Aug. 30, pp. 192–193.

Ministry of Housing and Local Government. *Clever Road Development, Ronan Point. The Structural Safety of the Building prior to the Explosion on 16th May 1968. A Report on an Examination undertaken for the Tribunal of Inquiry,* MOHLG, Sept., 23 p.

Building Research Station. *Wind loading on buildings,* Digest 99, HMSO, Nov. 1.

Inquiry report, Nov.

Report of the inquiry into the collapse of flats at Ronan Point, Canning Town; presented to the Minister of Housing and Local Government by Hugh Griffiths (and others), HMSO, 71 p.

Ronan Point Flats (Report), *Hansard,* Vol. 772, HC Debate, Nov. 6, col. 902–910.

'Aftermath of Ronan Point', *Arch. J.,* Vol. 148, Nov. 13, pp. 1111–1113.

'Ronan Point prompts . . . urgent review of codes of practice', *Contract J.,* Vol. 226, Nov. 14, p. 211.

Stone, H. P. 'Flats collapse tip of iceberg of potential building failures? Ronan Point report', *Munic. Eng.* Vol. 145, Nov. 15, pp. 2297–2298.

'Ronan Point', *Building,* Vol. 215, Nov. 15, pp. 131–134, 153–154.

'Ronan Point collapse: design faults', *Surveyor,* Vol. 132, Nov. 15, p. 42+.

Ministry of Housing and Local Government. *Flats constructed with precast concrete panels. Appraisal and strength of existing high blocks; design of new blocks,* Circular 62/68, HMSO, Nov. 15.

Institution of Structural Engineers. *Structural stability and the prevention of progressive collapse,* and *Notes for guidance on Ministry of Housing and Local Government circular 62/68,* Technical reports RP/68/01 and RP/68/02, ISE.

'Ronan Point aftermath (MOHLG's standards)', *Building,* Vol. 215, Nov. 22, pp. 107–108.

'Windy future for high buildings (BSI, BRS, NPL)', *Engineering,* Vol. 206, Nov. 22, pp. 756–759.

'Ronan Point, who is to blame?', *Nature,* Vol. 220, Nov. 23, pp. 733–734.

Newby, F. 'Ronan Point aftermath continues', *Arch. J.,* Vol. 148, Nov. 27, pp. 1243–1244.

'Standards for Ronan Point-type flats', *Contract J.,* Vol. 226, Nov. 28, p. 465+.

'Closer look at Ronan Point', *Building,* Vol. 215, Nov. 29, p. 83.

'Failure of a high-rise system: how safe should the structure really be?', *Archit. Rec.,* Vol. 144, No. 5, Nov., pp. 169–170.

'Systems appraisal (NBA)', *Off. Arch. Plann.,* Vol. 31, Nov., pp. 1428–1431.

'New standards for Ronan Point-type tower blocks', *Civ. Eng. Publ. Wks. Rev.,* Vol. 63, Dec., p. 1355.

'Structural behaviour of Ronan Point', *Concr.,* Vol. 2, Dec., pp. 488–491.

'Repercussions from the failure of a sub-standard brass nut', *op. cit.,* Vol. 2, Dec., pp. 480–481.

Ronan Point flats (Tribunal's findings), *Hansard,* Vol. 774, HC Debate, Dec. 3, col. *403–404.* (Minister's qualifications, especially over BRE's alleged failures.)

Wilson, N. 'High-rise is inevitable', *Arch. Build. News,* Dec. 4, p. 36–39.

Bate, S. C. C. (Letter), *Munic. Eng.,* Vol. 145, Dec. 13, p. 2530.

Ministry of Housing and Local Government. *Flats constructed with precast concrete panels. Appraisal and strength of existing high blocks; design of new blocks,* Circular 71/68, HMSO, Dec. 20 (approves and encloses Institution of Structural Engineers' comments on MOHLG's circular 62/68).

Institution of Structural Engineers. *Guidance on the design of domestic accommodation in loadbearing brickwork and blockwork to avoid collapse following an internal explosion,* Technical report RP/68/03, ISE.

1969

Building Research Station. *Wind loadings on buildings, 2–3,* Digests 101 and 105, HMSO.

Yallop, H. J. 'Ronan Point: the detective work', *New Sci.,* Vol. 41, Jan. 9, pp. 75–77.

Alonso, W. *et al. In-Cities Experimental Housing Research and Development Project. Innovations in Housing Design and Construction Techniques as applied to Low-cost Housing: A Collateral Literature Survey,* Kaiser Engineers, Oakland, Calif, March, 210 p. (PB–184 164).

'GLC starts to strengthen high system flats', *Surveyor,* Vol. 133, March 21, pp. 50–51.

'Larsen-Nielsen flats', *Building,* Vol. 216, March 21, pp. 121–122.

Davies, R. M. 'Progressive collapse: some notes on the present position and thoughts from an engineering point of view', *Syst. Build. Des.,* April, pp. 37–45.

Short, A. and Miles, J. R. 'Introduction to the new Code of Practice for large panel construction', *Concr.,* Vol. 3, April, pp. 121–123.

'Strengthening system-built blocks of flats', *op. cit.,* Vol. 3, April, pp. 119–120.

Short, A. and Miles, J. R. *Large-panel structures: notes on the draft addendum 1 to CP 116,* Tech. paper PCS 47, Concr. Soc., May 12, 12 p. (repr. BRS current paper 30/69).

'Strengthening tall blocks', *Building,* Vol. 216, June 13, p. 126.

'Implications of Ronan Point', *RIBA J.,* Vol. 76, June, p. 250.

Entwisle, F. D. 'Inadequate jointing: major cause of building collapse', *Munic. Eng.,* Vol. 146, July 11, pp. 1369–1371.

Institution of Structural Engineers. *Aims of structural design,* ISE, August.

Rodin, J. 'Statistical design against progressive collapse', *Consult. Eng.,* Vol. 33, August, pp. 66–68.

Reynolds, I. and Nicholson, C. 'Living off the ground', *Arch. J.,* Vol. 150, Aug. 20, pp. 459–470.

'TW solution to progressive collapse', *Ind. Build.,* Vol. 6, Sept., pp. 22–25.

Rasbash, D. J. 'Explosions in domestic structures, pt. 1: Relief of gas and vapour explosions in domestic structures', *Struct. Eng.,* Vol. 47, Oct., pp. 404–408 (also in *J. Inst. Heat. Vent. Eng.,* Vol. 37, Oct., pp. 142–146).

Stretch, K. L. 'Explosions in domestic structures, pt. 2: Relationship between containment characteristics and gaseous reactions', *Struct. Eng.,* Vol. 47, Oct., pp. 408–411 (also in *J. Inst. Heat. Vent. Eng.,* Vol. 37, Oct., pp. 146–149).

Diamant, R. M. E. 'Improved jointing and gas in Ladywood job', *Ind. Build.,* Vol. 6, Dec., pp. 28–29.

Pume, D. 'Structural behaviour of members and connections in large panel buildings', in Int. Assoc. Bridge and Struct. Eng., *Symposium on concepts of safety of structures and methods of design, London, 1969, final report*, pp. 222–229.

1970

'Cutting the chances of another Ronan Point tragedy', *Engineer*, Vol. 230, no. 5947, Jan. 15, pp. 38–39.

Alexander, S. J. and Hambly, E. C. 'Design of structures to withstand gaseous explosions', pts. 1–2, *Concr.*, Vol. 4, Feb., pp. 62–65/March, pp. 107–116.

Building (Fifth Amendment) Regulations, SI 109, HMSO.

Hodgkinson, A. 'What the post-Ronan Point building regulations mean', *Arch. J.*, Vol. 8, Feb. 25, p. 473.

Institution of Structural Engineers. *The Building (Fifth Amendment) Regulations 1970: Notes for discussion*, Technical report RP/68/04, ISE.

Entwisle, F. D. 'Urgent need for up-to-date comprehensive code (on wind pressure)', *Munic. Eng.*, Vol. 147, March 13, pp. 512–513.

Sibmac Proceedings. Proceedings of the 2nd International Brick Masonry Conference, Stoke-on-Trent, April 12–15 1970. (Papers on brickwork and gas explosions.)

Astbury, N. F. *et al.* 'Experimental gas explosions in brick buildings', *Building*, Vol. 218, April 17, p. 107+.

Fraser, J. S. 'The Building (Fifth Amendment) Regulations', *Building*, Vol. 218, April 24, pp. 90–100.

Arup, O. 'Architects, engineers and builders', *J. R. Soc. Arts*, Vol. 118, June, pp. 390–401.

Building Research Station. *The assessment of wind loads*, Digest 119, 12 p (replaces digests 99, 101, 105).

Stringer, P. 'Responsible to whom?', *RIBA J.*, Vol. 77, Nov., p. 521+.

USA

Pfrang, E. O. *Guide criteria for the evaluation of Operation Breakthrough housing systems, volume 1: Multifamily high rise*. National Bureau of Standards, Dec. 1, 577 p. (PB 212 055).

Greenfield, F. C. *et al.* 'Large-panel construction in a London Borough (Brent)', *Concr.*, Vol. 4, Dec., pp. 443–447.

Smith, B. S. 'Recent developments in the methods of analysis for tall building structures', *Civ. Eng. Public Works Rev.*, Vol. 65, Dec., p. 1417+.

British Standards Institution. *Code of basic data for the design of buildings, Chapter V: Loading, part 2: Wind loads*. BSI (revision of 1952 edn.).

British Standards Institution. *Large-panel structures and structural connections in precast concrete. Addendum no. 1 (1970) to CP 116: 1965 and CP 116: Part 2: 1969, The structural use of precast concrete,* BSI, 19 p.

Darke, J. *Health and environment: high flats,* Univ. Working paper 10, Centre for Environmental Studies, 34 p.

Institution of Structural Engineers. *The Resistance of buildings to accidental damage,* Technical report RP/68/05, ISE.

Ministry of Housing and Local Government. *Family living at high density: a study of estates . . .,* Design Bull., No. 21 (spec. issue), 69 p.

Morton, F. *Report of the inquiry into the safety of natural gas as a fuel,* HMSO, 88 p.

Stewart, W. F. R. *Children in flats: a family study,* NSPCC.

1971

'New Code of Practice for wind loads and its implications for the structural design codes', *Struct. Eng.*, Vol. 49, Feb., pp. 98–101.

'Resistance of buildings to accidental damage (progressive collapse): London Building (Constructional) Amending By-Laws, 1970', *Dev. Mater. Bull.*, March, pp. 4/1–10 (reproduced in full, with Notes for Guidance).

Rothblatt, D. N. 'Housing and human needs', *Town Plann. Rev.*, Vol. 42, April, pp. 130–144 (harmful effects of high-rise living).

Smolira, M. 'How safe are tall buildings?', *Conrad,* Vol. 2, no. 4, pp. 194–201.

'Integrating the design team: report of the NJCC Engineering Advisory Group', *Building,* Vol. 220, April 30, p. 64.

Ravetz, A. 'The history of a housing estate: Quarry Hill flats', *New Soc.*, May 27, pp. 907–910 (lessons of its planning failures).

Zienkewicz, O. C. 'Three-dimensional analysis of buildings composed of floor and wall panels', *Proc. Inst. Civ. Eng.*, Vol. 49, July, pp. 319–332.

Fry, J. F. 'Gas explosions attended by fire brigades in dwellings', *J. Inst. Fuel,* Vol. 44, Aug./Sept., pp. 470–471.

Brondum-Nielsen, T. 'Prevention of structural collapse', *Build. Int.,* Sept./Oct., pp. 280–283.

Jameson, C. 'Human specification in architecture: a manifesto for a new approach', *Arch. J.,* Vol. 154, Oct. 27, pp. 919–941.

Haseltine, B. A. 'Explosion-proof buildings would be totally uneconomic', *Munic. Eng.,* Vol. 148, Nov. 12, pp. 2139–2140.

Terner, I. D. 'Lessons from failure: a housing innovations agenda', *Ind. Forum,* Vol. 2, No. 3, Dec., pp. 19–30.

Construction Industry Research and Information Association, Study Committee on Structural Safety. *Report . . .,* CIRIA, 24 p. (Chairman: Sir Alfred Pugsley).

Canada Ferahian, R. H. *Design against progressive collapse,* Nat. Res. Council Canada, Div. Build. Res., Tech. pap. no. 332, 30 p. (background data; recommendations; British 1970 Build. Regs.).

TW history Jenkins, A. *On site, 1921–1971,* Heinemann, 226 p. (Taylor Woodrow Ltd).

Jephcott, P. *Homes in high flats,* Oliver & Boyd, 208 p.

Austria Panzhauser, E. *The danger to tall buildings due to internal explosions with special reference to prefabrication.* Osterreichisches Institut für Bauforschung, Forschungsberich 76 (in German).

Spyer, G. *Architect and community: environmental design in an urban society,* Peter Owen, 168 p.

1972 Creasy, L. A. 'Stability of modern buildings', *Struct. Eng.,* Vol. 50, Jan., pp. 3–6.

Hodgkinson, A. 'Structural safety: building legislation and structural safety', *Arch. J.,* Vol. 155, Jan., pp. 1287–1291.

'Inhuman high-rise apartments', *Ekistics,* April, pp. 296–299.

Lind, N. C. and Basler, E. 'Safety level decisions', in *Preprints from ASCE–IABSE Int. Conf. Plann. & Des. Tall Buildings, Lehigh Univ., Penn., Aug. 1972,* Vol. 1b–10, pp. 55–64.

Moses, F. and Tichy, M. 'Safety analysis for tall buildings', in *Preprints ASCE–IABSE Int. Conf. Plann. & Des. Tall Buildings, Lehigh Univ., Penn., Aug. 1972,* Vol. 1b–10, pp. 89–101.

Bruce, R. D. 'Gas services in high-rise buildings', *Build. Serv. Eng.,* Vol. 40, no. 9, pp. 131–138 (statutory requirements, codes and safety precautions).

Bartle, P. R. 'Partial stability: problems of progressive collapse', *Construction,* no. 3, Sept., pp. 2–4.

British Standards Institution. *Code of basic data for the design of buildings, Chapter V: Loading, part 2: Wind loads,* BSI, Sept., 49 p. (information additional to 1970 revision).

Hanlon, J. 'Ronan Point: four years after', *New Sci.,* Vol. 56, Oct. 19, pp. 158–159.

'More troubles with tower blocks: bulging brick panels', *Arch. J.,* Vol. 156, Nov. 1, p. 993.

'Ronan Point: the antidote', *Contract J.,* Vol. 250, Nov. 30, p. 52.

Proceedings 8th Systems Building Seminar: Planning and design of tall buildings with emphasis on fire and life safety systems, Kentucky Univ., College of Engineering, Dec., 64 p. (Pb–219 288/8).

Building Regulations 1972, SI 317, HMSO.

1973

Mainstone, R. J. *The hazard of internal blast in buildings,* Current paper CP11/73, Build. Res. Stn.

Barr, C. *et al.* 'Five views of industrialised building', *Built Environ.,* Vol. 2, Jan., pp. 12–16.

Martin, B. 'Systems of building', *Built Environ.,* Vol. 2, Jan., pp. 17–20.

'Missing the point: Ronan Point is the symbolic spearhead of a £25m attempt at bolt-on safety', *Build. Des.,* no. 134, Jan. 19, p. 14.

Beckmann, P. 'Investigations of structural failures', *Arup J.,* Vol. 8, no. 1, March, pp. 2–5.

'Progress in structures: collapse in large panel structures', *BRE News,* no. 23, Spring, pp. 8–9.

Coull, A. and Smith, B. S. 'Structural analysis of tall concrete buildings', *Proc. Inst. Civ. Eng.,* pt. 2, Vol. 55, March, pp. 151–166.

Entwhistle, F. 'Building failure: why it is a modern phenomenon'. *Build. Maint.,* Vol. 7, no. 3, May/June, pp. 22–27.

Pugsley, A. 'The prediction of proneness to structural accidents', *Struct. Eng.*, Vol. 51, no. 6, June, pp. 195–196.

Majid, K. I. and Onen, Y. H. 'Elasto-plastic load analysis of complete building structures', *Proc. Inst. Civ. Eng.*, pt. 2, Vol. 55, Sept., pp. 619–634.

Smith, B. S. and Rahmann, K. M. K. 'Theoretical study of the sequence of failure in precast panel shear walls', *Proc. Inst. Civ. Eng.*, pt. 2, Vol. 55, Sept., pp. 581–592.

Designing to survive disaster, Conf., Ill. Inst. Technol. Res. Inst., Chicago, Nov. 1973, IITRI, 283 p.

Leach, S. J. and Bloomfield, D. P. 'Ventilation in relation to toxic and flammable gases in buildings', *Build. Sci.,* Vol. 8, no. 4, Dec., pp. 289–310.

1974

McGuire, W. 'Prevention of progressive collapse', in *Reg. Conf. Tall Build., Proc., Bangkok. Jan. 1974,* pp. 851–865.

Allsop, B. 'Whose-fault?', Extracts from 'Toward a humane architecture', *RIBA J.,* Vol. 81, March, pp. 18–26.

Hirst, M. J. S. 'The structural platform of large panel buildings and design against progressive collapse', *Build. Int.,* Vol. 7, no. 3, May–June, pp. 253–263.

MacGinty, L. 'Rise and fall of the high-rise block', *New Sci.,* Vol. 63, Sept. 9, pp. 723–725.

Buildings and the hazard of explosion: proceedings of the BRE symposium, Garston, Oct. 1972, BRE, 75 p.

Bate, S. C. C. 'Structural failures', *Arch. Surv.,* Vol. 19, Nov.–Dec., pp. 7–9.

Building Design Partnership. *A treatment of structural safety of buildings taking account of consequences of failure – summary report,* Current paper CP63/74, BRE.

MacEwen, M. *Crisis in architecture,* R. Inst. Br. Arch., 111 p.

Mainstone, R. J. *The hazards of explosions, impact and other random loadings on tall buildings,* Current paper CP64/74, BRE (read at ISE/IABSE Conf. *Tall buildings and people,* Oxford, 1974).

Sutcliffe, A. (ed.) *Multi-storey living: the British working class experience,* Croom Helm, 249 p.

Newberry, C. W. *Wind loading handbook*, HMSO, 74 p. (guide and expansion to BS CP3: Chapter V: Part 2: 1972, *Wind loads*).

Taylor, N. and Alexander, S. J. *Structural damage in buildings caused by gaseous explosions and other accidental loadings,* Current paper CP 45/74, BRE (Statistics from 2 year survey as base for new design regulations).

1975 Freeman, I. L. 'Building failure patterns and their implications', *Arch. J.,* Vol. 161, no. 6, Feb. 5, pp. 303–308.

Malpass, P. 'Professionalism and the role of architects in local authority housing', *RIBA J.,* Vol. 82, June, pp. 6–29.

Bate, S. C. C. 'Structural failures', *Chart. Surv. Build. Quant. Surv. Q.,* Vol. 3, no. 1, Autumn, pp. 8–11 (Failure and collapses of buildings).

Entwhisle, F. D. 'Building regulations: the role of the structural engineer', *Struct. Eng.,* Vol. 53, Dec., pp. 543–544.

1976 Scott, G. *Building disasters and failures,* Construction Press, 169 p.

Case Study 5

1956 Hammond, R. *Engineering structural failures: the causes and results of failure in modern structures of various types,* Odhams, 224 p.

1958 *Symposium on the Failure and Defects of Bridges and Structures, Tokyo, 1957, Proceedings,* Japan Society for the Promotion of Science, 110 p.

1959 Freeman, R. and Otter, J. R. H. 'The collapse of the second Narrows Bridge, Vancouver', *Proc. Inst. Civ. Eng.,* Vol. 12, April, pp. N36–N41.

Hrennikoff, A. 'Lessons of the collapse of Vancouver second Narrows Bridge', *Proc. Am. Soc. Civ. Eng., J. Struct. Div.,* Vol. 85, no. ST10, Dec., pt. 1, paper 2305, pp. 1–20.

1962 Short, W. D. 'Accidents on construction work with special reference to failures during erection or demolition', *Struct. Eng.,* Vol. 40, no. 2, Feb., pp. 35–43.

1963 Victoria. Royal Commission of Inquiry into the failure of Kings Bridge. *Report,* Melbourne, Govt. Printer, 115 p.

1966

Kerensky, O. A. 'Recent developments in highway bridge design and construction', *J. Inst. High. Eng.,* Vol. 13, July, pp. 16–33.

1967

'Australia's longest clear span will be stayed girder bridge', *Eng. News-Rec.,* Vol. 178, no. 5, Feb. 2, pp. 32–33 (Lower-Yarra design outline).

Merchant, W. 'Three structural failures: case notes and general comments', *Proc. Inst. Civ. Eng.,* Vol. 36, March, pp. 499–505.

Shepherd, R. and Sidwell, G. K. 'Dynamic behaviour of Yarra River Bridge, Melbourne', *NZ Eng.,* Vol. 22, no. 3, March, pp. 109–111.

Short, W. D. 'Structural collapses during erection or demolition', *Proc. Inst. Civ. Eng.,* Vol. 36, March, pp. 507–522.

Galambos, T. V. *et al.* 'Trends in the design of steel box girder bridges', *Proc. Am. Soc. Civ. Eng. (J. Struct. Div.),* Vol. 93, no. ST3, pp. 165–180.

'Melbourne's Lower Yarra Bridge will be Australia's biggest', *Aust. Civ. Eng. Constr.,* Vol. 8, no. 5, May, p. 15+.

'Calder disaster', *Consult. Eng.,* Vol. 31, Sept., pp. 49–51.

'Structural models in action', *Engineering,* Vol. 204, no. 5300, pp. 790–791 (model tests for Yarra Bridge).

1968

Fountain, R. S. and Mattock, A. H. 'Composite steel-concrete multi-box girder bridges', *Proc. Can. Struct. Eng. Conf.,* Toronto, Feb., pp. 19–53.

Short, W. D. 'Study of bridge failures in the UK', *Highw. Public Works,* Vol. 36, June, p. 12+.

Pugsley, A. 'The safety of bridges', *Struct. Eng.,* Vol. 46, no. 7, pp. 197–201.

Cox, M. E. 'Milford Haven bridge', *Highw. Public Works,* Vol. 36, Dec., p. 39+.

Parr, D. H. *An ultimate strength analysis of box girder highway bridges,* New Mexico State U., 121 p.

1969

Brundan, W. 'Milford Haven high level bridge', *Civ. Eng. Public Works Rev.,* Vol. 64, Feb., pp. 118–119.

Shirley-Smith, H. 'Disasters in bridges and dams', *Adv. Sci.,* Vol. 25, June, pp. 386–390.

International Association for Bridge and Structural Engineering. *Symposium on concepts of safety of structures and methods of design,* final report, London.

Walshe, D. E. *The aerodynamic investigation for the proposed Lower Yarra Bridge – supplement,* National Physical Laboratory, 9 p.

1970

Brown, K. 'Erskine Bridge nears completion', *Engineering,* Vol. 209, May 22, pp. 523–525.

Milford Haven collapse, June
Yarra collapse, Oct.

'Loading in collapse range (Milford Haven)', *Consult. Eng.,* Vol. 34, Oct., pp. 36–37.

'Kerensky speaks out', *Consult. Eng.,* Vol. 34, Oct., pp. 37–38.

'Melbourne bridge: question mark over advanced design', *Contr. J.,* Vol. 237, Oct. 22, pp. 847–848.

Phillips, M. 'Design of the bridges that failed (Milford Haven and Yarra)', *Engineering,* Vol. 210, Oct. 23, pp. 419–421.

'West Gate bridge collapse in Melbourne', *Civ. Eng. Public Works Rev.,* Vol. 65, Nov., p. 1329.

1971

'Yarra Inquiry', *Consult. Eng.,* Vol. 35, Jan., pp. 21–23.

McKay, C. 'Composite bridge deck construction using steel hollow trapezoidal girders', *J. Inst. Highw. Eng.,* Vol. 18, Feb., pp. 5–16.

Chapman, J. C. *et al.* 'Structural behaviour of steel and concrete box girder bridges', *Struct. Eng.,* Vol. 49, March, pp. 111–120.

'Safe as houses?', *Economist,* Vol. 239, June 19, p. 79.

Lenssen, S. 'Downfall of the box-girder bridge?', *New Sci.,* Vol. 50, June 24, pp. 741–743.

'Erskine Bridge passes safety check', *Contr. J.,* Vol. 241, June 24, p. 788.

Davis, D. 'Bridge of sighs, Melbourne', *Surveyor,* Vol. 138, July 16, p. 39.

Manser, M. 'Bridging the Clyde', *Design,* July, pp. 70–77.

Scott, A. 'Slim strength across the Clyde', *Engineering,* Vol. 211, August, pp. 550–555.

Yarra Inquiry report, August

Victoria. Royal Commission into the Failure of the West Gate Bridge. *Report,* Melbourne, 143 p.

'Why the Yarra bridge collapsed (Royal Commission of Inquiry)', *Contr. J.*, Vol. 242, August 19, p. 735.

'Yarra – the burden of responsibility', *op. cit.*, Vol. 242, August 26, pp. 859–861.

'Yarra: final report', *Consult. Eng.*, Vol. 35, Sept., pp. 36–38.

Merrison interim report and appraisal rules, Sept.

Committee on Steel Box Girder Bridges. *Inquiry into the basis of design and method of erection of steel box girder bridges,* Interim report (Abridged version), HMSO, 22 p. (Chairman: A. W. Merrison).

Committee of Investigation into the Design and Erection of Steel Box Girder Bridges. *Criteria for the assessment of steel box girder bridges with particular reference to the bridges at Milford Haven and Avonmouth. Appendix A: interim design appraisal rules 1 September 1971,* Department of the Environment (Scottish Headquarters), 114 p.

'Merrison orders double check on bridge designs', *Contr. J.*, Vol. 243, Sept., pp. 100–102.

'Merrison interim', *Consult. Eng.*, Vol. 35, Oct., pp. 39–40.

Douglas, R. H. R. and Port, S. R. 'Determination by computer of reinforcement in box-girder bridges', *Civ. Eng. Public Works Rev.*, Vol. 66, Nov., pp. 1215–1218.

Hazards in construction: proceedings of the conference held at the Institution of Civil Engineers, November 1971, Inst. Civ. Eng., 106 p.

Koblenz collapse, Nov.

'Something's wrong (Koblenz collapse)', *Economist*, Vol. 241, Nov. 13, p. 92.

'Koblenz Bridge failure raises fresh doubts over box girder designs', *Contr. J.*, Vol. 244, Nov. 18, pp. 264–265.

'Box girder bridges: the current position', *Building,* Vol. 221, Dec. 10, p. 75.

Rockey, K. C. *et al.* (ed.) *Developments in bridge design and construction: proceedings of the international conference . . .,* University College of South Wales and Monmouthshire, March 29 to April 2, Lockwood, 616 p.

1972

'Koblenz November 1971', *Consult. Eng.*, Vol. 36, Jan., pp. 23–24.

Kerensky, O. A. *et al.* 'Erskine bridge', *Struct. Eng.*, Vol. 50, April, pp. 147–170.

'Box girder blues', *Economist,* Vol. 243, April 29, p. 88.

'Merrison design rules will aim for safety plus simplicity', *Contr. J.,* Vol. 247, May 4, pp. 22–23.

Box girder bridges, *Hansard,* Vol. 836, HC Debate, May 12, col. 1807–1816.

'Research in retrospect', *Consult. Eng.,* Vol. 36, June, p. 41+.

Das, P. C. 'Analysis of box-type structures', *Proc. Inst. Civ. Eng.,* pt. 2, Vol. 53, June, pp. 19–40.

Maquoi, R. and Massonnet, C. 'Lessons learned from accidents which occurred to four large steel box girder bridges', *An. Trav. Publics Belg.,* no. 2, 1971–72, pp. 69–84 (French).

1973

Steel box girder bridges: proceedings of the International Conference organised by the Institution of Civil Engineers in London, 13–14 February 1973, Inst. Civ. Engrs., 315 p.

'Coping with Merrison', *Contr. J.,* Vol. 251, Feb. 8, pp. 26–27.

Allinson, W. 'Steel box girders for bridges', *Met. Constr. Br. Weld. J.,* Vol. 5, Feb., pp. 43–49.

Harper, W. J. and Upstone, T. J. 'Side trends towards the big lift', *Contr. J.,* Vol. 251, Feb. 22, pp. 21–23.

Bradney, D. 'Box-girder bridges – what price safety?', *Munic. Eng.,* Vol. 150, Feb., p. 257.

Knowles, P. R. 'Steel box girder bridges', *Highw. Des. Constr.,* Vol. 41, April, pp. 34–35.

Atkinson, I. 'Huntworth – in the Merrison mode', *Contr. J.,* Vol. 254, Aug. 9, pp. 22–23.

Loddon Inquiry report, August

Report of Her Majesty's Factory Inspectorate on the collapse of falsework for the viaduct over the River Loddon on 24 October 1972, HC paper 425, HMSO, 54 p.

'Loddon Bridge – why it fell', *Economist,* Vol. 248, August 25, p. 68.

Merrison recommendations (cont.), Sept.

Committee of Inquiry into the Basis of Design and Method of erection of steel box-girder bridges. *Inquiry . . . report of the Committee,* Abridged version, HMSO, 33 p. *Appendix 1: Interim design and workmanship rules, Pt. 4: Materials and workmanship,* 38 p. *Appendix 1: Interim design and workmanship rules, Pt. 1: Loading and general design requirements, Pt. 2: Design rules,* 225 p.

Maisel, B. I. *et al.* 'Concrete box girder bridges', *Struct. Eng.*, Vol. 51, Oct., pp. 363–376.

Patey, D. 'Box girder delays', *Contr. J.*, Vol. 255, Oct. 4, pp. 40–41.

Atkinson, I. 'Avonmouth: anatomy of a gap', *op. cit.*, Vol. 256, Nov. 1, pp. 28–29.

Davies, J. D. *Famous failures and structural safety: inaugural lecture delivered at the University College of Swansea on Dec. 4 1973*, UCS, 24 p.

1974 Merrison (cont.)

Committee of Inquiry into the basis of Design and Method of Erection of Steel Box-Girder Bridges. *Inquiry . . . report of the Committee. Appendix 1: interim design and workmanship rules, Pt. 3: Basis for the design rules and for the design of special structures not within the scope of part 2*, HMSO, 128 p.

Wolfram, H. G. and Toakley, A. R. 'Design modifications to West Gate Bridge, Melbourne', *Inst. Eng. Aust. Civ. Eng. Trans.*, Vol. CE 16(2), pp. 143–150.

'Avonmouth bridge: main span closure', *Highw. Road Constr.*, Vol. 42, April, pp. 4–7.

Dubas, P. 'Safety considerations concerning the buckling of box girders', *Schweiz. Bauztg.*, Vol. 92, no. 33, August 15, pp. 769–773 (in German).

Culver, C. G. 'Steel box girder bridges: ultimate strength considerations', *Proc. Am. Soc. Civ. Eng., J. Struct. Div.*, Vol. 100, no. 12, Dec., pp. 2433–2448.

1975

Jones, B. H. 'Probabilistic design and reliability', *Compos. Mater.*, Vol. 8, pp. 33–72 (Structural design criteria; over- and under-design).

Catastrophe theory

Thompson, J. M. T. 'Experiments in catastrophe', *Nature*, Vol. 254, April 3, pp. 392–395.

Gmund collapse, May

Ferguson, H. 'Concrete box deck jack-knives in Austria', *New Civ. Eng.*, no. 144, May 22, pp. 8–9.

Studzinski, S. H. *et al.* Application of the Merrison report: Appraisal and strengthening of Coombe Lane flyover, *Proc. Inst. Civ. Eng.*, Pt. 1, Vol. 58, Aug., pp. 401–410.

Dowling, P. J. 'Strength of steel box-girder bridges', *Proc. Am. Soc. Civ. Eng.*, J. Struct. Div., Vol. 101, no. 9, Sept., pp. 1929–1946 (review of UK research).

Catastrophe theory

Stewart, I. 'The seven elementary catastrophes', *New Sci.*, Vol. 68, Nov. 20, pp. 447–454 (incls. collapse of box-girder bridges).

Institution of Structural Engineers, *Communication of structural design: a report of the ISE,* 16 p.

1976 Walker, A. and Sibley, P. 'When will an oil platform fail?', *New Sci.,* Vol. 69, Feb. 12, pp. 326–327 (discusses box-girder bridges).

Brown, W. C. Platform risks (letter), *New Sci.,* Vol. 69, Feb. 26, p. 465 (author, from Freeman Fox and Partners, attacks I. Stewart's and A. Walker's *New Sci.* articles, and Merrison Committee conclusions).

Case Study 6

Annual survey *Casualties to vessels and accidents to men: vessels registered in the United Kingdom, return for . . .,* HMSO (Supersedes *Shipping casualties and deaths,* and *Deep sea trawlers: casualties to vessels and accidents to men*).

1957 Ministry of Transport and Civil Aviation. *The Merchant Shipping Act, 1894: report of Court no. 7999: M.V. 'Traquair' ON 16720,* HMSO, 4 p.

1965 *International Convention for the Safety of Life at Sea, 1960: London, 17 June 1960 . . .,* Cmnd 2812, HMSO, 388 p.

IMCO Code Inter-governmental Maritime Consultative Organization. *Code of safe practice for bulk cargoes including ores and similar bulk cargoes, concentrates and similar materials,* IMCO (revised in 1972).

Gaches, P. L. 'Bulk sea carriage of ore concentrates and thixotropic commodities', *Q. Trans. R. Inst. Nav. Arch.,* Vol. 107, no. 4, Oct., pp. 529–538 (Difficulties in rough weather and how overcome).

Manley, C. V. 'Merchant ship losses – a general review', *Q. Trans. R. Inst. Nav. Arch.,* Vol. 107, no. 4, Oct., pp. 539–548.

1966 Waters, J. M. *Rescue at sea,* Van Nostrand, 264 p. (US Coast Guard, Search and Rescue Division).

1967 Bonwick, G. J. *Lifeboat handbook,* 12th edn., Maritime Press, 99 p.

Inter-governmental Maritime Consultative Organization. *Merchant ship position reporting systems,* IMCO, 15 p.

1968 Barnaby, K. C. *Some ship disasters and their causes,* Hutchinson, 272 p.

Thomas, R. E. *Stowage: the properties and stowage of cargoes,* 6th edn., Brown & Ferguson, 562 p.

1969 Work of IMCO in maritime safety, *Shipbuild. Shipp. Rec.,* Vol. 114, Sept. 26, pp. 31–33.

Whiteside, H. N. E. 'Marine safety', *Trans. Inst. Mar. Eng.,* Vol. 81, Dec., pp. 405–409 (International requirements and organizations, ship losses 1958–67, life-saving appliances).

Committee of Inquiry into Trawler Safety. *Trawler safety: final report . . .,* Cmnd 4114, HMSO, 168 p.

Inter-governmental Maritime Consultative Organization. *International code of signals, 1969 . . .* HMSO, 149 p.

1970 Committee to Review the Marine Search and Rescue Organization of the United Kingdom. *Marine search and rescue organisation: report . . .* HMSO, 49 p.

MERSAR Inter-governmental Maritime Consultative Organization. *Merchant ship search and rescue manual,* IMCO, 54 p.

Report of International North Atlantic Air and Surface Search and Rescue Seminar, Oct. 26–29 1970, N.Y., US Dept. of Transportation, 116 p. (AD–722 191).

1971 'Coast guardians', *Flight Int.,* Vol. 99, April 8, p. 502.

Covich, P. 'New approaches to safety for shipboard systems', *Nav. Eng. J.,* Vol. 83, no. 4, August 1971, pp. 85–90 (System safety techniques and the development of shipboard systems).

Fagerberg, B. and Stavang, A. 'Determination of critical moisture contents in ore concentrates carried in cargo vessels', *Proc. 1st Int. Symp. Transp. & Handl. Miner., Vancouver, Oct. 1971,* pp. 174–186 (Plus further six pages of discussion).

Guerra, F. 'The transportable moisture limit for the transportation of ore concentrates in vessels', *Proc. 1st Int. Symp. Transp. & Handl. Miner., Vancouver, Oct. 1971,* pp. 192–200.

Admiralty list of radio signals, Vol. 1: Coast radio stations, 1971, Hydrographer of the Navy, 299 leaves.

Brook, N. *Mechanics of bulk materials handling,* Butterworth, Pantech Press, 176 p.

Department of Trade and Industry, Standing Advisory Committee on the Carriage of Dangerous Goods in Ships. *Carriage of dangerous goods in ships: report . . .* 2nd edn., HMSO, 304 p. (The Blue Book).

Post Office. *Handbook for radio operators working installations licensed by Ministry of Posts and Telecommunications,* 13th edn., incorporating Amendment no. 1, HMSO, 250 p.

Scarlett, B. *Shipminder: the story of Her Majesty's Coastguard,* Pelham, 207 p.

1972 Burtonia founders, Nov.

Madsen, S. A. 'Aviation/Marine: a study of contrast', in *Amer. Pet. Inst., Div. Transp., Ann. Tanker Conf., 17th Coronado, Calif., May 1972,* pp. 193–223.

National Transportation Safety Board. *Survivor-locator systems for distressed vessels, Special study,* NTSB, Aug. 16, 26 p. (PB–211 867).

Danton, G. C. *The theory and practice of seamanship,* 4th edn., Routledge & Kegan Paul, 542 p.

Hydrographic Department. *Admiralty notices to mariners in force on 1st January 1972,* Hydrogr. Dept., 156 p.

Revised IMCO code

Inter-governmental Maritime Consultative Organization. *Code of safe practice for bulk cargoes, including ores and similar bulk cargoes, concentrates and similar materials,* rev. edn., IMCO (Prev. edn. 1965).

Parker, J. D. *Present and future systems of navigation in maritime distress, search and rescue,* in Adv. Mar. Navig. Aids, Int. Conf., London, July 1972, IEE Conf. Publ. 87.

1973

Miles, S. 'Shipwreck and survival', *Shipp. World Shipbuild.,* Vol. 166, Jan., p. 55+.

National Research Council, Maritime Transportation Research Board, *Human error in merchant marine safety: interim report,* Nat. Acad. Sci., June, 15 p.

Stewart, J. P. 'Basic causes of marine casualties', *Tanker & Bulk Carrier,* Vol. 20, June, p. 18+.

Earl, G. E. *Munro's seamanship primer: containing the 1960 collision regulations, life-saving rules, grain rules and many official notices,* 11th edn., Munro, 129 p.

Farr, A. D. *Let not the deep: the story of the Royal National Life-Boat Institution,* Impulse Books, 210 p.

1974 Inquiry report, July 31

The Merchant Shipping Act 1894, report of Court no. 8062, MV 'Burtonia' (ON 300222), formal investigation, HMSO, 46 p.

Summaries of report

''Burtonia' owners partly to blame for loss of ship', *Lloyd's List,* Aug. 1, p. 1.

'Findings of Court of Inquiry into loss of MV 'Burtonia', *Trade & Ind.,* Aug. 8, pp. 271–272.

(Editorial on 'Burtonia'), *Lifeboat,* Vol. 43, Autumn, p. 199.

'Burtonia findings', *Coastguard,* Vol. 8, no. 4, Oct., p. 107.

Loughton, A. 'The AMVER system', *Port of London,* Sept., pp. 285–287.

Francey, J. B. 'Life saving appliances: the historical development', *Mar. Week.,* Vol. 1, no. 33, Dec. 6, pp. 31–32.

McDonald, G. J. 'Maritime radio – still some serious deficiencies', *op. cit.,* Vol. 1, no. 33, Dec. 6, pp. 34, 37–38.

US Coast Guard. 'AMVER revolutionises search and rescue operations', *op. cit.,* Vol. 1, no. 33, Dec. 6, pp. 38–41.

'Automatic marker buoy pin points distressed ships', *op. cit.,* Vol. 1, no. 33, Dec. 6, p. 51.

International Conference on Safety of Life at Sea, 1974: final act of the Conference, with attachments, including the International Convention for the Safety of Life at Sea, 1974, IMCO, 36, 266 p.

Malster, R. *Saved from the sea: the story of life-saving services of the East Anglian coast,* Dalton, 296 p.

Martin, N. *Search and rescue: the story of the Coastguard Service,* David and Charles, 95 p.

Warner, O. *The life-boat service: a history of the Royal National Life-Boat Institution, 1824–1974 . . .* Cassell, 321 p.

1975
Loss of the Lovat, Jan.

Sirrett, V. G. 'Royal Navy search and rescue facilities', *Aeron. J.,* Vol. 79, April, pp. 161–165.

Hopkins, D. L. 'Marine communication and safety at sea (summary)', *Mar. Week.,* Vol. 2, May 23, p. 23+.

DoT report on SAR

Department of Trade. *United Kingdom marine search and rescue organisation 1975,* HMSO, 83 p.

1976 Lovat Inquiry opens, March	Post Office. *Handbook for radio operators working installations licensed by the Home Office/Post Office,* 14th edn., HMSO, 258 p.

Case Study 7

Annual survey	*Accidents to aircraft on the British register: a survey . . .,* Civil Aviation Authority (1971 and before, under the aegis of the Dept. or Board of Trade. Reports on individual accidents are published in the *Civil Aircraft Accident Reports* series, and, before Dec. 1970, the *Civil Aviation Publications* series.)
1959	Evrard, E. (ed.) *Medical aspects of air safety: the unexplained aircraft accident . . .,* Pergamon (for Agard, Nato), 308 p.
1964	Gillman, R. E. 'Flying Trident', *Flight Int.,* Vol. 85, April 2, pp. 537–540.
	Major, E. R. 'Trident engineering', *op. cit.,* Vol. 85, April 2, pp. 541–543.
	'Hawker Siddeley Trident IE airliner', *Aircr. Eng.,* Vol. 36, no. 6, June, pp. 157–198 (special issue, including Evolution and basic design philosophy, Aerodynamic design and flying controls, Aircraft systems, etc.).
	'Trident: a comprehensive evaluation', *Hawker Siddeley Rev.,* Winter, pp. 21–28.
	Walker, P. B. 'Scientific investigation of aircraft accidents', *Inst. Mech. Eng. Proc.,* Vol. 179, pt. 1 (1964–65) pp. 997–1014.
1966 Trident stall accident, June 3	Rasmussen, E. A. and Terry, R. A. *Human factors literature relevant to civil aviation: a guide for management and design engineers,* Oklahoma Med. Res. Found., 76 p.
1967	Miller, C. O. Dynamics of accident prevention information, *Can. Aeronaut. Space J.,* Vol. 13, no. 6, June, pp. 273–277.
	Gordon-Burge, H. K. 'Practical and legal problems of disseminating air safety information, pt. 1: Practical problems', *J. R. Aeron. Soc.,* Vol. 71, Nov., pp. 773–781.

Caplan, H. 'Practical and legal problems of disseminating air safety information, pt. 2: Possible solutions to some of the problems', *J. R. Aeron. Soc.*, Vol. 71, Nov., pp. 781–788.

Allward, M. F. *Safety in the air,* Abelard-Schumann, 176 p.

Launay, A. F. 'Historic air disasters', Allan, 171 p.

1968 Burrows, A. A. and Mastropaolo, J. A. 'Human error research and analysis program (HERAP)', *J. Aircr.,* Vol. 5, no. 5, Sept.–Oct., pp. 497–501.

Felthorpe Trident report, Nov. 6 Board of Trade. *Report on the accident to Trident G–ARPY near Felthorpe, Norwich on June 3, 1966,* CAP 311, HMSO, 26 p.

'Deep stall disaster (Trident G–ARPY)', *Flight Int.,* Vol. 94, Nov. 28, pp. 909–911.

Board of Trade. *The safety performance of U.K. airline operators: a special review,* HMSO, 108 p.

1969 Beaty, D. *The human factor in aircraft accidents,* Secker & Warburg, 196 p.

1970 Rolfe, J. M. 'Air safety: human error, the cause behind the cause', *Flight Int.,* Vol. 98, August 27, pp. 307–310.

Godson, J. *Unsafe at any height,* Blond, 176 p.

Hardwick, M. *The world's greatest air mysteries,* Odhams, 254 p.

1971 Gillman, R. E. 'From the left-hand seat', *Flight Int.,* Vol. 99, April 8, pp. 489–492 (Trident 313).

Black, H. C. 'Objectives and standards for air safety', *Aeron. J.,* Vol. 75, Aug., pp. 551–559.

Hoekstra, H. D. *Safety in general aviation,* Flight Safety Foundation, 126 p.

1972 Yanowitch, R. E. *et al. The psychosocial reconstruction inventory – a post-dictal instrument in aircraft accident investigation,* US Federal Aviation Authority, Off. Aviat. Med., Jan., 5 p (FAA–AM–72–2).

Wooley, D. 'Enter the CAA', *Flight Int.,* Vol. 101, March 30, pp. 439–441.

Martin, P. 'The Law of the Civil Aviation Authority', *op. cit.,* Vol. 101, March 30, pp. 441–442.

Cowin, H. 'Trident 3 stall protection', *op. cit.,* Vol. 101, March 30, p. 449.

Trident crash June 18

Aircraft accident, Staines, *Hansard*, Vol. 839, HC Debate, June 19, col. 44–50.

'Inquiry briefing', *Flight Int.*, Vol. 101, June 29, pp. 932a–934a (Trident crash).

Kluak, L. L. *et al.* 'Study of in-flight pilot incapacitation', *ITA Bull.*, Sept. 11, pp. 641–646.

Tye, W. and Neill, J. R. 'Reporting safety matters', *Flight Int.*, Vol. 102, Oct. 26, pp. 567–569 (discussion of CAA Aeronautical Information circ. 122/1972 on incident reporting).

Bennett, G. 'Pilot incapacitation', *op. cit.*, Vol. 102, Oct. 26, pp. 569–571.

Wooley, D. 'Outlook on safety', *op. cit.*, Vol. 102, Nov. 23, pp. 737–739.

Inquiry begins

'Trident disaster analysis begins', *op. cit.*, Vol. 102, Nov. 30, pp. 769–772.

'Trident inquiry: tests and procedure', *op. cit.*, Vol. 102, Dec. 7, pp. 807–809.

Captain X. *Safety last: the dangers of commercial aviation: an indictment by an airline pilot*, Dial Press, 264 p. (Published in England by Millington, 1974. Author: B. Powers-Waters).

US National Transportation Safety Board. *General aviation stall/spin accidents, 1967–1969: special study*, NTSB, 18 p. (NTSB–AAS–72–8).

1973

Field, H. 'Small step back', *Flight Int.*, Vol. 103, Jan. 18, pp. 91–94 (survey of 1972 accidents).

'Trident inquiry – conclusion', *op. cit.*, Vol. 103, Feb. 15, p. 218.

'Bringing the message', *op. cit.*, Vol. 103, April 5, p. 541 (Gasco's Flight Safety Bull.).

Inquiry report, May

Department of Trade and Industry, Accidents Investigation Branch. *Trident 1 G–ARPI: report of the public inquiry into the causes and circumstances of the accident near Staines on 18 June 1972*, Civil aircraft accident reports 4173, HMSO, 84 p.

Trident aircraft accident (report), *Hansard*, Vol. 856, HC Debate, May 9, col. 489–497.

'Trident crash findings', *Flight Int.*, Vol. 103, May 10, pp. 694–695.

'Accident prevention', *op. cit.,* Vol. 103, May 17, p. 723 (Trident inquiry editorial).

'Trident report – accepted with reservations', *op. cit.,* Vol. 103, May 17, pp. 728–729.

'How safe?', *op. cit.,* Vol. 103, May 17, pp. 743–746.

Shannon, R. H. and Waag, W. L. *Human factors approach to aircraft accident analysis,* Nav. Aerospace Med. Res. Lab., Pensacola, June 18, 46 p.

Ramsden, J. M. 'Air safety: when and why it happened', *Flight Int.,* Vol. 104, Aug. 9, pp. 237–239.

Field, H. 'Whose mandate?', *op. cit.,* Vol. 104, Aug. 9, p. 242 (mandatory reporting procedure discussed with CAA Controller (Safety)).

Tye, W. 'Safety – the role of the Authority', *Aeron, J.,* Vol. 77, Sept., pp. 449–452.

Veal, J. B. 'The CAA and safety – the regulatory framework', *Aeron, J.,* Vol. 77, Sept., pp. 446–448.

Keith-Lucas, D. 'Design for safety', *Aeron, J.,* Vol. 77, Oct., pp. 483–488.

Ramsden, J. M. 'After an airliner accident', *Flight Int.,* Vol. 104, Nov. 8, pp. 791–792.

Gilson, C. 'After a military aircraft accident', *op. cit.,* Vol. 104, Nov. 8, pp. 781–783.

Zeffert, H. 'Airliner flight deck design for crew co-ordination', *Aeron, J.,* Vol. 77, Dec., pp. 639–648.

Dodds, R. L. 'Airline pilot's views on medical licensing standards', *Pilot,* Winter, pp. 10–12.

Corkindale, K. G. G. (ed.) *Behavioural aspects of aircraft accidents,* Agard Conf. Proc. no. 132 (AD–775 208) (causes and prevention of pilot error accidents).

International Air Safety Seminar, 26th, Annual, Lisbon, November 1973, Flight Safety Found., Arlington, 208 p. (Papers on pilot error accidents, monitoring of heart failure, cockpit design, incident analysis, etc.).

1974

Mason, J. K. 'Disease of aircrew as a cause of aircraft accidents', *Commun. Health,* Vol. 6, no. 2, pp. 62–67 (includes remarks on Trident crash).

Ramsden, J. M. 'Air safety: the uncommon cause', *Flight Int.,* Vol. 105, May, pp. 691–696.

Richardson, G. R. 'Pilot medical career terminations', *Log,* Oct.–Nov., pp. 226–227/Dec., pp. 252–253.

Ramsden, J. M. 'The safe airline, pt. 2: Government regulator', *Flight Int.,* Vol. 106, Nov. 28, pp. 761–764.

Ramsden, J. M. 'Human factors', *op. cit.,* Vol. 106, Nov. 28, pp. 764–768.

'Towards an overall safety index?', *op. cit.,* Vol. 106, Nov. 28, pp. 768–769.

Ramsden, J. M. 'Safe airline, pt. 3: Airline', *op. cit.*, Vol. 106, Dec. 26, pp. 906–908.

Bartel, R. C. *Identification of aircraft accident causation and factors: a systems approach survey,* Bowie, Md., 1 Vol.

Godson, J. *Papa India: the Trident tragedy,* Compton, 164 p.

Kowalsky, N. B. *et al. An analysis of pilot error-related aircraft accidents: final report,* Lovelace Found. Med. Educ. Res., 72 p. (N74–26434).

Sanders, M. G. *Personality aspects of pilot-error accident involvement,* US Army Aeromed. Res. Lab., 21 p. (AD–782 976).

US Defense Documentation Center. *Human factors in design and control of aircraft . . .,* DDC, 235 p. (AD–782 700).

1975

Ramsden, J. M. 'Flight safety: the healthy pilot', *Flight Int.,* Vol. 107, April 17, pp. 647–649.

Smith, C. W. 'The measures of air transport risk', *op. cit.,* Vol. 107, April 17, pp. 650–651.

Doetsch, K. H. 'Proper symbiosis of the human pilot and automatic flight control', *Aeron, J.,* Vol. 79, June, pp. 247–260.

Dodds, R. L. 'Human factors in aircraft accidents', *Log,* Winter, pp. 47–49

'Human factors', *Flight Int.,* Vol. 108, Dec. 4, p. 814 (IATA Conference).

Barlay, S. *Aircrash detective: the search for air safety,* rev. edn., Coronet, 395 p. (prev. edn., Hamilton, 1969).

Godson, J. *The rise and fall of the DC–10,* New English Library, 351 p.

'Airworthiness', *Flight Int.,* Vol. 108, Nov. 20, p. 737 (stick pushers).

1976 Chapman, P. J. C. 'Do we really need stress heart tests?', *op. cit.,* Vol. 109, March 20, pp. 688–689.

Turner, N. 'Revolt on the flight deck', *New Sci.,* Vol. 70, April 8, pp. 77–79 (pilots accuse CAA of over-reacting to Papa-India crash).

Eddy, p. *et al. Destination Disaster,* Hart-Davis, 435 p. (DC–10 crash, Paris, April 1974. Extracts serialized in *The Sunday Times*, from Oct. 17 1976).

Acknowledgements

Grateful acknowledgement is made to the following for material used in these case studies:

Case Study 1

Extracts from *Report of the Public Inquiry into the Accident at Hixon Level Crossing, January 6th, 1968,* Cmnd 3706 reproduced by permission of the Controller of HMSO. *Figure 2* Sunday Mirror; *Figure 3* Chief Constable, Staffordshire Police.

Case Study 2

Extracts from *Report of the Tribunal appointed to inquire into the Disaster at Aberfan, October 21st, 1966,* reproduced by permission of the Controller of HMSO. *Frontispiece* Keystone Press; *Figures 1, 2, 7 and 9* reproduced from the Ordnance Survey map with the permission of the Controller of HMSO, Crown copyright reserved; *Figures 3, 4, 6 and 10 Report of the Tribunal appointed to inquire into the Disaster at Aberfan, October 21st, 1966,* reproduced by permission of the Controller of HMSO; *Figure 5* C. J. Lloyd; *Figure 8* Chief Constable, Merthyr Tydfil Borough Police.

Case Study 3

Extracts from the abridged version of the *Report of the Summerland Fire Commission, 1974,* reproduced by permission of the Lieutenant-Governor and Government of the Isle of Man. *Figure 1* H. E. Lieutenant-Governor, Isle of Man; *Figures 2, 5, 6 and 7* Manx Press Pictures; *Figures 3 and 4* based on The Architects' Journal; *Figures 8 and 9* Keystone Press.

Case Study 4

Extracts from the *Report of the Inquiry into the Collapse of Flats at Ronan Point, Canning Town, 1968,* reproduced by permission of the Controller of HMSO. *Figures 1 and 2* from the *Report; Figure 3* London Fire Brigade; *Figures 4 and 5* London Express News and Features Services; *Figure 6* The Commissioner of Police of the Metropolis; *Figures 7–10* Taylor-Woodrow Group.

Case Study 5

Reproduced by permission of the Honourable the Speaker of the Legislative Assembly of Victoria.

Case Study 6

Extracts from *MV Burtonia (O.N. 300222) Report of Court No. 8062– Formal Investigation* reproduced by permission of the Controller of HMSO. *Figure 2* RNLI; *Figure 3* Ministry of Defence; *Figures 4, 8 and 9* The Eastern Daily Press.

Case Study 7

Extracts from the *Report of the Public Inquiry into the causes and circumstances of the accident near Staines on June 18th, 1972,* reproduced by permission of the Controller of HMSO. *Figures 1 and 4* Flight International; *Figures 2, 5 and 6* Keystone Press; *Figure 7* Evening Mail, Slough.